AN INTRODUCTIO[N]
SPECIFICATION WIT[H]

THE McGRAW-HILL INTERNATIONAL SERIES IN SOFTWARE ENGINEERING

Consulting Editor

Professor D. Ince
The Open University

Titles in this Series

AN INTRODUCTION TO FORMAL SPECIFICATION WITH Z AND VDM

Deri Sheppard

McGRAW-HILL BOOK COMPANY

London · New York · St Louis · San Francisco · Auckland
Bogotá · Caracas · Lisbon · Madrid · Mexico
Milan · Montreal · New Delhi · Panama · Paris · San Juan
São Paulo · Singapore · Sydney · Tokyo · Toronto

Published by
McGRAW-HILL Book Company Europe
Shoppenhangers Road, Maidenhead, Berkshire SL6 2QL, England
Telephone 01628 23432
Fax 01628 770224

British Library Cataloguing in Publication Data
Sheppard, Deri
  Introduction to Formal Specifications
  with Z and VDM. – (McGraw-Hill
  International Series in Software Engineering)
  I. Title II. Series
  005.1

  ISBN 0-07-707907-8

Library of Congress Cataloging-in-Publication Data
Sheppard, Deri.
  An introduction to formal specifications with Z and VDM / Deri
Sheppard.
    p. cm. – (The McGraw-Hill international series in software
engineering)
  Includes bibliographical references and index.
  ISBN 0-07-77907-8 :
  1. Z (Computer program language) 2. Computer software-
-Development. I. Series.
QA76.73.Z2S48 1994
005.1'01'5113–dc20   94-20024
                                                        CIP

1234 CUP 98765

Typeset by Alden Multimedia, Northampton
and printed and bound in Great Britain at the University Press, Cambridge

For my family
Marilyn, Huw and Wyn, Gypsy and Brumby

CONTENTS

LIST OF TRADEMARKS

Smalltalk Xerox
IBM International Business Machines Corporation
SADT Softech Inc.
Oracle Oracle Corporation
GENESIS Imperial Software Technology
INMOS Thompson CSF
Rolls-Royce British Aerospace
CADiZ York Software Engineering Ltd.

PREFACE

Software engineering is a young discipline yet it has to tackle problems of enormous complexity. In doing so it has evolved a 'structure' intended to provide a systematic approach to control this complexity. Typically, software engineers will capture the system specification using a natural language, the design might be expressed through a graphical notation while a programming language is used for the implementation. Unfortunately, natural languages and graphical notations are ambiguous and difficult to reason with. It is not possible to show that a graphical design correctly expresses a natural language specification, neither is it possible to be entirely sure that an implementation is a correct reflection of the design. On the other hand, it is equally true to say that structured approaches to software engineering are well understood and have been enormously successful. Even so, it was interesting to note the discomfort experienced by a company spokesman on a recent television programme (*The Net*, BBC2 (Wales) 20 April 1994) when closely questioned about the methods used to construct the computerized safety systems of a nuclear power station about to be commissioned. 'These systems', he insisted, 'have been constructed by a well-known company experienced in the application of structured methods'. 'Yes', the interviewer continued, 'but have these systems been subjected to any kind of mathematical proof?' The spokesman paused...then ran out the same strained reply.

The questioner was referring to the application of formal methods, mathematically-based notations whose descriptions are capable of being subjected to rigorous proof, and when used with programming languages that have a precise semantics, they are capable of establishing the correctness of an implementation with regard to its specification. The interviewer was also speaking on behalf of 'the man on the Clapham omnibus' whose understanding of mathematics may be vague but whose confidence in its application to design has been well-founded by experience with traditionally-engineered products such as aircraft, bridges and, of course, televisions.

This book is an attempt to bring the benefits of one aspect of formal methods, namely formal specification, to an undergraduate audience. It has been written specifically for students on modular courses where a broad spectrum of interest and mathematical ability is often found. These courses often include Information Engineers, Computer Studies/Science students, Combined Studies students as well as Software Engineers, and this profile will become the norm at many universities as the country moves towards a mass higher education system.

Because of the composition of its intended audience the book can be used in a variety of ways, but fundamental to its proper use is a thorough understanding of 'traditional' software engineering techniques, their benefits and problems. In this respect I notice that another author in this series suggests that 'some broad understanding of what constitutes "software engineering" would also be useful' for his book. In this text I go further and devote the whole of Part 1 to a coarse-grained but nevertheless detailed review of the contemporary software engineering scene. These chapters can be read by students who may have some 'holes' in their understanding of what currently constitutes the discipline. After reading Part 1, I would hope to avoid being asked the question 'Why are we studying formal specification?' while those who have a well-founded knowledge of the subject can use Part 1 for reference and proceed directly to Part 2.

Part 2 presents the basic ideas and problems associated with establishing the 'correctness' of software and examines each of the various options open to us. This is done in a largely non-technical fashion and gives a broad understanding of the subject area. However, formal approaches to software development can only be understood by studying the mathematics they use (there really are no short-cuts to this) and we begin this in Part 3. Many authors of books on formal specification/methods declare that the mathematics should present no barriers to the reader. This is not my experience. When dealing with a modular course at one of the typical 'new' universities (as opposed to (say) the staff of a particular industrial company) the audience varies tremendously in its numerical ability and interest. Consequently, I have employed a number of devices to make the mathematics more approachable. These involve case studies relating to everyday situations, the use of informal English equivalents for many of the predicate calculus expressions, diagrams that illustrate important mappings between sets and a degree of 'poetic licence' when using Z ideas in the typed set theory.

The remaining parts of the book can be used in a variety of ways. Chapters 15 and 20 can be read by those who want some understanding of the structure and history of one or both of the leading notations, Z and VDM. The Epilogue in Chapter 26 will be useful to those wanting some understanding of contemporary experience using the techniques. Those who wish to have a firm understanding of Z can read Parts 4 and 5, while those who prefer to tackle VDM can read Parts 6 and 7. But the full potential of the book will be realized by reading all four parts and to facilitate comparison, all the Z case studies in Part 5 have been re-worked through VDM in Part 7. I believe this to be a unique feature in my approach.

The case studies are generally used to illustrate the practical application of the notation. My use of stacks, queues and symbol tables has been criticized on the grounds of originality, but they are familiar and well understood and leave the reader free to concentrate on the techniques and not on the functionality of the object we are specifying. Such techniques include generic definitions, error handling, the structuring of large specifications and proofs. It is in this latter respect that much of the power of formal specification lies. Consequently, the book addresses initial state proofs, implementability proofs and property proofs in both Z and VDM. The much neglected topic of bags also has a prominent place in the book and goes some way to giving these objects some well-earned respectability.

Some consideration of the progression from specification to implementation is made in the Epilogue in Chapter 26. However, it is my opinion that in an introductory course it is best to emphasize such a migration through *ad hoc* or structured techniques rather than by the full rigour of refinement. The intellectual effort currently demanded by the latter is formidable for all but the most trivial of projects and much more support work needs to be provided before we can raise this activity to the same level of respect as specification.

I was pleased to receive the comments made by the anonymous reviewers as the book progressed through the various quality control mechanisms at McGraw-Hill. Originally, the text was very large and as a result of the comments it has been knocked into a much more acceptable form — I can only hope that the scars of the various excisions do not show! It goes without saying that the book has benefited directly and indirectly from reading many other works and I hope that full acknowledgement has been made at the appropriate point. Any mistakes are of course entirely my own — the price that has to be paid for the freedom of being the only author.

I would like to thank both McGraw-Hill — for making the project a (relatively!) painless experience — and my family. In particular I must thank my wife Marilyn whose continued support has always encouraged me, and my sons Huw and Wyn for letting me get on with my work when I should have been playing rock guitar with them! I must also thank the other members of our 'family' — Gypsy and Brumby — who never failed to give their time and affection whenever it was needed. It might also be appropriate to mention the various quotations that appear throughout the book and which I use to break the continuous flow of formalism and add a little reflection. My favourite however, applies to the process of authorship itself which in this case — as for another in this series — extended over four years.

Life is what happens to you while you're busy making other plans
John Lennon, *Beautiful Boy*, 1980.

Budding authors be warned!

Deri Sheppard
University of Glamorgan

PART ONE

Contemporary Software Engineering

One never notices what has been done;
one can only see what remains to be done....

Marie Curie (1867–1934), from a letter to her brother, 18 March 1894

INTRODUCTION

The term *software engineering* can be traced back at least as far as 1968. Fritz Bauer introduced an early definition at a conference held at Garmisch (West) Germany, sponsored by the NATO Science Committee (Nauer *et al.* 1976). The conference was the first held to discuss issues arising directly from the software crisis that was perceived to afflict the industry generally. Bauer's definition was less than comprehensive, and many more have appeared since, yet it underlined from the outset the essence of his approach towards software production:

> *The establishment and use of sound engineering principles in order to obtain economically, software that is reliable and works on real machines.*

Of the major extensions to this definition, Boehm (1976, 1981) has included the 'practical application of scientific knowledge' and the production of associated 'documentation' in an attempt both to broaden the catchment area of the subject and to address the problem of the communication of technical detail to the users and among developers. These are hallmarks of the traditional engineer. In a further comment, Boehm (and previously Hoare (1978)) has also incorporated the notion of 'usefulness', in that engineered software should display qualities that make it efficient, usable and secure.

It is not this book's purpose to quote the various 'definitions' that have appeared over the years. These are frequently vague and seem divorced from the actual act of software production. What is far more relevant is to present the *framework* of activities that are currently recognized as being the essence of the engineering approach and to isolate the principles, techniques and sequence of events that have to occur in our attempt to produce reliable software. The next few chapters are therefore dedicated to a review of the

1

current state of software engineering. Such a review is important in a number of respects. First, students studying software engineering courses often tend to concentrate on the detail of particular techniques and forget about the relation(s) one technique has to another and their role in software production. Secondly, the main parts of this book are concerned with relatively recent developments in the engineering of software and, unless the reader is familiar with the scope and difficulties of current concepts, the significance of the new methods may be lost.

This review provides a 'coarse grained' picture of software engineering and omits many of the subdivisions of the subject found in dedicated textbooks. In particular, it concentrates on commercial data processing aspects rather than those of real-time referencing the latter only when necessary to preserve some continuity. Interested readers may use the references to pursue the detail of a particular area, while established software engineers may prefer to move directly to Part 2, having familiarized themselves with the basic content of Part 1.

Probably the most widely accepted view of software engineering encapsulates the process in three major life cycle phases: *definition*, *development* and *maintenance*. These phases are encountered in all software development regardless of size, application or complexity and are applied in strict sequence. But we begin at the beginning, by reviewing those events that have led to an understanding of the nature of software and its proper role within computer systems.

1

THE NATURE OF SOFTWARE

CHECKLIST OF OBJECTIVES

After reading this chapter you should be able to:

- Understand the nature of the problem facing the software industry and outline some of the reasons why it has arisen.
- Understand why the production of software was outpaced by developments in hardware and appreciate the contribution that traditional engineering methodologies have made to the latter.
- Understand what the term *engineering* implies.
- Appreciate the need to apply an 'engineering' methodology to the production of software.
- Outline the differences that exist between software and a traditionally engineered product and appreciate that these differences should be reflected in any methodology used to improve software production and quality.

1.1 INTRODUCTION

This book concerns itself with concepts of computer science. In its broadest sense, the subject has developed in terms of both hardware and software. The relationship between the two is symbiotic in that neither can fulfil its function without the other. However, it is true to say that developments in software have been largely catalysed by those in hardware. File access utilities and concurrent programming are obvious examples, relying as they do on disk and parallel processor technologies, respectively. Innovations such as these have emerged as natural progressions in the development of physics and electrical engineering. Indeed, most hardware can be seen as a direct result of applied science(s).

In its construction, hardware benefits from the tried and tested principles of engineering. The strict discipline associated with engineering has developed because the object of a traditional engineering exercise, such as a bridge or an aircraft, must satisfy a whole host of criteria concerning its use. Foremost among these are safety, cost and the environment. Engineering failure can kill, pollute, lose money or destroy jobs and these horrifying consequences can occur at local, national or global levels. As a result, professional engineering has long recognized the need to *prove* the suitability of a design and to construct/test prototypes with appropriate components before ever attempting to put the object into use. In this fashion we can be reasonably sure that the object will perform within the professional and technological limits used in its design. The result of true engineering is an object that *at least* performs to requirements but is usually capable of much more.

Because of the consequences of bad engineering, we have come to expect all practitioners to be fully trained and appropriately experienced in its methodologies. Such training is a long process. Consequently, building quality into a final product by the proper application of engineering principles is expensive as a result of both the nature of the process itself and the cost of the talent of those who achieve it for us. Frequently, the cost of an engineered object is also related to the degree of responsibility the designers carry for its failure. Such cost is twofold; the cost of injury to others and the cost of putting it right.

In contrast to the effort put into the production of hardware, the early 'manufacture' of software was 'cheap'. As a result, much of it failed to reach even basic levels of reliability, quality and user satisfaction. The generally abysmal state of software since the 1960s was sufficient for the the term *software crisis* to be a melodramatic but appropriate description. Even so, until relatively recently the consequences of its failure have been limited, causing inconvenience and often amusement rather than tragedy. This in turn relieved most manufacturers of software of the burden of responsibility carried by the traditional engineer, and both aspects militated heavily against any approach to software manufacture which ensured that it 'worked' in advance.

The disturbing state of software was revealed and heightened by the parallel developments in hardware. As hardware became smaller, it also became cheaper and far more reliable. These developments opened up a bewildering array of complex and sophisticated applications for which software was totally unprepared. Software was unable to meet the challenge, for those principles that guided the engineer to increasingly sophisticated developments in hardware were not applied to the development of the associated software. In short, the principles, tools and techniques used in software development were generally ad hoc and inadequate, they lacked an underlying rationale or theoretical basis and there was little, if any, methodology in their application. Software manufacture was an enigmatic process practised by many but understood by few. A number of points contributed to the software crisis, but four are of particular significance.

First, software manufacture was a completely new activity. It had no history, no guiding principles and no developments in other areas that it could instantly modify and develop. The rapid evolution of hardware and the confusion surrounding software during this period is therefore a frequently used but rather unfair comparison. Successful and reliable hardware was produced by the amalgamation of a wide range of existing sciences and techniques that developed progressively over very many years. Hardware engineers were (and still are of course) often able to draw upon the fruits of the labour of workers in a wide variety of other fields. Two examples taken from opposite ends of the chronological spectrum of hardware development illustrate the consistency of this point:

1. The diode valve was created in the mid-1920s. Its usefulness in electronic computers was not realized until some 10 years later. During this time physicists had developed

the device to a fairly reliable level (by the standards of the day!). At the time of its role in computing it was a well understood and available component.

2. The phenomenon of liquid crystals was thoroughly researched for some 20 years by workers at Hull University's Department of Chemistry. The work was regarded then as pure research, having no obvious uses other than furthering the understanding of the correlation between molecular structure and physical properties. In the laboratory, molecular structure was adapted to such an extent that liquid crystals could be 'engineered' to activate at a variety of temperatures and with varying applied voltages. Not until there appeared a requirement for a small, cheap, main-tenance-free display device with minimal power requirement (early 1970s) was the industrial significance of the research realized. Today the LCD has become a standard and widely used component. Once again the engineer benefited from 'insider dealing'.

Because engineering has a comparatively long history and freely accesses other dis-ciplines, it is not surprising that hardware developments proceeded at such a pace. The contrasting performance of software during this period is therefore understandable purely in terms of its youth and naïvety.

Secondly, many of the problems of the software crisis could be attributed directly to the introduction of 'third-generation' languages. These were immensely powerful by the standards of the day and yet were presented to an industry that had no clear idea of how to use them. The structure of the languages themselves compounded the situation, for since concepts of bad practice were hardly understood, features which led to unreliable software were not suppressed.

Thirdly, the approach towards system development became progressively 'application centred'. Programmers took an increasingly isolated and individual view of a corporate data resource. Very frequently there was a one-to-one correspondence of a program with its file(s). Definitions of the data file were to be found in the program. Changes in the structure of data necessitated changes to the program. Additionally, the data in the file became the sole responsibility of its 'guardian' programs. Other programs could not access the data unless temporary transfer files were created. Not only did this generate unproductive maintenance, it also duplicated data unnecessarily and both of these spread rapidly almost without control. It is somewhat ironic to realize that the duplication of data was encouraged by the falling cost of hardware during this period.

Finally, the situation was aggravated by the lack of education of programmers at independent institutions. The majority of systems were developed 'in house' with the commercial pressures of their associated companies driving the programmers' solutions, rather than codes of good practice.

Whatever the reason for the software crisis, its effects have been profound. Managers responsible for software development concentrated on the 'bottom line' issues: schedules and estimates were often grossly inaccurate; the productivity of the software people could not keep pace with the demand for their services; while the quality of software was often less than adequate. As a consequence, developments have occurred rapidly in languages and methodologies in an attempt to put the production of software on a firm theoretical basis. Progress in these areas has been paralleled by an increased dependence on the performance of software and this in turn has generated enhanced responsibility for failure on those who produce it.

Today the computer plays a central role in finance, defence, transportation and many other areas of daily life. It has become accepted as a standard (and very frequently safety-critical) component in a wide range of engineered products. Many aircraft, for example, are *totally* reliant on their computer systems, and software failure now has tragic consequences across a wide spectrum of human activity. It is generally fair to say that the hardware associated with a computer system has reached acceptable levels of reliability, due principally to the role of engineering. Hardware costs have tumbled over the past decade, so much so that the cost relationship between hardware and software has now inverted, with software the major expenditure. Because of the software crisis, costs and the effects of failure, our attention has turned to the production of software to the same high standards as we have for hardware.

1.2 CAN ENGINEERING HELP?

Most readers would be prepared to accept the general case made in favour of the engineering process in the previous paragraphs. This implicit acceptance stems from an exposure either directly (as professionals) or indirectly (as users) to a wide variety of engineered products in our everyday lives. As users of aircraft, cars, television sets, etc., we well appreciate the care that has gone into their design and construction. Our first-hand experience of their safety and performance convinces us of the correctness of the principles used in their design and construction. Indeed, even though most members of the public are unsure as to exactly what these principles are, society demands that they are employed. At this point, then, it seems relevant to formalize the role of the engineer, to identify what it is that an engineer does, and to see if the general principles used in the construction of reliable hardware can help produce software in an equally robust form. In short, we need to know just what engineering is.

The Engineers' Council for Professional Development defines *engineering* thus:

Engineering is the profession in which a knowledge of the mathematical and natural sciences, gained by study, experience and practice is applied with judgement to develop ways to utilise economically the materials and forces of nature for the benefit of mankind.

The relevance of the term 'engineering' can be appreciated more fully by enumerating the major activities that contribute to the formulation, design and manufacture of almost any complex but reliable product. Briefly these activities are:

- Analysing the problem
- Specifying what is required for a successful solution
- Designing a solution that matches the specification
- Implementing the design
- Production (often large-scale) of the end product
- Assuring the quality of the end product
- Maintaining the end product

- Planning and controlling all of the above
- Selecting, applying, and creating principles, tools, techniques and materials to effect all of the above

The major point to appreciate, therefore, is that engineering resolves itself into a strict sequence of separate activities. Whatever the product, analysis precedes specification, specification precedes design, etc. This is very much a 'divide and conquer' approach which results in the reduction of overall complexity and permits progression from one stage to the next in a controlled fashion. The major success of engineering is that this structured approach has been long realized.

The engineer has a whole host of tools and methodologies to help in this approach. Each is applied within specific areas of the process and with a singular purpose in mind. It is precisely this combination of the *structured* application of a set of comprehensive *methods*, *tools* and *procedures* together with the sensibility of *practical experience* that contribute to that which we term 'engineering'.

1.3 CAN WE ENGINEER SOFTWARE?

In the early days of computing, systems development concentrated heavily on hardware management techniques. This was quite natural because hardware was the single largest budget item. To control hardware costs, managers instituted formal controls and technical standards. They demanded thorough analysis and design before something was built. In this respect, computer systems were engineered in a traditional sense. In contrast the software—the result of programming—was developed very much as an afterthought, reflecting its low status in the overall scheme of things. During this period it was not unusual to describe the process of programming as akin to an art or a craft where experience and intuition were of more use than calculation or logic. This was understandable, for the activity had very few formal methods and even fewer people used them. The production of software was 'jargonized', undisciplined and in no way related to the engineering process applied to hardware.

Because of the inversion of the hardware/software cost curves, the software profile has now risen to centre stage. Practitioners and managers have had to examine ways to make the production of software quicker, cheaper, more reliable and subject to the proper measure of progression that we would expect in any other production environment. However, software is a *logical* rather than a *physical* component of a computer system, and therefore has characteristics that are quite different from those of hardware. Some of the more important of these are discussed briefly below.

'Software is often custom built and rarely assembled in traditional engineering terms from a multitude of existing components'   The traditional engineer is afforded the luxury of specifying, selecting and then assembling components into a final product. Sadly, software designers have no reciprocal luxury. There are no catalogues of software components. Although it is perfectly possible to purchase ready-made software, we can only do so for a complete product. The disassembly of such software to its component parts or the purchase of the individual components such that we can (re-)assemble them into a different product is not possible. Frequently, the software components that comprise a finished product have been written in a specific rather than a generic fashion and their suitability as a general utility is questionable. There is, however, no reason why software components cannot be written and used even for one-off solutions.

'Software does not wear out as time progresses'   Figure 1.1 shows the (idealized) failure curves for hardware and software. Hardware suffers a relatively high failure rate early in its life owing to design and manufacturing faults. When these defects are corrected the failure rate stabilizes. As time passes, however, the rate increases again as the cumulative effects of wear and tear take their toll. At some point on this curve the device simply 'wears out'. In contrast, software is not susceptible to environmental maladies and the failure curve, after initial problems have been remedied, continues at the same rate until obsolescence. Although this is a gross oversimplification, the implication is clear—software cannot 'wear out'. This should be an important characteristic of software, but we should equally be aware of the fact that it does deteriorate.

Deterioration occurs either because of its use in an environment that has changed from the original or as a result of the effects of maintenance. When a large software system is introduced into an environment the original environment is altered by its presence. For example, successful software often has the effect of generating higher and

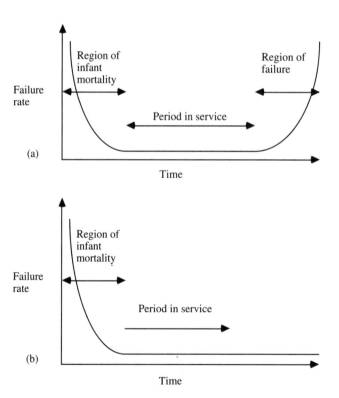

Figure 1.1   The idealized failure curves for (a) hardware and (b) software.

higher workloads for itself, consequently the design limitations may be exceeded and the performance suffers. Frequently, users modify their behaviour as they become more experienced with the software. Their expectations are redefined and in that sense the original system no longer satisfies. Again it has deteriorated.

Additionally, Fig. 1.2 shows that all software undergoes changes during its lifetime and, as each change proceeds, new defects are introduced that increase the failure rate and cause it to spike. After such a change the curve rarely relaxes back into the previous steady state before another change occurs. If each such change has the same effect then the background failure rate begins to gradually rise, i.e. the software deteriorates as a result of maintenance.

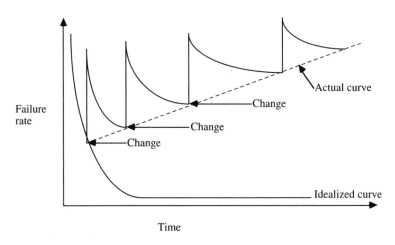

Figure 1.2 Failure curve for software undergoing modifications.

As a final point, we have come to accept that deterioration in hardware is remedied by replacing it with a new component. In software there are no 'spare parts'. More importantly, every software failure signals an error in design or coding. Therefore software maintenance can be an extremely complex process.

'Software is developed, it cannot be manufactured in the classical sense' Although there are some parallels between software development and hardware production, the two activities are quite different. In both cases high quality is achieved by good design, but the manufacturing phase for hardware has no real equivalent in software development. This means that the distribution of costs is quite different for each activity. Both activities are often labour intensive but people are used in different ways and their contribution is quite different.

In traditional manufacturing more people mean more production. In a software development that is running behind, adding more people simply makes it even later. As more people are added, the extra time needed for education and communication leaves less for production. The distribution of costs and the effect of people means that the 'software factory' would have to be managed quite differently from one engaged in traditional manufacture.

'Software cannot benefit from the scaled-up models frequently used in traditional engineering' The problems of building large software systems are not simply those of scaling-up smaller ones. Because software exhibits a systemic behaviour, the overall performance can equate to more than the sum of its parts. We have already argued that the allocation of additional workers, for example, has a somewhat perverse effect. In contrast, traditional engineering often exploits a working model of a design, the purpose of which is to simplify concepts, clarify specifications and, by scaling up, act as a projection to the performance of the final product. Scale models in engineering help in situations where the essential elements contributing to the behaviour of interest are easily perceived but their interactions are extremely complicated. Problems of this sort are frequently encountered in those fields of engineering that have to do with fluids, i.e. with liquids or gases. Consequently, scale models are often used in studies for the design of aircraft, ships, auditoriums, pumps, turbines, harbours and coastal protection schemes, and for problems concerning the movement of silt in an estuary or the dissipation of heat from a power station. Once the scale model has achieved its purpose it is discarded.

The concept of modelling has an important role in software development also, but its use and evolution follow a quite different path. The term *prototyping* is frequently applied to the creation of a restricted software model and, unlike scale modelling in engineering, it is applicable in a wide range of situations. Just like the engineer's scale model, the prototype serves as a vehicle to simplify concepts and clarify requirements. A working prototype can be produced quickly using existing programs such as report generators, screen painters, etc. The customer sees what appears to be a working version of the software, however, unlike the scale model, the techniques holding together a prototype will often not translate to large-scale production. An inappropriate operating system or language may well be employed or a simplistic algorithm used just to demonstrate capability. Frequently, the designer may become familiar with these choices and forget why they were inappropriate. There is a chance that the less-than-ideal choice may find its way into a final part of the system and eventually be delivered to a customer. The fundamental difference between the engineer's model and the software prototype is that in the former case the model is always discarded, in the latter case it may not be. Discarding the software model once it has served its purpose is *throwaway prototyping*. Developing the prototype to a level where it eventually becomes the final system is *evolutionary prototyping* and requires careful management by a development team.

1.4 SOFTWARE MYTHS

Recognition of the realities of software is an essential precursor to the development of a strategy that attempts to put software production on a sound basis. Unfortunately, the realities are also intertwined with software 'myths' which developed along with the problems that caused the software crisis. Software myths had a number of attributes that made them appear to be reasonable statements of fact (sometimes containing elements of truth), they had an intuitive feel by the standards of the day and were often subscribed to by respected practitioners. The myths were misleading, subjective judgements that caused serious problems for managers and technical staff alike. In the drive towards a more sustainable approach to software development, myths needed to be debunked. Unfortunately, even today the myths range widely and are embedded with customers, managers and practitioners alike.

For the customer, myths lead to false expectation and ultimately dissatisfaction with the performance of a delivered product. Frequently, the customer may assume that a general statement of objectives is sufficient to begin writing programs and that detail can be added later. Similarly, software is seen as a much more flexible entity than hardware so that changes can easily be accommodated. However, poor initial definition is a major cause of software failure, while the effect of change depends very much on the time it is introduced. Changes have least effect in the definition phase and greatest effect during maintenance.

For the manager, often under extreme pressure to maintain budgets, keep to schedules and maintain quality, myths represent a straw to clutch which relieves the pressure, albeit temporarily. Managers often resist changes in software development methods simply because they are developing the same kinds of programs as they were 10 years ago. This is the inertia of past practice and it lies heavily with many computing professionals. Frequently, the purchase of the newest computer(s) for staff is associated with the provision of state-of-the-art development tools, while the availability of sets of standards and procedures for building software is implicitly associated with its *use*.

All three examples are dangerous misconceptions. Although application domains do not change for long periods of time, volume of work, productivity, quality and the ability of an information system to expand in line with business objectives do. The mere provision of standards is insufficient to ensure that they are reflected in the software production. Indeed, are their concepts modern or complete? Finally, it takes more than the latest mainframe or PC to do high-quality software development. Software tools (software that helps build software) are often much more important than hardware in achieving quality and productivity.

At the practitioner level we find possibly the greatest number of myths. Fostered by four decades of a programming culture, the insular nature of program development and the reluctance of programmers to find fault with their own work has led to many difficulties. Programmers are often suspicious of methods of design, analysis and testing, and feel that the 'sit at my terminal and code' approach will always succeed—it will not. Others feel that the success of a design can only be determined when the program 'runs' and if it works, their job is done—it is not. Maintenance is seen as a necessary evil but it can be handled quite easily as and when needed—it cannot. The overall success of a project is determined not only by delivery of compliant software but also by the standard of its associated documentation. Documentation forms the basis of software development and maintenance so that a fixation with the development of compliant software exclusively, abrogates responsibility for its maintenance, which frequently causes major expenditure within a department.

The software crisis will not disappear overnight but a realization of the characteristics of software and the fallacy of the software myths has to be the first step in formulating a more practical and sustainable solution for software development. The software crisis has left as its main legacies indiscipline and entrenched attitudes, a lack of structure in the use of tools and methodologies, poor integration of the major phases of software development and a consequent overall lack of control. If anything is to be learned from engineering it is that discipline and structure are essential and that these must be applied in a comprehensive fashion to the whole development process and not in isolated parts. If the software crisis is to be solved, it can be done only by developing methodologies for all phases of software production, by providing tools to automate software production, by providing more powerful mechanisms for implementing software, better techniques for quality assurance at all stages and the provision of an overriding philosophy for the coordination, control and management of each. There is no reason why such a discipline could not properly be called 'software engineering'.

2

THE DEFINITION PHASE OF SOFTWARE ENGINEERING

CHECKLIST OF OBJECTIVES

After reading this chapter you should be able to:

- Appreciate the subdivision of traditional requirements analysis in terms of functional and data-oriented views and understand the contribution and scope of each.
- Understand the role of and the relationships between data flow diagrams, entity–relationship diagrams and entity life histories.
- Appreciate the techniques used to determine the 'correctness' of the specification.
- Realize the importance of the specification in driving the remainder of the engineering process.

2.1 INTRODUCTION

The role of the definition phase within the overall life cycle is to produce a precise and independent description of the structure and purpose of a computer-based system. Such a description is a *specification* and it acts as a foundation for the whole of the remaining engineering work. The definition phase concentrates on *what* is required and not on how it is achieved. It consists essentially of two separate activities: the computer system analysis and the software requirements analysis. Computer systems analysis is the first step in the evolution of a new computer-based system, while the software requirements analysis is the first step in its associated software engineering process. Throughout this stage the development team find out about the existing system using a number of techniques such as interviewing, studying the current system documentation, circulating questionnaires, observing the system in practice, looking at the results of previous studies and conducting surveys. Each of these has been well documented in standard textbooks and we shall not discuss them further here.

During computer systems analysis, the engineer determines the customer's needs and assesses their technical and economic feasibility. The result of the systems analysis is a system specification document and this forms the basis of all the engineering that follows. The document contains descriptions of each system function, the information structure and requirements, hardware and software allocation, constraints, costs and schedules. Clearly, if this phase is incomplete or imprecise the whole of the future work is at risk. The systems analysis phase is therefore one of intense communication between customer and analyst. Customers must be able to state and understand system goals, analysts must know what to ask of the customer, offer advice on a whole range of topics and research those that are necessary. The specification document represents the first 'deliverable' in the engineering process. It will be closely studied by the customer and reviewed if necessary. Once its contents are stabilized by customer–engineer consensus, the next step can begin.

Software requirements analysis is the first step in the software engineering process. Its purpose is one of discovery and refinement. The scope of the software identified by the systems analysis as a series of generalized statements is distilled into a concrete specification that forms the basis of the development phase. Although the requirements analysis is usually associated with the definition phase, it naturally bridges the gap between definition and development since the objects and functions that it identifies form the basis of the data, architectural and procedural design philosophy. Frequently then, the techniques used during this aspect of the engineering process are often referred to by the general term '...analysis and design'. However, the term 'design' refers to the overall (abstract) description of the system rather than the software. The latter is the exclusive responsibility of the development phase.

2.2 PRINCIPLES OF REQUIREMENTS ANALYSIS

Over the last 20 years or so a number of analysis and specification methods have emerged, each with a unique notation, graphical representation and point of view. However, all methods are driven by the need to address the three fundamental principles of requirements analysis:

- To understand and describe the *information domain* of the system.
- To reduce complexity by partitioning the problem into manageable levels.
- To present implementation-independent descriptions of the functions to be accomplished and information to be processed.

The information domain is a conceptual picture of the data held by an organization and processed by the computer. Traditionally, the domain has been viewed in at least three different ways: as a *flow* of information described by the ways in which processes change data as it moves through the organization; as information *content* describing precisely what data the items of information contain; and as an information *structure* describing the way one piece of information is related to others and (to some extent) what that means. It is understandable therefore that most requirements analysis techniques make use of one or more of these views of the domain. It is not our intention to develop the full detail of any particular method here. Indeed, I hope readers will be familiar (or soon will be) with the major methods through first year or on-going second year studies, but an appreciation of the range of techniques available and their integration into large-scale manual or automated methodologies is a useful exercise which reinforces the point that the production of software has moved some way towards the levels of analysis and design long associated with traditional engineering.

The techniques most familiar to requirements analysis fall into two broad classes: those which are oriented towards data flow and those which describe data structure. Considerations of data content tend to appear naturally as a feature of both. Most of the techniques described in the next sections have been used in requirements analysis for many years and to some extent they can be regarded as representing a 'traditional' approach—at least as far as the term can be applied to the subject. During the late 1970s and early 1980s, however, other methods emerged, notably *Jackson Structured Design* (JSD) and the object-oriented approach. Some mention will be made of these for the sake of completeness.

2.3 DATA FLOW DIAGRAMS

Of the data flow school, the major technique is *data flow diagramming*. As information moves through an organization, it is transformed by the application of a series of processes. A data flow diagram (DFD) is a graphical technique that captures the flow and transformation of data as it moves from input(s) to output(s) or from a net originator to a net receiver. Figure 2.1 shows a very simple DFD illustrating the manager of a department registering a new programmer and associating that individual with a particular project. The diagram also shows the dismissal of an existing programmer. The key explains the diagram notation.

A DFD is therefore a process-oriented technique composed of four basic elements: *data stores*, *data flows*, *processes*, and external entities of *source* and *sink*. The description of the information domain would be incomplete, however, if these elements were not considered further. Each arrow in the DFD represents the 'flow' of an item or items of information and some mechanism to represent content must also be available. The same mechanism must also define the content of a data store. Similarly, each box represents a process, and a description of that process should also augment the diagram. Consequently, a data dictionary and procedural description language are also available to analysts using the technique.

Data dictionaries usually employ a 'quasi-formal' grammar to describe the content of an information item in a manner similar to that indicated in Fig. 2.2. Here the dictionary entry describes the composition of a departmental telephone number. The notation used in this grammar is as follows:

$$= \quad \text{is composed of}$$
$$| \quad \text{or (a selection)}$$
$$+ \quad \text{and (a sequence)}$$

The dictionary statement may therefore be read: a telephone number is composed of either a local extension or an outside number or 0 (for operator). Local extension and outside number represent composite data items themselves and are further defined in other dictionary statements. In these definitions we assume the usual understanding of the terms 'subscriber access number' and 'area code'.

Key

| Process | Data store | Source | Sink | Flow line |

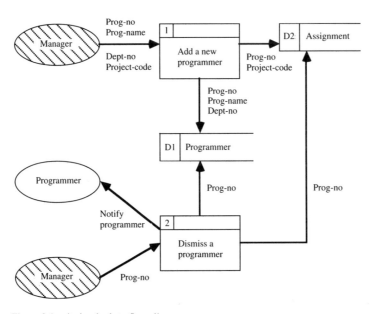

Figure 2.1 A simple data flow diagram.

Telephone number	= [local extension | outside number | 0]
local extension	= [1001 | 1002 | .. | 1999]
outside number	= 9 + [local number | long distance number]
local number	= subscriber access number
long distance number	= area code + local number

Figure 2.2 Data dictionary notation. The entry defines the composition of a departmental telephone number in terms of composite data (data that can be further divided) and elementary data (data that cannot be further divided).

The dictionary expands until all composite items have been represented in terms of elementary items or until all composite items are represented in terms that are well known and unambiguous to all readers. For large systems where the DFD is extremely complex, the dictionary grows rapidly. Maintaining the dictionary manually is a difficult task, and most systems ultimately automate the process. The process descriptions can be achieved in a number of ways, such as structured English, pseudo-code, decision tables or trees. With a similar quasi-formal approach to the description of processes, these too can form part of the data dictionary.

2.4 DATA ANALYSIS

A DFD represents the dynamic view of organization where the concept of change plays a major role in the descriptive process. However, a description characterized purely in these terms is somewhat unstable, in that old processes are often dropped or altered and new ones frequently added. Although processes may come and go, the data they operate upon remains relatively stable and forms the bedrock upon which the applications are built. Figure 2.3 draws an analogy with the foundations of skyscraper blocks. The foundations represent the data while the skyscrapers represent processes. The height of the skyscraper is proportional to its process activity.

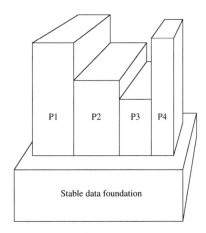

P1   P2   P3   P4

Stable data foundation

Figure 2.3 The skyscraper analogy.

This observation therefore presents the analyst with an alternative (but complementary) view of an organization through an understanding of the structure and content of its data. Techniques developed here are grouped together under the general term 'data analysis' and normalization and entity–relationship (E–R) modelling are the foremost available. Both have been closely associated with relational database theory, but as techniques they are much more widely applicable. Indeed, even if we were to consider them as a purely relational concept, the wide use of that data model for information systems development would be sufficient for them to be included as important analytical techniques for the software engineer.

Normalization developed originally as part of the theory of large databases proposed by Codd (1970) and to some extent should be seen as part of its wider philosophy of relations, relational operators and integrity constraints. Normalization has two fundamental objectives. First, to reduce the information domain to a description that consists of elemental rather than composite (array-like) data items (this was both a theoretical and a performance requirement of the approach) and secondly, to remove certain undesirable features of its maintenance. It is a process of successive decomposition whereby an original (complex) entity is reduced to progressively simpler forms. When properly executed, it retains the original information content, removes the maintenance anomalies and achieves this without introducing any redundant material that would otherwise consume storage space or processing time.

Normalization proceeds in discrete steps. Unnormalized data sets are converted progressively to first, second, third and even fourth or fifth normal forms. For most purposes however, third normal form is acceptably stable. The process is somewhat subjective in that it depends heavily on the identification and use of data dependencies. For systems that are new and where representative data does not yet exist, exactly what depends on what is often open to discussion. When existing systems are analysed, data samples presented to an analyst may not contain occurrences of all possibilities so that, again, the set of dependencies is not absolute. The method, however, is flexible enough to accommodate changes to design made as a consequence of a better understanding of the system.

An information domain reduced to a third normal description is capable of being represented and manipulated by a wide range of software. For all implementations, the technique provides the developer with the assurance that the information domain is represented with minimal redundancy and is capable of being maintained consistently. The method does not address the question of functionality directly, but it is possible to subject the analysis to a thorough examination such that we become confident that it can support the functionality expected of it.

A subtle consequence of normalization is that it imposes, via the process of decomposition, implicit *semantics* (i.e. meaning), to the information domain. By 'meaning' we imply the establishment of relationships between entities. Relationships have been described as 'the stuff of data models' and they are imposed when the primary key of one entity appears as a foreign key in another, thereby establishing a connection between the two. This is sometimes called 'posting' the key. The semantics is implicit for it was not the primary consideration during the normalization process, rather it appears naturally as it proceeds. Normalization therefore begins with the detail of data occurrences, and while considering the maintenance of the data, develops a degree of meaning.

E–R modelling, introduced by Chen (1976) has its origins in the pioneering work of Bachmann (1969) in network and hierarchical data models. E–R modelling was an attempt to unify the view of data in an information domain by imposing from the outset an obligation to reveal relationships between entities (i.e. a more explicit semantics) together with a consideration of the maintenance of the data.

E–R modelling begins by considering the meaning of the information domain. Major entity types of interest to us are recognized and associated with unique identifiers (keys). The relationship(s) that one entity has to another (for example a customer to a sales order or an employee to a department) are enforced by posting keys as in the normalization approach or even by the creation of new relationship entities. The difference, however, is that such postings are a *primary* consideration of the E–R model. Once major entity types have been recognized and identified, the detail of the final analysis is achieved by associating attributes with entities in such a way that a set of third normal form tables results. In its simplest form then, E–R modelling can be seen as a process that inverts the philosophy of normalization. It begins the analysis at the relatively uncluttered level of entities and relationships and slowly develops to add detail. While normalization is a bottom-up data analysis technique, E–R modelling is best described as top down.

Like normalization, the result of E–R analysis is capable of implementation on a wide variety of software supporting relational, network or hierarchical data models. Chen (1976) suggested a series of operators to help achieve functionality but these are far less powerful than those of relational theory. Consequently, E–R models benefit from the application of relational operators and some authors (Date 1986) have commented that the model is merely a 'thin veneer' on the surface of the basic relational model. It is interesting to note, however, that since the widespread acceptance of E–R modelling as a data analysis technique, Codd (1979) has proposed a comprehensive extension to the relational model that considers semantics explicitly. Such 'semantic data models' contain data about the relationships that exist among entities as well as data about the entities themselves. Traditional databases contain entity data only, while the meaning of that data is stored at the conceptual level, not at the database level itself.

Finally, it is important to realize that a set of entities in third normal form is easily converted to an equivalent E–R diagram so that ultimately the two techniques converge to a common view of the structure, content and meaning of an information domain. Figure 2.4 shows a set of third normal form tables together with the associated E–R diagram for the original unnormalized entity 'programmer'. The structure of this entity is such that it describes a number of relationships within a single logical unit thus forcing the whole unit to be processed even when only one relationship may require updating. Some of the relationships we can easily deduce are those between programmers and departments, programmers and projects, etc. Note that the attribute 'project' associated with each row in 'programmer' is composite, in that values in this domain are repeated a number of times depending upon the individual programmer concerned. Some of the maintenance problems associated with the entity in this form are:

- To amend the name of a project we have to search the whole table and alter occurrences wherever they are found.
- New programmers cannot be added until they are associated with a project and a new project cannot be added until it has at least one programmer assigned to it.
- If a project has just one programmer assigned and the programme's details are removed from the table, then we lose details of the project as well.

The third normal form entities in the E–R diagram however consist of 'atomic' elements and avoid the problems of maintenance associated with 'programmer'. In addition, we can see almost by inspection that the table set would efficiently satisfy the functionality embodied by the addition, amendment or dismissal of programmers or even projects. Notice also the explicit reference to relationships amongst the entities of an E–R diagram ($l:l$, $l:m$ and $m:n$) and the equivalent postings of keys in the third normal form tables. Later parts of the book make quite extensive use of this scenario.

Prog-no	Prog-name	Dept-no	Dept-name	Man-no	Man-name	Project-code	Project-name	Time-spent
P1	Jack	D1	Systems	P10	Jenny	J1	Notes	3
						J3	Biblio	3
						J3	Normal	7
P2	Jill	D1	Systems	P10	Jenny	J2	Biblio	6
						J3	Normal	7
P3	Julie	D2	Operations	P15	Jocasta	J1	Notes	8
						J2	Biblio	4
						J4	RDBMS	12
P4	Jenny	D2	Operations	P15	Jocasta	J2	Biblio	5
						J4	RDBMS	9

Figure 2.4(a) The original unnormalized data *programmer*.

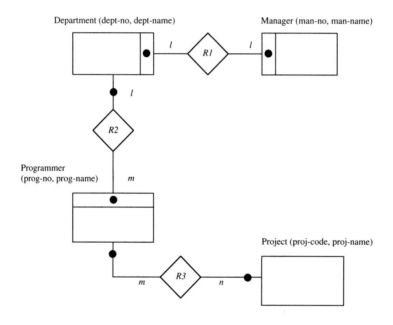

Explanation of relationships

R1 (*l*:*l*) a manager manages just one department, a department has just one manager
R2 (*l*:*m*) a department has many programmers, programmers belong to one department
R3 (*m*:*n*) a programmer has many projects, projects involve many programmers

Obligatory membership   Optional membership

Figure 2.4(b) The E–R diagram.

Programmer(prog-no, prog-name, dept-no)
Department(dept-no, dept-name, man-no, man-name)
Project(project-code, project-name)
Assignment(prog-no, project-code, time-spent)

Figure 2.4(c)   The third normal form table definitions (primary keys underlined).

2.5 ENTITY LIFE HISTORIES

For the engineer using an E–R or normalization approach to analysis, the entity life
history (ELH) diagram adds an extra dimension. An E–R diagram (however obtained)
represents a static description of the real-world events it is meant to model. An entity,
however, has a dynamic aspect to its nature in that it participates in a particular life
cycle of creation, use and obsolescence and the fact that it is *used* indicates a connection
with the processing requirements. An ELH diagram is therefore used by the analyst to
chart the use of an entity by the processes involved in an information system. Clearly it
has a primary objective to connect those entities of an E–R model with the processes of
a DFD that use the entity. The ELH in Fig. 2.5 represents part of the programmer–
project system we used earlier and illustrates the life history of the programmer entity
from registration with the company, through a particular series of project assignments
to a final dismissal.

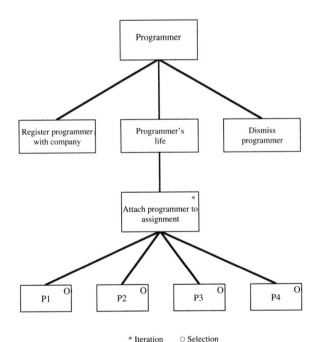

Figure 2.5   A simple entity life history diagram for the *programmer* entity.

2.6 RECONCILING THE THREE VIEWS

It is important to realize that the three views of a system presented to us by DFDs, E–R diagrams and ELHs are closely related, and strenuous efforts must be made by analysts to preserve consistency between them at all times. Data stores, for example, will always be made up from a whole number of entities and these must be present in the E–R diagram. Items of information that flow through a DFD must similarly be associated with the attributes of these entities, and an ELH diagram must associate each entity of the E–R diagram with a process in the DFD. Entities that exist without participating in an associated process must be treated with suspicion. Much of the information associated with these techniques is trapped in the data dictionary which therefore acts as a powerful check on the consistency of these three views.

2.7 JSD AND OBJECT-ORIENTED ANALYSIS

Of the remaining techniques, Michael Jackson's system design (JSD) has been widely used since the publication of his influential book (Jackson 1983), while increasing interest has been focused on 'object' oriented approaches (OOAs) to analysis and design (Booch 1986, 1991).

JSD is a technique which covers most of the project life cycle either directly or as a framework in which more suitable techniques can be embedded. In its latest edition (Cameron 1986) the method consists of three phases, the modelling phase, the network phase and the implementation phase: The first two phases of JSD address the problem of system analysis and design rather than software—although the latter can be derived directly once the former is established. OOAs on the other hand constitute a partial life cycle technique focusing on the design and implementation only. OOAs have matured in the last decade, so much so that Rentsch (1982) predicted that:

> Object oriented programming [*and presumable analysis/design*] would be to the 80s what structured programming [*analysis/design*] was to the 70s.

This prediction has a partial ring of truth to it, for object-oriented languages such as Smalltalk (Goldberg and Robson 1983) formed the basis of a wide range of products during the 1980s. But whereas JSD has become reasonably well established among the academic and commercial communities, the time does not yet appear to have fully come for OOAs and this may be due to a number of factors: there seems to be confusion between object-oriented analysis/design and object-oriented programming, some argue that not all systems benefit from the approach and traditional analysis techniques provide only partial support when an object-oriented solution to a problem is foreseen. OOAs however, offer important advantages to the software engineer and the method is quite literally 'bubbling' beneath the surface and about to become a substantial influence in the very near future.

2.8 CORRECTNESS

The final stage of requirements analysis should establish that we have achieved the elements of a solution that meets the needs of the customer. The next major phase, the engineering process, is geared towards the code that ultimately becomes the final delivered product, and the production of that code is guided totally by what has been discovered and refined by the analysis. The correctness of the analysis in forming the basis of a successful solution therefore has to be explored both with the customer using techniques of rapid prototyping and among developers with the structured walkthrough. Just what constitutes a correct analysis is, of course, open to discussion, but we must at least establish that our analysis is complete, consistent and a sound basis for the development phase.

Prototyping is concerned primarily with the fact that the final product, based on the results of the analysis, meets the requirements of the customer *before* it is actually engineered. Most methods for defining requirements are designed to establish a final, complete, consistent and correct set of requirements before the system is designed and constructed, but often before it is eventually experienced by the user. In many cases the user may reject applications as neither correct nor complete upon delivery even though the developer may be satisfied. Consequently, much (expensive) remedial work is necessary to harmonize the performance of products with customer needs. The prototype represents a small-scale model of the final software in appearance if not in performance. Ideally, existing software such as report generators, screen painters, etc., are used to create a facsimile of the system in rapid fashion. The customer 'test drives' the application, and suggests modification. Applied iteratively, this process strengthens the original analysis and ensures that the developer knows precisely the form a product acceptable to the customer will take. It must be emphasized however, that when throwaway prototyping is used, no real programming or development has yet occurred and that any form of prototyping is a consensus rather than an absolute technique.

Structured walkthroughs, on the other hand, are internal group meetings held among members of the development team, the primary purpose of which is to expose the analysis (or any other phase of software engineering) to a peer group review. This technique, developed originally both by Weinberg (1971) and at IBM as 'team debugging', tries to remove the natural tendency that an analysis is seen as an extension of the analyst. As we are unlikely to find fault in our own work an informal review by colleagues is desirable.

As a final point, the role of the data dictionary should be mentioned as an element in the drive towards 'correctness'. References herein are capable of automatic checks for consistency, such that a data store of a DFD has a corresponding entity in the E–R diagram. The fact that such a correlation exists does not make the design correct, but it does help the overall process in that it eliminates an inconsistency which could otherwise contribute to an incorrect solution. Prototyping, dictionaries and structured walkthroughs, therefore, represent the extent to which 'correctness' is traditionally examined prior to the development phase.

2.9 SUMMARY

We have spent some time reviewing those aspects of software engineering that contribute to the definition phase of the life cycle. Because this phase forms the basis of all future engineering work, it is critical that the final specification, however expressed, is shown to be capable of leading on to a successful product. During the analysis the designer may 'paint with a broad brush' and it is possible (indeed desirable) that the final specification will incorporate many different techniques in an attempt to capture as complete a view of the system as possible. The wide range of methods available to the design team helps communication with the customer, in that alternative and more easily understood representations can be presented in order to clarify certain aspects. A continual review of this stage between customer and designer is essential to ensure that both have the same perception of the system to be built. Clearly, the definition phase of the life cycle will be applied iteratively until customer–designer consensus stabilizes the specification.

The techniques discussed here are largely diagramming and notational ones having some parallels with those in traditional engineering (engineering drawings might serve as a useful comparison). We have already noted that there are differences between the engineering of software and that of a real-world object and so we could not expect to see many similarities in the two sets of design techniques. What has emerged, however, is that the computing community has made great efforts with the introduction of these techniques to structure and discipline the design process and this aspect correlates well with the methods of traditional engineering.

There are still points to discuss concerning the requirements analysis phase, such as its integration into a large-scale life cycle methodology (see Sec. 3.8). But more important is its role in driving the remainder of the engineering work. All the techniques discussed so far have been semi-, quasi- or 'soft' formalisms making heavy use of diagrams to express the specification. Such formalisms are subject to a variety of standards and are therefore inherently ambiguous. When using soft formalisms, it is not possible to create an absolute standard against which the correctness of the subsequent program code can be measured. The remaining engineering work is therefore always at risk.

3

THE DEVELOPMENT AND MAINTENANCE PHASES OF SOFTWARE ENGINEERING

CHECKLIST OF OBJECTIVES

After reading this chapter you should be able to:

- Appreciate the basis of the techniques used by software engineers to convert specifications into reliable software systems.
- Understand that software development is a highly structured and disciplined activity.
- Understand the influence software development techniques and their application have on the subsequent maintenance effort.
- Appreciate the role of large-scale methodologies and CASE.

3.1 INTRODUCTION

Having completed quite a detailed review of software definition, this chapter addresses the *development* and *maintenance* phases of contemporary software engineering. Whereas definition is concerned with *what* the software must achieve, development deals with *how* this is to be brought about. Since the early 1970s or so the software engineering community has made great strides to discipline its approach to definition such that its final description is a stable and well-understood document; in this respect certain techniques of analysis and design have become widespread and standard. In parallel with developments in definition, techniques have been introduced into the development phase which have imparted equal discipline to the activity; these techniques are closely related to, and dependent upon, those of the definition phase. In this way, contemporary software engineering has emerged as a highly organized activity proceeding in discrete steps in much the same way as traditional engineering.

The final product of the development phase is a software system of some sort, the characteristic behaviour of which has to be determined and compared with the requirements of the definition phase. This aspect of the development phase is termed *testing* and a wide range of test strategies aimed at causing a software unit to fail have been developed. Even though the development of software always proceeds with the definition phase in mind, we must accept testing as a necessary part of software production because contemporary software engineering has not yet developed techniques which engender a high degree of confidence in the product produced by their primary application.

Once software has been released and goes 'live', problems usually arise and modifications have to be made to alter its behaviour. This is the final phase of the process and is known as maintenance. In this chapter we take a brief look at the various techniques involved in software development and maintenance so that the reader has a balanced view prior to reading the remaining parts of the book. We should also point out that although software development (on a large scale) is subject to project planning and control, we do not address this aspect of the life cycle.

3.2 PROGRAMMING LANGUAGE DEVELOPMENT

By the late 1960s, powerful new third-generation languages had been introduced which offered programmers unparalleled opportunities to build the complex software systems beginning to be demanded by the user communities. However, the ad hoc techniques associated with software production at this time guaranteed unproductive use of these new languages, leading to products that suffered slippage in delivery times and proved difficult to maintain. Indeed, many pieces of complex software simply were not delivered or did not work at all! The developments in programming that occurred around this time were therefore largely concerned with imparting standardization and discipline to the development process. As with analysis, the software engineering community saw *structure* as a primary tool in this mechanism; structure not only in the programming language itself but also in its associated design, such that aspects of design were supported directly by constructs within the language, making the migration from one to the other relatively straightforward.

In this respect *structured programming and design* emerged as a major influence in the late 1960s and early 1970s. This movement was seen as an attempt to offer a disciplined methodology for software development based on what were generally accepted ideas as to an appropriate syntax for the procedural languages of the time. Software produced in this fashion offered at least some of the following attributes—although this is neither a complete nor universally accepted list:

- has been developed according to some well-known appropriate method or authority or
- has been built from simple language constructs such as sequence, selection and iteration or
- has eliminated the 'goto' statement or
- has been developed in top-down fashion or
- any combination of the above

Structured languages emerged before the techniques of design were properly formulated. This was largely as a result of the dependence of the latter on the former and the ease with which the syntax of existing languages could be modified to those of 'classic' structured languages such as Algol and Pascal. Features of all structured languages were the elimination of the 'goto' and support for relatively few program control structures. In fact, advocates of structured programming (Dahl *et al.* 1972) suggested only three control structures were necessary: the *sequence*, the *selection* and the *iteration*.

These were often accompanied by codes of best practise which guided the circumstances under which they were to be used together with `begin...end` block formats which, in the absence of the goto, forced program execution into a continual forward advance. At the same time, styles of program writing emerged such as the indentation of program lines within blocks and explanatory comments in the source code. (See Kernighan and Plauger (1974) as a typical example of the writings of the time.)

The simplest of the control structures is the sequence in which each sentence (*S*) in the software is executed just once, for example:

```
begin
  S1;
  S2;
  ⋮
  Sn
end
```

Selection, on the other hand, is a control construct that permits us to deal with a number of different situations in different ways. Typical examples of this construct are:

- A single branch selection: `if` *condition* `then` *action* `endif`
- a double branch selection: `if` *condition* `then` *action*1 `else` *action*2 `endif`
- or finally a multibranch selection:

```
case
condition1 : action1
condition2 : action2
  ⋮
conditionn : actionn
else action
end
```

In each example the *conditions* and *actions* are often compound constructs themselves.

The final control structure is the iteration or loop which permits a number of software sentences to be executed over and over until some terminating condition is met. Once again a number of variations exist:

- Looping a fixed number of times is achieved by the `for...next` structure:

```
for n times
begin
  action
end
next n
```

- Looping at least once can be achieved with the repeat...until... construct:

```
repeat
begin
  action
end
until condition
```

- While looping only if a condition is *true* can be achieved with the while...do... construct:

```
while condition do
begin
  action
end
endwhile
```

Writing structured programs has a number of advantages among which are *readability*, *portability* and *maintainability*, because only a fixed number of construction units are used in accordance with well-accepted codes of conduct. At the same time, the program logic has become amenable to a process of reasoning from which its behaviour can be deduced. It is not surprising therefore to learn that at this time serious research into provability and correctness began.

3.3 TECHNIQUES FOR DERIVING STRUCTURED PROGRAMS

Program design is simply a process whereby the specification embodied in the definition phase is transformed to a description close to actual code. This final description is detailed enough to be used to produce programs in a variety of appropriate languages. There are essentially two schools of thought concerning how this transformation should be achieved. These are based on the two possible views of a system and both represent techniques for structured program design. In the first of these, Yourdon and Constantine (1979) propose the achievement of structured design through a *functional* decomposition approach, i.e. one that takes a process-biased view. Typical components of this approach are:

- Program modularity
- Module hierarchies
- Black box descriptions
- Cohesion and coupling

together with the use of a graphical device called the *Structure Chart* which helps produce structured programs.

In the second approach (due largely to Warnier (1971) and Jackson (1975)), the basic premise is that the structure of the *data* determines the structure of the program. *Jackson Structured Programming* (JSP) uses the notion of a *structure diagram* to represent the structure of both the data and the program(s). Structure diagrams are converted easily to a language-independent pseudo-code using a *schematic logic* developed by Jackson.

The functional approach was introduced and made fashionable by Edward Yourdon and Larry Constantine through their influential book first published in 1979. The authors' main theme was that the fundamental problem with software is its complexity. They introduced a number of techniques for dealing with complexity dubbed simply 'structured design'. Structured design embodies two principal aspects:

- Partitioning of the system into a collection of communicating black boxes.
- Organizing these boxes into a hierarchy with well-defined roles at each level.

A black box is a software module which has a single identifiable purpose with clearly defined inputs and outputs. The term 'black box' is derived from another property that reduces complexity—we need not know how the module functions in order to be able to use it. Separate black boxes are needed for each well-defined part of the problem, and the partitioning of the system should be carried out such that any connection (communication) between the boxes is introduced only if there is some logical relationship between those parts of the problem. All connections are therefore essential ones and are kept as simple as possible. Excessive connectivity is seen as adding to complexity and Yourdon and Constantine introduced two empirical concepts which acted as a measure of the connectivity of the elements of the solution—*coupling* and *cohesion*.

Coupling is a measure of the degree of interdependence between the software in black box modules. The objective of good design is to achieve low coupling, for this in turn minimizes *ripple effects*—errors in one program appearing as symptoms in another—and permits changes in one module to be made with minimum effect on others. Low coupling denotes a well-partitioned system, and to help designers achieve this Yourdon and Constantine detailed major (graded) categories of coupling and suggested ways in which each could be achieved or avoided.

Cohesion, on the other hand, describes how closely the elements within a single module are related to each other. What is needed are strong, highly cohesive modules whose elements are genuinely related to one another. Clearly, cohesion and coupling are related in that the greater the cohesion the lower the coupling. In order that modules be made as cohesive as possible Yourdon and Constantine developed an empirical scale of cohesion which suggested that a strongly functionally cohesive module is one which contains elements that all contribute to only one problem-related task. Using this scale, designers could again determine ways to achieve or avoid the various degrees of cohesion.

The second aspect of good design concerns the way in which the black boxes are organized into hierarchies to achieve some overall functionality. Here it is useful to draw an analogy between the structure of the software and that of some business organization which carries out its tasks according to the general guidelines applying to most information systems, for example:

- Modules may be segregated into managers and workers.
- Managers should have no more than seven workers subordinate to them.
- Actual work must be performed by the workers with the managers acting as coordinators and facilitators.

In such an architecture control is present in the upper parts of the hierarchy while work is done at the lower levels. Communication between the various levels is achieved through well-defined channels with strict protocols and simple messages.

Designs based on the general principles suggested by Yourdon and Constantine are eventually converted to structured programs via a device called the structure chart, which in turn is derived from an appropriate data flow diagram (DFD) (see Sec. 2.3). A DFD is a statement of requirement; it declares what transformations on data have to be achieved. It represents the last step of the definition phase but the first step in the development phase. A structure chart is a statement of design; it shows how that transformation is to be brought about using the principles of good structured design. Those developing structured programs using Yourdon therefore have to master both the notation of structure charts and the mechanism that enables such charts to be drawn from DFDs.

Structure charts are graphical tools which represent the hierarchical nature of a well-designed system. A typical chart is shown in Fig. 3.1.

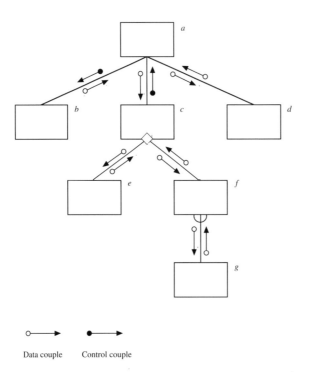

Figure 3.1 Basic elements of Yourdon and Constantine's structure chart.

Each labelled rectangular box represents a software module—a set of contiguous programming language statements, the detail of which need not concern us at this stage of the design, i.e. it is a black box. The lines between modules represent connections and suggest that the subordinate module is 'called' from the superior module; this of course imposes hierarchy in the diagram. Whether a call involves an element of data or control passing between the modules is denoted by the data or control couples—

directed arrows running along the connection lines. Data couples have open tails; control couples have filled tails. The connections and couples therefore show the communication (interface) between the components by showing what data and flags are passed to an operation when it is called and what data and flags are returned by the operation once it has completed its task. Sequential control over module calls is shown in the diagram when subordinate modules are called from superior modules. The modules are called in left to right order. Thus, *a* calls *b* followed by *c* followed by *d*. Conditional choice is indicated by the decision lozenge ($\Diamond$) while iteration on the call is denoted by the curved line across the appropriate connection. In Fig 3.1, module *c* conditionally chooses *e* or *f* while module *f* calls *g* iteratively. With structured programming constructs corresponding to each of these forms of control, the chart is converted quite readily to program code.

The semantics behind a structure chart is really quite informal; the basic idea is simply to produce a hierarchical diagram with a control module (manager) calling one or more processing modules (workers) and where each worker module corresponds largely to a process in the DFD. Yourdon and Constantine suggested a method of *transform analysis* to convert DFDs to structure charts. Transform analysis separates processes that deal with high-level inputs and high-level outputs from those that are associated largely with physical input and output. High-level inputs and outputs are defined as those that are as far removed from physical I/Os as possible, yet still constitute inputs to the system. An example might be a data item that has first been input through the keyboard, then validated, then added to an index and finally used as input to some process. Only in its final form is it a high-level input and transform analysis isolates processes that operate with it in this form. Once central transforms like these have been revealed, we build the structure chart with a top-level control module and subordinate modules to get–validate–index the data flow, transform the data flow and finally 'output' the data flow. Each of these modules may require further factoring, such that each becomes a control with its own crop of workers. In this fashion, a structure chart gradually emerges.

The alternative to Yourdon suggests that data rather than functionality determines the structure of the program. Probably the best-known data-oriented structured program design methodology was developed by Jackson in the mid 1970s (Jackson, 1975). Much of this work eventually became incorporated into JSD mentioned in the previous chapter. JSP therefore represents the technique by means of which the model processes of a JSD network diagram are realized. Given that we are now designing programs from data, we need a notation for representing both data structures and program structures; JSP achieves this with a hierarchical device called a structure diagram. Structure diagrams are really only entity life history diagrams (see Sec. 2.5) which link entities (data) to the process(es) that use them. This in turn suggests that the diagrams are best constructed once the E–R modelling exercise and DFDs have been completed.The diagram uses three basic constructs corresponding to sequence, selection and iteration with the same notation as the ELH in Chapter 2.

The structure diagram looks similar to Yourdon's structure chart. As far as the overall program structure design is concerned both diagrams are equivalent. However, only the structure chart shows data passing between modules, while only the structure diagram has an associated schematic logic (or structured text) designed to translate the diagram into a form more amenable to coding. The schematic logic is essentially a language-independent pseudo-code corresponding to the various sequences, selections and iterations in the diagram. This pseudo-code is similar to that introduced earlier in the chapter. Structure diagrams therefore generate pseudo-code that migrates readily to any target language.

3.4 IMPLEMENTATION OF OBJECT-ORIENTED DESIGNS

The techniques of structured programming described in Sec. 3.3 evolved to support 'traditional' software development based largely on descriptions in terms of DFDs and ELHs. It might therefore be assumed that the need to implement object-oriented designs has generated corresponding techniques based on the analysis and design tools of the object model (class hierarchies, Booch diagrams, etc., see Booch (1991)). However, this has not been quite the case. In the object-oriented approach, emphasis is placed on the design stage which produces descriptions in terms of communicating objects with clearly defined interfaces and functionality. Implementation of these designs requires a commitment to the interface first, followed by 'stubbing out' the representational and procedural detail of the object itself. In this respect, traditional third-generation languages *can* be used and therefore benefit from the techniques of deriving structured programs described in Sec. 3.3. However, object designs are probably more sympathetically implemented using object-oriented languages whose syntax and structure have evolved to mirror closely the terminology used in the object-oriented design itself. Object-oriented languages are those which possess direct constructs to support objects that are data abstractions with an interface of named operations and a hidden local state, that have an associated type or class and which may inherit attributes from supertypes or superclasses. In this respect languages such as C++ are widely used so that the methodology of structured program design for object-oriented solutions corresponds largely to that suggested for the proper construction of (say) C++ programs with an appropriate correspondence between the features of the design and the facilities of the language. Such techniques are described in most books on C++. (See for example Cantu and Tendon (1992) which describes program construction using Borland C++ version 3.1—a standard form of the language.)

3.5 SOFTWARE TESTING

The correctness of a specification is determined by walkthroughs with the design team and prototyping with the customer. Subsequent structured design techniques largely ensure that the requirements embodied in the specification are translated to appropriate program code. So why then test the software we produce? The reason lies primarily in the informal semantics associated with the techniques used throughout the definition and development phases. Even in the most carefully controlled software development environments, misconceptions, misunderstandings and ignorance of what is required will exist because the diagrams and notation of the various techniques are often open to more than one interpretation, while none of the techniques at the development phase have ever attempted to address the retrospective process of being able to show that structured code they produced actually satisfies the requirements. This process of course being confounded by the poor semantics which is insufficiently rich to capture all the requirements of the real world. Consequently, because we cannot prove our software correct by some process of formal verification, we have to establish confidence in the product by some kind of machine testing. It is interesting to note that Booch (1991) has observed that these points apply equally well to object-oriented implementations.

A machine test involves the examination of the behaviour of a particular software unit under actual or simulated operational conditions with one or more carefully selected inputs. From the observed behaviour of the unit we deduce its acceptability. A good test is essentially a destructive activity—one that causes the unit to fail. When devising test plans input should be chosen that is most likely to cause failure. This of course suggests that if the data is badly selected, or if a particular test case cannot be achieved simply because test time is limited, then an error will go undetected and be present when the software is released. Testing is therefore an inherently inadequate verification technique which, in the absence of anything better, has to be made as effective as possible. In this respect we should ensure that testing is.

- Thoroughly planned and its results well documented.
- Executed methodically with sensibly devised strategies and appropriate techniques.
- Subject to judiciously chosen test cases so that eventual failure-free behaviour indicates a high probability of its operational correctness.

Most contemporary test strategies regard software units as 'boxes', in particular black boxes or white boxes. Black boxes have the same properties as those in structured design, namely their functionality is known in terms of inputs and outputs but the internal detail of how that transformation is achieved is not. When a unit is regarded as a white box its internal detail is also available to us. Black box testing therefore simply ensures that a unit's output(s) are as expected when fed with input(s) within the tolerance of its specification. White box testing, however, is largely concerned with examining each of the various pathways through the unit from inputs to outputs, that each is achievable under appropriate circumstances, and that when executed they perform adequately and without side-effects. In practice, testing is a combination of both approaches and testing a large software system as boxes occurs at various levels:

- *Subprogram testing*   White box testing with emphasis on internal structures
- *Program testing*   White box on program structure, black box on subprograms
- *Subsystem testing*   Interface testing on black boxes of the subsystem assembly
- *System testing*   Demonstration that overall the system meets its specification

As the software system evolves from program(s) to final system the integration of the various units is carefully controlled. *Bottom-up integration* is the classic approach to software testing. Units are all tested individually and then combined one by one (vertically or horizontally) into higher assemblies which in turn are tested until the top level is reached. *Top-down integration* begins by testing the overall control structure then adds the subordinate units one by one, migrating eventually to the lowest level. As each new unit is added (vertically or horizontally) the partially complete structure is tested again. Various other strategies are also possible, especially in cases where the structure of the system as a whole is not hierarchical and therefore would not respond well to the previous integration techniques. The final phases of the integration involve acceptance tests usually conducted by independent parties to obtain corroborative evidence that the system fulfils its specification. Finally, under customer control the system goes live. Of course this represents the ideal case; not all component test levels necessarily occur.

It is clear from the previous paragraphs that software testing is a necessary but time-consuming business. Consequently the industry has developed tools to aid the testing process together with debuggers to find and cure the problems. With all this effort, one feels duty bound to ask the question: what has software testing contributed to an overall philosophy of program design? The answer is: nothing.

3.6 THE MAINTENANCE OF SOFTWARE

Maintenance is very much a blanket term used to cover all the activities that occur once the software goes live and has to be reconfigured. Reconfiguration of software is quite common and gives rise to a number of maintenance categories. The first and most obvious of these is *corrective maintenance* which arises simply because errors (either known or unknown at the point of software release) are usually present in the product. Secondly, changes may occur externally to the software but may impinge upon it. Such changes may involve operating system upgrades, database reorganization, etc., and lead to *adaptive maintenance*. Finally, small-scale on-going developments may occur which make the software more acceptable to the users, e.g. improving response times or redesigning the human–computer interface. Such activities come under the heading of *perfective maintenance*.

In 1980, the results of a very large-scale investigation into maintenance were published, covering almost 500 organizations (Leintz and Swanson 1980). The survey found that of the total time devoted to maintenance, just over 20 per cent was taken up with corrective work, just under 25 per cent by adaptive work and over 50 per cent by perfective work, while user-driven enhancements accounted for 42 per cent of total maintenance effort. Indeed, both user demands for enhancements together with poor quality documentation were seen as the two most severe problems facing us in the maintenance of software. In the intervening years there has been no real evidence to suggest that much has changed—especially in traditionally organized 'data processing' departments—although a more recent examination of maintenance can be found in IEEE (1987).

Maintenance is responsible for by far the largest cost in the software engineering life cycle so reducing maintenance is an important consideration. There are two ways to achieve it:

1. By making software more reliable thereby reducing the need for maintenance in the first place.
2. By building maintainability into software.

Achieving both of these revolves around engineering *quality* into the final product.

Quality software implies that it has been produced by a disciplined process of specification and development with due regard to the detection and correction of defects. This of course cuts down the incidence of corrective action and contributes to point 1. Maintenance of the adaptive and perfective types will always be unavoidable and this observation leads directly to point 2. In this latter respect, maintenance is enhanced if the product is modifiable, understandable and testable, which in turn suggests that quality software can only be regarded as such if it is accompanied by quality documentation. In traditional software engineering environments, engineering quality is the domain of the *quality assurance* personnel.

3.7 QUALITY ASSURANCE

Quality assurance (QA), the term applied to the general activities involved in attempting to ensure that a product will satisfy prespecified levels of performance and reliability, applies to all phases of the software life cycle from definition through to documentation and maintenance. In this respect QA cannot be addressed properly unless we have effective standards, procedures and techniques which are seen to be applied within the organization. Quality assurance is therefore enhanced when companies adopt large-scale methodologies for their software developments, because these often impose strict standards on the products at each phase of the life cycle. Such methodologies are discussed in the epilogue where this point can be borne in mind.

QA attempts to provide measurement data concerning the well-being of a project. Such quantitative data may be gathered about resource allocation, time spent, defects detected or cured and scheduling estimates for work yet to be performed. However, when most people think of QA they normally think in terms of the various *software metrics* that have evolved over the years, which attempt to provide indices of merit that can support quantitative evaluations and comparisons of software together with its associated design, development, use, maintenance and evolution. One of the simplest of the quality metrics has been suggested by DeMarco (1982) who defines quality in terms of the absence of 'spoilage'—the money and effort spent over the life cycle of the software in rectifying defects. DeMarco's metric is:

$$\frac{\text{Total cost of rectifying all defects}}{\text{Product size (usually in bytes)}}$$

where of course, the smaller the value the better. Software metrics have been the subject of a number of interesting books, two of the most influential being McCabe (1976) and Halstead (1977). Both attempt to measure software complexity; McCabe approaches the problem from the perspective of control flow complexity: within a program, while Halstead measures counts of operators and operands. The usefulness of metrics such as these has been the subject of much debate over the years, with a number of important correlations being claimed between the metrics and our understanding of software. The use of QA and software metrics will no doubt be extended and enhanced in future years. Once again it is interesting to note that Booch (1991) has observed that QA must be applied to object-oriented solutions with the same vigour as in traditional solutions.

3.8 LARGE-SCALE METHODOLOGIES

Previous chapters discussed a number of techniques that could be used in the various phases of software engineering. To some extent the techniques can be viewed in isolation and manufacturers are free to select those they feel appropriate during the life cycle of a project. Consequently, when assembling sets of techniques to facilitate the definition, development and maintenance of software, a large number of different engineering methodologies could be created. Indeed, it is possible for methodologies to be customized for each individual project but this is rarely the case. More frequently, a large-scale methodology is adopted and applied by an organization to all its software developments.

The association of techniques would be expected to be constrained by the obligation that they all belong to one of the two basic ways of considering design—functional or object-oriented. Functional designs tend to concentrate on developing process components with state information held in some shared data area. Object-oriented designs, on the other hand, associate data with processes. Whereas the techniques of functional design are well established (see for example Yourdon and Constantine (1979)), those of the object-oriented school are much less so. Indeed, the latter actively uses many techniques of the former. The line of distinction between the two approaches is therefore clearly drawn in terms of the final description of a system, but less so in terms of the techniques used to get there.

Whatever the methodology, the adoption of a development standard has clear benefits in terms of consistency, communication and understanding among the development teams. When selecting a large-scale methodology we have the choice of developing one in house, purchasing one off-the-shelf or the compromise choice of purchase with modification to company practice. The most popular of these is to purchase off the shelf. Customers as well as developers are often aware of the details of such products and by this choice the important aspects of communication and consistency are extended to include customers as well as developers. Many agencies are aware of this advantage and consequently a large number of off-the-shelf products are available to engineer real-time or commercial software. Representative examples are SADT (Schoman and Ross 1977) a structural analysis and design tool from Softech Inc., SREM (Alford 1977) a software requirements engineering methodology developed for time-critical, distributed real-time systems (such as in large defence systems), CORE, the controlled requirements expression method (Mullery 1979), MASCOT, the modular approach to software construction and testing for real-time systems, and SSADM, a structured systems analysis and design method developed originally by LBMS and CCTA in London and adopted by the UK government since 1981 for development of its projects (Ashworth and Goodland 1990). Additionally, JSD represents a flexible methodology certainly applicable to traditional solutions and (to some extent) object-oriented ones as well. No large-scale methodology has established itself for OOAs exclusively, although a number of different approaches have been suggested.

It is not our intention to develop the full detail of these techniques, but an exposure to the organization of exemplary methods permits a more complete understanding of the software engineering process as it is applied by the majority of practitioners today. In this respect a brief review of SSADM is certainly relevant.

3.8.1 SSADM: A structured systems analysis and design method

Figure 3.2 details the six stages of SSADM and the sequence in which they are applied. The activities embodied in these stages correspond closely to those we identified previously concerning the major phases of software engineering.

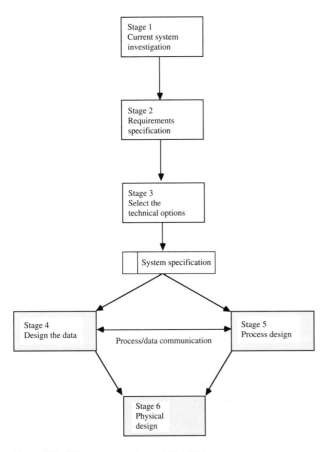

Figure 3.2   The stage structure of SSADM.

Each stage of SSADM is a large-scale activity in itself, consequently stages are divided into individual steps and each step is characterized by its input, output and tasks. The number of steps within a stage varies and each is labelled with a unique step number. The concept of a step decomposes the stage to manageable levels, while the step number indicates the sequence in which the aspects of the stage are to be applied and assists the documentation of each.

SSADM does not include specific procedures for project management and control as the various stages are traversed. Standards for project management and control must be selected before an SSADM methodology is applied. Many such standards are available and most address a common set of factors such as:

- Detailing what must be produced at each stage
- Defining how estimates, plans and budgets are developed, maintained and presented
- Defining how quality assurance is to be applied at each stage

Standards may be available internally within an organization. Alternatively, a commercially available project management and control methodology may be purchased and applied. The UK government, for example, uses PROMPT (Yeates 1986) and this has been specifically developed to complement an SSADM approach. The point to take on board is that SSADM responds to most techniques and users are able to integrate almost any methodology they feel appropriate. The free integration of SSADM with most project management methodologies is of course made possible because of its subdivision into stages, steps and tasks. Each of these can be treated in isolation by the monitoring processes or can be reviewed in groups.

Of the six major phases of SSADM, only stage 6 concerns itself with the physical design. Stages 1, 2, 4 and 5 discover, develop, specify and detail the system in a logical fashion. In this way a commitment to a particular architecture or hardware configuration can be left to as late a point as possible so that the technical options available to the customer via stage 3 can be fully evaluated and assessed. Changes and backtracking within a design can therefore be made freely. This approach clearly defers questions of cost (in terms of both the hardware purchased and cost of correction if the wrong commitment is made) until as late as possible. Recall from Chapter 3 that the cost of error is least in the design phase and greatest in the development and maintenance phase; SSADM therefore tries to give developers as much time as possible to 'get it right'.

3.8.2 Summarizing SSADM

In many ways SSADM typifies a large-scale functional methodology. It is highly structured, incorporates and integrates many different techniques, and has good documentary support. It has, however, been strictly limited to applications within the commercial sector, having facilities that ultimately address file structures and file-handling processes. In the same fashion, SSADM is rarely applied to real-time solutions and neither does it address questions of parallelism. The method is quite different from any other technique and therefore users cannot easily migrate. It relies for its solutions upon consensus and the understanding of its practitioners. SSADM places great emphasis on the separation of the logical and physical views of a system, but the techniques it uses to capture the abstract view are merely collections of notation and diagramming aids. SSADM possesses no ability to reason about the nature of its logical description neither does it support a mechanism to prove the correctness of the realization of its specifications. Whereas SSADM undoubtedly benefits from automation, automation does not imply an improved or indeed optimal solution. Large-scale methodologies are not standardized and, as such, SSADM practitioners cannot claim to have a universal language with which to develop system specifications.

When SSADM was introduced (1980), it addressed the majority of software development problems in the commercial sector. Since then, it has tried to move with the times and has developed new sets of first-cut rules as the popularity of various commercial products has increased. However, developments in the future may require commercial software to encompass not only traditional aspects but also more complex structures such as those of a manufacturer's database. Consequently, SSADM may well have to continue to expand its techniques in order to survive as a sustainable methodology in the long term.

3.9 AUTOMATING THE SOFTWARE ENGINEERING PROCESS

Until very recently, software development was a labour-intensive, unmanageable, unreliable, high-cost and high-risk activity. The appearance of large-scale methodologies by leading practitioners and procurement agencies can therefore be seen as a direct response to the problems of a variety of industrial sectors. Whereas these methodologies have undoubtedly contributed to an improvement in software quality and development times, the process of software engineering is still a costly activity that suffers slippage. Companies that commit themselves to a particular methodology expect their productivity to benefit by its application, but the benefits can be reduced because:

1. Many of the activities of a typical methodology are repetitive, mundane and therefore error prone when applied manually.
2. Documentation of the engineering process is important but can lead to an unmanageable proportion of paperwork and an unproductive use of staff resources.
3. Because of point 2, the communication is often less than it should be.
4. The techniques of a particular methodology may respond well to initial developments, but as an organization expands they may prove rigid and inflexible in its changing environment and therefore ultimately inappropriate.

A growing realization within the industry is that to gain maximum benefit from large-scale methodologies they really need automated support from a range of high-quality 'tools', i.e. software that helps build software. We have already introduced the concept of the software factory (see Chapter 1) and while the production of software differs from that of a tangible product, the analogy that tools are required to build software just as much as they are to build ships or cars is a valid one. Historically, the most significant increases in productivity have been associated with the replacement of human efforts by those of machines. Automation confers the same benefits to the engineering of software as it does to a traditional product.

A very productive area for software developments over the last few years has been in computer-aided software engineering (CASE), and today a wide variety of CASE tools are available to help automate the activities involved in a large-scale methodology. CASE is really just a new term for an old concept. Software tools to aid (say) programming have been available for some time. However, these tools were typically used with large time-sharing machines which were restricted in the amount of computational time they could devote to each user. CASE tools are generally computational and storage intensive, and it is only with recent developments in powerful, networked, single-user workstations that CASE has advanced significantly on a broader front.

Clear targets for automation are support tools for E–R, DFD and ELH diagrams integrated with a data dictionary acting as repository for these different views. Cross-referencing mechanisms within the dictionary permit consistency to be imposed and allow the automatic generation of parts of one diagram from the information held in another. The creation and editing of these diagrams are linked to the dictionary so that changes are captured immediately, while anomalies and errors can be reported directly during diagram creation or amendment. Other targets for automation are normalization, screen and document painting, report and sample data generators and code generators which generate code (or code segments) directly from a design captured in the central store. CASE products that support these features are called *workbenches*. Most workbenches tend to support the early stages of software engineering, being oriented towards automating the various graphical techniques. Some can be configured to support aspects of a specific methodology such as SSADM, while others simply support the techniques common to most methodologies.

Most CASE workbenches are first generation systems and Martin (1988) has indicated a number of deficiencies. Typical complaints are: workbenches are not integrated with other document preparation tools; they are all different, making migration across benches difficult; and most systems embody rigid rules for methods and standards and cannot be reconfigured. Frequently, the diagramming tools are described as slow. In an area of rapid transition, the vendors' attitudes to configurability and integration will be a critical factor in determining the sustainability of CASE products.

CASE has become an area of intense development since the mid-1980s. Large numbers of independent companies now offer CASE products while most computer manufacturers have embraced CASE technology and integrated it into their existing range. The broad range of problems treated by CASE and the products available can be seen by the major conferences devoted to the subject, together with the various special interest groups of the major professional organizations. CASE is still relatively new and few standards are available against which we can compare different products. Indeed, what should actually be automated when CASE is applied to a particular methodology is still unresolved. However, the technology seems set to impact more and more as an aid to the continuing problems of productivity, maintainability and cost. One interesting observation, however, is that by far the largest amount of time in software development is spent actually *fixing* software. Currently CASE has little to offer here and therefore may not contribute to productivity as effectively as some might lead us to expect.

3.10 SUMMARY

This chapter has presented a short review of the principal techniques used by contemporary software engineers to make the development and maintenance of software as successful as possible. The distribution of effort in software maintenance suggests that the structured design methods that ultimately provide program code are relatively successful, but the large amount of time devoted to perfective work indicates that the current specification techniques used by software engineers may be less than adequate in capturing and demonstrating the users' requirements. Poor specification then is responsible for much of the most costly effort in software engineering, therefore the major parts of this book are devoted to areas of research that raise specification to a much more accountable level, thereby contributing to the production of more reliable software systems.

SUMMARY OF PART 1

There seems little doubt that software engineering is a concept whose time has come. This is clearly evidenced by the success of the various structured methods applied to software production and the subsequent appearance of the related disciplines of information and knowledge engineering. Software engineering is still very young, yet it tackles problems of enormous complexity. In developing systematic approaches to control this complexity, software engineering can be expected both to evolve current methodologies and to incorporate a variety of new practices.

To what extent then should current practices be retained by the software engineering of the foreseeable future? The structured methods of contemporary engineering have been applied successfully in countless large projects and have resulted in measurable improvements in costs, productivity and reliability. A primary advantage of such methods is simply the presence of structure which imposes discipline and standards upon an historically confused process. Another apparent advantage lies in the soft (descriptive) formalisms that these techniques employ as the means of expressing their specifications. Such formalisms are understood by engineers and customers from a wide variety of backgrounds and can help establish a consensus in the critical initial phase of the software life cycle. Undoubtedly, the software engineering of the future will retain the structural aspect of current methodologies for the same reasons it is employed now. But the role of soft formalisms may be downgraded from one that acts as a vehicle for both specification *and* communication to one that simply addresses the latter. This reassessment of the role of soft formalism springs from an understanding of its disadvantages, which in terms of the ultimate goal of software engineering—the production of *error-free correct code*—outweigh its advantages.

In this respect it is somewhat paradoxical to realize that the major advantage of soft formalism is also its major disadvantage. Software specified in such terms is always capable of being checked for consistency but never fully capable of determining the correctness of the code it is used to generate. It cannot be used to reason about its logical descriptions (other than in an informal manner) neither is it unambiguous nor standard, for its notation and mode of employment often vary from one institution to another. The software engineering of the future will not be able to mechanize the intuitive and creative processes that lead to a specification, such activity is uniquely human. But we should expect it to be capable of expressing that specification in a form that avoids these current disadvantages.

The use of object-oriented approaches to software engineering will not be the immediate panacea that some have supposed, especially in the commercial sector. Indeed, whatever else we may say about structured methods developed around the functional approach, they *are* successful and deserve continued time and effort devoted to them. The obvious major contribution that we can expect from object-oriented approaches is one of software 'reusability'.

Most of the methods described in the review of contemporary software engineering have benefited from CASE technology and, whereas there are currently some good products on the market that actually do something for us, the vast majority are just diagramming and documentation aids supporting the soft formalisms of modern structured methods. Although the future role of CASE will be essentially the same as it is now, namely to make the production of software more rapid, less mundane and ultimately 'safer', it has the potential to achieve this not simply by performing those boring aspects of software production that lead to human error, but by automatically generating correct code from precise specifications. Consequently, the full advantages of CASE might not be realized through soft formalism. From each of these perspectives the productive evolution of software engineering lies not so much in the development and maintenance of software but in its specification. Indeed, given the obvious differences that exist between the engineering of software and that of a tangible product, the only other area where the two disciplines differ profoundly is in the nature and use of their formalisms. Current software engineering practice uses very little of the elegant mathematics that lies at the heart of the description of a complex engineered product such as an aircraft or bridge. Mathematics has long been used by the traditional engineer to express the qualitative and quantitative aspects of a problem. It is used to express an independent standard against which the performance of a product can be compared. Although these abstract descriptions are ultimately realized in terms of engineering drawings, the latter are an aid to construction and communication rather than specification.

Similar standards have to be set for software before it can be engineered. Liskov and Berzins (1986), for example, have stated:

> Every program performs some task correctly. What is of interest to computer scientists (and software engineers and their managers) is whether a program performs its *intended* task. To determine this, a precise and independent description of the desired program is needed. Such a description is termed a specification.

The requirements analysis phase of the software engineering life cycle is primarily charged with the production of the specification. The description produced by current methodologies is certainly independent, but it is neither precise, standard, unambiguous nor predictive. Soft formalisms therefore, always have the potential to place the remaining engineering work at risk. Indeed, the formalisms of current software engineering are only analogous to engineering drawings, yet they serve as specifications as well as in construction and communication.

Mathematical specification has the potential to remove much of the imprecision associated with soft formalism. It can generate proof obligations that can be used to show that software enjoys certain properties; ultimately, it could present us with a mechanism to determine the correctness of code. It is essential, however, that such formalisms are not applied in isolated areas but form part of a complete 'formal method' where the term is meant to imply a structured approach to the whole software life cycle based on a precise and verifiable description of its requirements. The adoption of a more formal approach to the specification of software does not preclude the use of current formalisms such as E–R diagrams or DFDs, it simply reduces their role to that of a language of communication rather than specification. There will always be a need to express a mathematical description in a simpler form to communicate with customers and development team alike. The careful use of soft formalism fulfils this role admirably and exactly parallels its use by the traditional engineer.

Software engineering has learned much from the principles of traditional engineering. With ever more powerful hardware making even more complex developments possible, it is time to consider the advantages of the adoption of the more formal notation of mathematics in our specifications, not simply from a point of dogma but from a realization of the benefits such formalism could ultimately confer. Soft formalisms can lead to specification–implementation conflict which generates more development and maintenance work than should be necessary. Because the cost of software production is greatest in these areas, the application of a more formal approach to specification should represent a most fruitful area in which to direct our efforts.

There may be initial disadvantages with a formal approach. Obvious contenders are that programming languages will have to develop features that enable them to be used effectively with these abstract descriptions, while software engineers may have to develop their mathematical awareness to appreciate and communicate such specifications fully. The added intellectual effort required however will be repaid, for as Dines Bjørner observes: '...It is refreshingly relaxing to develop beautiful software embodying elegant theories formally...'.

Having now established the state of contemporary software engineering, the remaining parts of this book are devoted to developing the roles that such formal approaches could play in its continuing evolution.

PART TWO

Formal Software Development

From the very beginning of my life I never doubted that words were my metier. There was nothing else I ever wanted to do except use them; no other accomplishment or achievement I ever had the slightest regard for, or desire to emulate. I have always loved words, and still love them, for their own sake. For the power and beauty of them; for the wonderful things that can be done with them.

Malcolm Muggeridge (1903–90), *Chronicles of Wasted Time*

INTRODUCTION

In the first part of this book the current state of software development was reviewed and a picture was presented which emphasized engineering quality into software by using techniques that had little or no basis in formal science but were structured and applied in a systematic manner. This approach corresponds to the notion of 'traditional' software engineering. Throughout Part 1 the emphasis was on the improvements in software that these techniques have brought about, but we must be equally aware of the fact that software produced in this fashion has to be tested to establish its correctness, rather than proved correct.

Current mechanisms used to establish correctness involve prototyping and walk-throughs at the specification stage, followed by systematic destruction aimed at detecting errors by attempting to cause the resultant software unit to fail. The latter activity is euphemistically known as *debugging* and consists of an iterative process of testing followed by correction. A *bug* is simply a software error. During the software crisis, a new version of a major software component (such as an operating system) had typically 1000 bugs per release. At a conference on software engineering in 1969 (Nauer *et al.* 1976) it was suggested that programmers preferred to call their errors bugs simply because that number of 'mistakes' would prove psychologically unacceptable.

Debugging, however, is not a scientific way to determine correctness, for it can neither establish the correctness of a correct program nor the incorrectness of an incorrect one. This may be an uncomfortable fact to accept yet it is well within most programmers' experience. Take, for example, a program that calculates the square of some integer. In order to prove this program correct by testing, its output has to be examined for every possible integer that could be input. Even in such a simple case this is clearly impracticable. Similarly, a bug in a program can be detected only if we have had the good fortune to devise a test to show that it exists, or the misfortune to suffer from its effects. Edsger Dijkstra summarized this flaw in debugging with the now famous quotation:

> *Program testing can be used to show the presence of bugs, but never to show their absence.*

The process of debugging contributes nothing to a methodology of program design. What is ideally required is that the construction of software should benefit from a methodology of determining correctness such that a discipline for the development of software emerges which reflects the relationship between the two.

In this second part of the book the scene is set for the development of software by an alternative to debugging and soft formalism—one that seeks to establish a firm formal foundation for software development in the crucial areas of *specification* and *verification* such that software of proven correctness could become a reality. In this respect, whereas the use of natural language by eminent practitioners enriches and fulfils our everyday life, we will see that the wordsmiths of a 'Muggeridge School of Software Engineering' would not contribute effectively to the primary aspects of this mechanism.

4

SPECIFICATION, VERIFICATION AND CORECTNESS

CHECKLIST OF OBJECTIVES

After reading this chapter you should be able to:

- Distinguish between syntactic and semantic 'correctness'.
- Appreciate the distinction between partially and totally correct software.
- Within an approach to software engineering that attempts to produce correct software, appreciate the implications of the terms 'specification' and 'verification'.
- Understand the changes that programming languages have undergone to make them more amenable towards a mechanism of verification.
- Enumerate the requirements of a specification language.
- Appreciate the advantages and disadvantages of natural languages, soft formalisms, programming languages and mathematics as vehicles for specification.
- Identify those branches of mathematics most suited to software engineering and give reasons for their use.

4.1 INTRODUCTION

There are many differences of opinion between the practitioners and recipients of software engineering but there is one thing upon which they all agree, the need to establish the correctness of every program or software system delivered to a customer. A program may have a number of attributes of quality—it may be fast, memory efficient, user friendly or robust—but if it is also incorrect then it is useless. The notion of 'correctness' lies at the heart of software engineering, yet it is not immediately apparent how the correctness of a program should be established. What has been established is that correctness is good, lack of it is bad. As a consequence, we cannot reasonably expect anyone knowingly to take delivery of an incorrect program. Unknowingly, it happens all the time!

Any statement about the correctness of software, such as the proposition 'the program is correct', must presuppose that there exists some external frame of reference against which its truth can be determined. This is really a very general observation that is not confined to software issues. For example, correct behaviour assumes some known code: in certain countries people drive on the right, in others they drive on the left; in some cultures people in mourning wear black, in others they wear white.

Without the underlying code we simply could not be sure that our behaviour was correct. With software as in real life, there may be potentially disastrous results.

There are several possible frames of reference within which the correctness of software may be considered. The two most important ones are *syntactic correctness* and *semantic correctness*. Syntactic correctness is relatively straightforward to establish. The 'known code' referred to earlier comprises the alphabet associated with the programming language and the rules used to construct valid software sentences. Establishing correctness in this sense simply requires the application of some algorithmic test to determine whether or not these rules have been obeyed. Determining the syntactic correctness of software is exactly analogous to determining the syntactic correctness of natural language, in that we must know how to tell the difference between sentences and non-sentences. *We shall assume that all the expressions we are interested in are syntactically correct.*

The second frame of reference, the semantics, concerns the meaning of the software sentences and is less disposed towards a simple evaluation. There is, however, only one practical approach to determine semantic correctness; we assume we know the purpose of the software sentences and proceed by establishing whether or not they express that intention. Semantic correctness therefore cannot be established unless there is also a known code in terms of an a priori stated intent. Determining semantic correctness is thereby reduced to a comparison of meanings, one expressed by the software and one expressed by its specification.

4.2 CORRECTNESS

How does one deduce the meaning of software to permit the comparisons required to determine semantic correctness? As an introduction to this problem we could assume that the meaning of software is expressed in terms of the set of consequences that are deducible from it. Let us illustrate the point with some examples. Consider the following three small program segments (which we can regard as software 'sentences' S_1, S_2, S_3):

Program S_1	Program S_2	Program S_3
Var x : natural;	*Var x : natural;*	*Var x : natural;*
begin	*begin*	*begin*
input x;	*input x;*	*input x;*
$x := x + 1;$	$x := inc(x);$	$x := x + random;$
output x	*output x*	*output x*
end.	*end.*	*end.*

The intention guiding the construction of these sentences was that they should all express the informal meaning:

if the input is a natural number x , the output is also a natural number x' such that x' is greater than x by 1

where natural numbers are those in the series 0, 1, 2, ... Among the consequences of this specification are:

if x equals 4 then x' equals 5   and   if x equals 0 then x' equals 1   and ...

together with a host of others all obtained by the same reasoning. The first program (S_1) seems to express this intent. We can see by inspection that it has a set of consequences that exactly correspond. Assuming the *inc* ( ) operator returns the immediate successor of a value, the second program (S_2) has the same meaning as the first because it has an identical set of consequences. Within this frame of reference both programs can be regarded as 'correct'. However, the third program (S_3) has a different meaning. If we take it as understood that *random* returns an arbitrary positive integer selected with equal probability from the whole domain of natural numbers, then the consequences of the first two programs appear as consequences of the third, but the third has additional consequences which cannot be deduced from the others, for example:

$$\text{if } x \text{ equals } 0 \text{ then } x' \text{ equals } 2$$

In principle then, whether one set of software sentences has the same meaning as another set, or whether a set of software sentences has the same meaning as the stated intent of that software could be established by the deduction and comparison of their respective consequences. (Such a comparison, however, makes no comment as to whether one piece of software is more efficient than another. That is an altogether different question.) The set of consequences provides the individual meaning while the comparison determines correctness.

In practice, having to convey meaning by the complete enumeration of consequences is neither a safe nor a satisfactory basis for the subsequent act of semantic correctness checking. It is unsatisfactory because some software or specifications may produce an inexhaustible list of consequences that take an infinite time to deduce, and unsafe because the situation where a consequence does not exist cannot be distinguished from one where it has not yet been generated. Because of this, we should be wary of a mechanism that tries to establish correctness by physically comparing the perceived consequences of the program with those of its specification. However, this is precisely what we do when we test software for compliance. The program has a set of consequences (outputs for given inputs) some of which we anticipate; these are then compared with the consequences of the intended program. When these correspond we are happy that the program serves its purpose. Unfortunately, most programs are complex and all their consequences simply cannot be anticipated. As a result software is placed in service without a complete knowledge of its behaviour. When we are made aware of certain consequences that do not correspond with what we intended, we call these bugs.

Clearly, we must propose a more manageable mechanism for correctness checking; one where meaning is stated implicitly rather than by explicit enumeration. A clue to one way of achieving this can be found in the previous examples where the expression of the consequences took a rather special form. With our specification, examples of what we take to be correct behaviour are:

- For a set of software sentences S_i, given that x is a natural number, x' is also a natural number and if x equals 4 we expect x' to equal 5.
- For a set of software sentences S_i, given that x is a natural number, x' is also a natural number and if x equals 0 we expect x' to equal 1.

In each of these these circumstances (and any we have not listed), x is an input and a statement such as 'x is a natural number' makes an observation about the environment *before* the execution of S_i. Similarly, x' is a result issued from the software and statements such as 'x' is also a natural number and if x equals 4 then x' equals 5' make observations about the relationship between the *before* and *after* environments once the execution has been completed. This suggests that the specification of software can be generalized in a form that captures all its intended consequences if we were to demand that:

> There must exist some condition which if *true* before the execution of S_i demands a corresponding condition to be *true* after the execution of S_i if the software sentences behave as intended.

These conditions are generally referred to as *preconditions* and *postconditions*, respectively. Preconditions state what must be true about the initial environment before the software can be legally applied, while postconditions state what must be true about the relationship between the initial and final environments if the software has behaved correctly. In our examples the preconditions are represented by 'x is a natural number', while their corresponding postconditions are 'x' is also a natural number and if x equals 4 then x' equals 5' together with 'x' is also a natural number and if x equals 0 then x' equals 1'. Of course, there are an infinite number of individual preconditions giving rise to an infinite number of corresponding postconditions. But the intended meaning of the software can be captured for all these possibilities if we generalize these conditions as:

> precondition   Given that x is a natural number
> postcondition   We expect x' to be a natural number and x' to equal $x + 1$

These pre- and postconditions tighten up and clarify our original informal requirement and express its meaning in a form that is much more manageable than the enumeration of its consequences. If we were to regard these as a specification, then the subsequent act of semantic correctness checking would require us to show that the program always satisfies a postcondition for a given precondition, rather than showing that a (possibly infinite) set of individual consequences correspond. While the latter corresponds to a process of testing and can never be complete, the former corresponds to a proof because pre- and postconditions are written to cover general rather than individual environments. In either case, the process of checking is called *verification*.

On the face of it then, the notion of a proof represents a marked improvement over testing but, as is usual in life, we cannot expect the notion to be without its difficulties. The first of these raises the question of implementability; pre- and postconditions cannot be simply quoted without some assurance that it is possible to achieve the latter from the former. If this obligation is not fulfilled, we are never sure that the specification can be realized in practice; such specifications are *infeasible*. Secondly, we must take care to phrase the pre- and postconditions in a fashion that precisely expresses our requirements. For example, if we wanted to specify the behaviour of a program that accepted two integers and then interchanged their values we might be tempted to write:

> pre x is an integer and y is an integer
> post x equals y and y equals x

Unfortunately, although this seems the obvious solution, if you look carefully at the postcondition it merely requires that both x and y have the same value—and it is not entirely clear exactly which one that is! Additionally, formulating pre- and post-conditions is further compounded by the lack of homogeneity among specifications. Some programs may require obvious results such as a root program that returns a real root within a certain tolerance. Here the pre- and postconditions are quite straightforward. With other programs, e.g. operating systems, text editors and games, the 'result' is much less obvious and the pre- and postconditions more difficult to define.

Specification with pre- and postconditions is usually called *constructive* or *model based* because the behaviour of the software is built up or described in terms of the operators of some other object(s) which act as a model. In our example, what the program should do is explained in terms of the properties of natural numbers. However, this has not been the only avenue explored in our attempt to capture semantics. Other approaches to proof of correctness begin with an *axiomatic specification*, i.e. one where the meaning of each of the various operators that characterize the software unit is expressed in terms of a series of equations or axioms. (Axioms are simply equations concerning the properties of some object of interest that are taken to be true in all possible circumstances.) The axioms are constructed in a manner that describe the outcome of any operation on the system and therefore completely define its behaviour. This is a less intuitive approach to specification but we can illustrate its general form if we use it to specify the behaviour of the earlier programs S_1 and S_2 whose purpose of course was simply to increment a number by 1. If we call such an operation **succ** (for *succ*essor) then the following axioms explain its intended behaviour by relating **succ** to some of the other operators that characterize natural numbers:

For all values of a and b that are natural numbers the following equations are true:

iszero$(0) = true$	(A1)
iszero(**succ**$(a)) = false$	(A2)
$0 + a = a$	(A3)
succ$(a) + b =$ **succ**$(a + b)$	(A4)

Using these axioms it is possible to show that for any natural number n, **succ**$(n) = n + 1$, which in turn describes what we want our software to achieve. In all honesty it is not immediately obvious how we can deduce such behaviour from the axioms[1] and this makes the approach generally less intuitive than a specification with pre- and post-conditions.

Unfortunately, our difficulties are not just confined to the construction and meaning of the specification. For example, if we conduct the process of verification using a specification phrased in terms of pre- and postconditions, proof of correctness requires us to show that a program satisfies a postcondition for a given precondition, which in turn suggests that we must be able to reason about the behaviour of the program. All programming languages have an alphabet and strict rules governing the correct

---

[1]An informal justification proceeds as follows. These equations are meant to be true for a universe where the set of natural numbers is to be interpreted as 0, 1, 2, ... and where every natural number except 0 can be generated from some other natural number. Axioms A1 and A2 show us that the successor to any natural number must be greater than 0. From this we deduce that $Succ(0) = 1$ because if it were anything else it would not be possible to generate 1. Because the equations are axioms they can be rewritten in terms of others. Thus, using axiom A3, $Succ(n)$ can be written as $Succ(0 + n)$ which in turn can be written as $Succ(0) + n$ (axiom A4). Finally, since $Succ(0) = 1$, $Succ(0) + n$ is the same as $n + 1$, i.e. $Succ(n) = n + 1$.

assembly of program sentences (a syntax or grammar), together with a formal semantics that enables us (theoretically) to deduce the consequences of any set of sentences admitted by the grammar. The term 'formal' is used with care here and is meant to imply that a particular set of legal sentences can have one meaning and one meaning only. If this were not so, the same program segment could produce different results with the same data on different occasions. Dismissing hardware errors, such spurious behaviour is of course totally unacceptable so that all programming languages generate software that behaves in deterministic fashion. Consequently, it should always be possible to reason about them to deduce their behaviour, and programming languages have been deliberately modified over the years to make them more amenable to this process.

Early programming languages, however, were particularly difficult to reason about. The liberal use of 'goto' statements disrupts the natural progression through a program which is from start to finish. Structured languages, on the other hand, permit a continual forward advance during execution. The avoidance of goto and the use of a small set of basic constructs (assignments, sequences, selections, iterations) in these languages require the development of correspondingly few reasoning techniques and reduce complexity. However, there are many different structured languages available, each geared towards a specific application area, and it would be neither sensible nor practical to develop individual deduction mechanisms for each language; a much more sustainable approach addresses their commonality. Programming in any structured language can ultimately be seen as an act of synthesis whereby basic constructs are assembled in a fashion which ensures that the final program achieves a particular function. These constructs, in one form or another, are common to all such languages, and so it is not beyond our imagination to conceive of a programming pseudo-code or indeed a representative programming language which simplifies the verification process in that:

- We can use it in place of a specific language because, once proven correct, its constructs can be translated into any target language (possibly automatically).
- One inferencing mechanism only need be used during proof of correctness, irrespective of the target language finally adopted.

To date, most work has centred upon Pascal-like languages which can be regarded as exemplary in this respect. There is, however, a further difficulty associated with software, one that we have so far avoided; some programs do not halt but otherwise behave as they should. Clearly we have to distinguish between two types of correctness:

1. *Partially* or *conditionally correct* software   The execution of S_i begins in a state that satisfies `Pre...` and if S_i terminates then the final state is guaranteed to satisfy `Post...`
2. *Totally correct* (or simply *correct*) *software*   If `Pre...` is satisfied, S_i terminates satisfying `Post...`

In other words, proving software correct according to the specification `Pre...` S_i `Post...` only proves its partial correctness. For sequential non-repetitive software this is also sufficient to prove its total correctness for we are guaranteed termination. For programs that employ loop constructs the burden of proof requires evidence of termination. To this end Hoare (1969) has provided proof rules to be used with Pascal-like statements and, for those who are interested, Backhouse (1986) elegantly illustrates their use in his book.

One final point to be made before leaving is that the view of verification presented here treats the process as a retrospective exercise performed after the software has been realized (and possibly partially tested). Unfortunately, although this is probably the most natural way for us to think about the problem, such retrospective proofs are always difficult to construct and require significant intellectual effort. One way to reduce this effort is to develop software in modular form, applying the verification techniques to relatively smaller but critical sections of code. The use of these modules within others then proceeds with total confidence. One way to avoid retrospective verification completely is to invert the mechanism; instead of proving an existing program correct, we use the specification to guide the evolution of a correct program in the first place, i.e. a constructive proof. Later in the book two specification languages—Z and VDM—are introduced, both of which develop their code using a process of *reification*, the term used to describe the process of gradually making a specification real or 'concrete'.

4.3 THE REQUIREMENTS OF A SPECIFICATION LANGUAGE

A primary requirement of semantic correctness checking is that the process is calculable, permitting us to proceed in a systematic fashion that avoids guessing. Therefore specifications, like programs, have to be based on some kind of linguistic system with an appropriate syntax and precise semantics, but when choosing a language for the specification of software it is also prudent to examine both the wider role the specification is meant to play and the nature of the problems that it is meant to specify.

In addition to its role in a proof of correctness, a specification language must be both communicable and comprehensible. In this respect Meyer (1985) considers that a successful specification should be free from the seven 'deadly sins':

- *Noise* The presence of irrelevancy and unnecessary duplication which masks the basic intent of the specification.
- *Silence* The (unintentional) omission of parts of the intention.
- *Overspecification* Providing details of how the specification may be realized thereby suggesting we employ a particular implementation which may or may not be appropriate.
- *Contradiction*
- *Ambiguity*
- *Forward referencing* Appealing to concepts that are defined later yet are used to make an important point early in the specification. This confuses us.
- *Wishful thinking* Including some feature(s) which, with all the goodwill in the world, cannot be realistically implemented.

Simple common sense tells us that each of these confounds both our understanding of the specification and our ability to communicate it effectively to others.

From the perspective of the problems we are meant to specify, software engineering often suffers from the sheer size and complexity of the task(s) it has to perform. Complexity is at its most severe in the early stages of software development where least is known about the problem or its solution. The key tool to use in managing complexity is *abstraction*. Abstraction is not an easy concept to define, but in terms of software engineering its most common usage relates to the elimination of unnecessary detail. Such detail exists in two forms: that which is totally irrelevant to our understanding of the problem, and that which is relevant but unnecessary at a given stage. Of course, determining what is relevant to a speci-fication and what is not is in itself no easy matter, but what we can all agree upon is that problem-specific issues, such as the name of a bank account or a department in an organization, together with algorithms (for sorting or searching, say) are not as appropriate to specification as are the identification of the classes to which individual bank accounts or departments belong or descriptions of the syntax and semantics of the operators that are meant to bring searching and sorting effects about. In other words, abstraction permits generalization beyond a specific problem and expresses what should be achieved by something without revealing how. It is preoccupation with problem-specific 'clutter' and the 'how' of a transformation that introduces complexity. Hiding the internal detail of how a particular operation is achieved also defers the decision on an implementation strategy until a point is reached where such decisions can be properly made. Decisions on implementation issues made too early in the software development life cycle are often thoroughly regretted. This view of abstraction therefore sees it as a mechanism that must simultaneously make concise, discard, hide and generalize.

In addition to complexity, software engineers also face a wide *range* of problems. This is evidently reflected by the various programming languages that have been developed over the years. We cannot change our specification language with each different application, for that would make specification problem specific and less abstract. Whatever language system is used as the specification vehicle it must therefore be flexible enough to deal with as wide a range of application as possible.

Communication, comprehensibility, a wide range of application and the ability to support abstraction, together with a calculable and precise deductive apparatus, therefore form our terms of reference when we evaluate a linguistic system as a basis for specification. In this respect we have four obvious possibilities:

- Natural languages
- Soft, quasi or semi-formalisms
- Programming languages
- Mathematics

The tone of the previous sections of this book make it clear that our final choice will be mathematics, but really we must not be allowed to get away with a *fait accompli* that appeals to prejudice rather than reasoned argument. If more formal approaches to the specification of software are to become widely accepted then software engineers must become convinced of their efficacy by understanding what each of these linguistic systems has to offer. We can begin such understanding by reviewing the characteristics of each system against these basic terms of reference.

4.4 PROPERTIES OF THESE LINGUISTIC SYSTEMS

The most instinctively appealing of our choices would be a natural language such as English. Unfortunately we know from experience that in terms of communication and comprehension it suffers from most of the deadly sins, whereas its clumsy syntax and semantics makes it difficult to reason about it in a fashion appropriate to the proper deduction of its consequences. A trivial example from *Through the Looking-Glass* illustrates the mischief that natural language deduction can cause.

> 'Contrariwise,' continued Tweedledee, 'if it was so, it might be; and if it were so, it would be; but as it isn't, it aint. That's logic.'

From the perspective of what this book is trying to achieve a more worrying example is that attributed to Bertrand Russell. Apparently, during a dinner conversation Russell claimed that it was possible to prove anything given a false statement from which to begin. An immediate challenge was made: 'if $0 = 1$ then prove that you are the Pope'. Russell proceeded:

> $0 = 1$. Hence $1 + 1 = 0 + 1$, i.e., $2 = 1$. The Pope and I are two, therefore the Pope and I are one!

On a more formal basis, studies have been undertaken in the restricted and careful formulation of natural language specifications and these have still been shown to contain many of Meyer's 'sins'. From the point of view of abstraction, the same nebulous semantics subjects our most careful generalizations to ambiguity. Such languages, although flexible enough to deal with the wide range of software engineering, are therefore fatally flawed as a primary vehicle for specification. Indeed, Wittgenstein (Monk, 1991) has made a general comment concerning the use of natural language in areas of philosophy such that we have

> a constant struggle against the bewitchment of our understanding through our language

This observation, however, does not preclude the use of natural language within a more formal method of software development. 'Informal' specification will always have a role in software engineering, but it should be one that supports and possibly enriches the primary specification language not one that replaces it. Evidence is mounting to show that the retrospective use of natural language to 'translate' a more formal speci-fication will often result in a much more precise statement than would otherwise have been possible.

The next most instinctive choice would be the quasi, semi or soft formalisms that we have seen used throughout Part One and embodied in SSADM and JSD. From the perspective of communication and comprehension, the wide use of diagrams by these methods is to be commended, as long as the diagrams are universally understood and standardized. This is not always the case, however. As a vehicle for abstraction, diagrams easily convey the notion of a black box and therefore support the classical view, while the techniques have been applied to a wide range of problems. However, soft formalisms are simply loose collections of notation, the consistency of which may be enforced by a data dictionary but whose formal semantics are often only poorly defined. As a consequence it is often difficult to prove properties of the system. In this respect consider the DFD of Fig. 2.1. We would sensibly expect that software engineered according to this specification would leave the 'database' unchanged if the *add a new programmer* process was followed immediately by the *dismiss a programmer* process using the same programmer number. This property can be discussed subjectively only at the walkthrough stage with analysts whose intuitive understanding and creativity led to the description in the first place. One experienced in such discussion may convince me that the database possesses this property even if it were not so; one less experienced may find difficulty convincing me even if it were so. This is not a mechanism that imparts confidence to correctness checking. Proceeding as it does through a natural language, its conclusions are always at risk.

The utilization of a programming language as the basis for specification is another obvious possibility to be explored. However, the whole point of our specification is that a wide range of equally valid realizations must be possible. The role of every programming language is one that manipulates machine representations of objects and not the objects themselves, which inevitably means that even if we use even a 'very high' programming language to express a specification, it will only be able to do so in a way that presumes a particular implementation.

All this of course leads us to consider mathematics—the major tool for abstract description with a wide range of application in keeping with a history that spans many thousands of years. From the perspective of communication and understanding, mathematics is universally understood among scientists and engineers but arguably less so outside these communities. In this respect the communication of the mathematics often has to receive support from natural language or diagrams together with prototyping languages such as Prolog that animate the descriptions. But these difficulties are placed in perspective when we consider the opportunities offered by its precise semantics. Mathematical descriptions are compact and unambiguous; they are not open to loose interpretation. Consequently, it becomes possible to reason about each system in a fashion that permits us to predict accurately how it would behave. This above all else has led to software engineers applying formal approaches to the specification of software to establish its properties *before* it is engineered. No other contender for a specification language offers us such potential and this has been the major reason for its adoption, especially in complex systems where the ability to predict behaviour is also accompanied by a reduction in specification size. On an industrial scale, formal approaches have been made possible by the relatively recent appearance of products which are now regarded as mature enough to contribute effectively to the software engineering process. Superficially, each of these products look quite different but really they share a common mathematical basis—the mathematics that is relevant to software engineering.

4.5 THE MATHEMATICS OF SOFTWARE ENGINEERING

We can illustrate the nature of the mathematics needed by software engineering by considering the execution of the following program segment which forms the sum of the series for some input n, (a natural number). (The sum of the series for some number

n is given by $1 + 2 + 3 + \ldots + (n - 1) + n$. Hence for a value of $n = 2$, the sum of the series is $1 + 2 = 3$.) The simplest way to describe the behaviour of this program is to follow the way in which the values in the variables n, *sum* and i change as the program execution proceeds. Table 4.1 illustrates the various changes that occur for an initial condition where the value of n equals 2.

> *Program Sum_Series;*
> *Var i, n, sum : natural;*
> *begin*
>   *input(n);*
>   *sum* := 0;
> i := 1;
>   *while* $(i <= n)$ *do*
>   *sum* := *sum* + i;
> i := $i + 1$
>   *end(*while*);*
>   *write(sum);*
> *end(*Sum_Series*).*

Table 4.1 Tracing the execution of the program *Sum_Series*

n	*sum*	i	Statement	
2	–	–	;*input(n)*	Program begins here.
2	0	–	;*sum* := 0	
2	0	1	;i := 1	
2	0	1	;*while* $(i <= n)$ *do*	
2	1	1	;*sum* := *sum* + i	
2	1	2	;i := $i + 1$	
2	1	2	;*while* $(i <= n)$ *do*	
2	3	2	;*sum* := *sum* + i	
2	3	3	;i := $i + 1$	
2	3	3	;*while* $(i <= n)$ *do*	Loop terminates here.
2	3	3	;*write(sum)*	
2	3	3	;*end.*	Program terminates here.

The behaviour of the program is expressed in terms of the effect of its sequence of statements and each *while ... do* loop iteration is written out in full. Each table entry reflects the situation after the execution of the statement to the left of the entry and before the execution of the statement immediately below. For example, the third line in the table:

$$2 \quad 0 \quad 1 \quad ;i := 1$$

reflects the situation after the execution of $i := 1$ but before *while* $(i <= n)$ *do*. The fact that the table is finite indicates that the program terminates and even for the most complex program this tabular description is a valid (yet impossibly inconvenient) equivalence.

From the table we notice that prior to and after the execution of each statement (or indeed the whole program) the variables exist in certain stable and identifiable conditions. At each point during execution therefore—including at the start and finish—the state of the program is described by the condition of its variables. The conclusion we draw is that a program's behaviour can be modelled in terms of a gradual progression from one clearly identifiable discrete state to another, while its specification could be based on certain aspects of the discrete states that exist before and after the execution of the program. In this particular case, given that n is an input and *sum* an output, the program specification is described by:

Pre n is a natural number

Post   *sum* is a natural number and $sum = n*(n + 1)/2$

where the formula is used to generalize the result for any natural number we care to input. As usual, the precondition describes what must be true about the input to the program before we can legally use it, while the postcondition describes the relationship that must exist between input and output if the program has behaved as intended. Clearly, $3 = 2*(2 + 1)/2$.

At this point it should be made clear that the mathematics required to understand the role of the hardware is entirely irrelevant. Software engineers are interested only in the stable discrete states that occur during program execution and not in what happens between such states. Any mathematics required to describe these intermediate effects and the rate at which they occur is therefore beyond our concern. This observation conveniently eliminates topics such as differential and integral calculus together with their attendant trigonometry, complex number theory, etc. The mathematics appropriate to the behaviour of software will therefore be characterized by topics that address the following:

- The *sorts* of data the program processes and the *individual values* they adopt
- The *composition of the discrete states* that are generated during program execution rather than events that occur during the changes between such states
- The *rules of the transformations* that characterize the conversion of one discrete state into another
- The *deductive apparatus* that establishes whether or not progressive transformations on some initial state by a program logic eventually terminate with a state that satisfies the specification of the software

Of all the mathematics that help us understand and describe events in such terms the most fundamental is *set theory*. Sets are simply collections of distinct items, the members of the set, enclosed with set braces { }. Sets are therefore discrete structures and any collection of interest can constitute a set just as long as we can decide whether an item is, or is not, a member. The sorts of data that a program processes (and therefore the individual values that program variables can adopt) could be described by sets such as:

Natural numbers	$\{0, 1, 2, 3, 4, \ldots\}$
Integers	$\{\ldots, -1, 0, 1, \ldots\}$
Customer names	{Phoenix Products, Lennox Mouldings, D. Sheppard & Sons, . . .}
Book titles	{Specification Case Studies, Software Development, . . .}
Author names	{I. Hayes, C. B. Jones, . . .}

Once we have decided which sets are to be used we will have also made a statement concerning the discrete states that can exist during a program's execution. Such states describe possible conditions for the program's variables and are composed from individual elements of the sets placed together in combination. In the specific case of program *Sum_Series*, Table 4.1 shows us that combinations such as the following are legal states when the number input is 2:

$$\{\dots(2,0,1), (2,1,1), (2,1,2), (2,3,2),\dots\}$$

The legal states themselves therefore constitute a set—a set where each item consists of three numbers representing the current values of *n, sum* and *i* (in that order). At any point in time, the condition of the program can be described by an element from this set—usually referred to as the *state space* for the program. Transformations upon the data by the program can be described in terms of movement from one element in the state space to another and these can be brought about by the set operators which in turn embody the rules such transformations must obey.

Although simple sets are useful, they are restricted in the way they can describe both the data and the transformations of interest to us. However, sets form the basis of relations, functions and sequences; mathematical objects that can be used to model relationships between data and order among data. By implication then, these topics are also useful to the software engineer and can be used to describe more complex situations. Of the remaining areas of mathematics, the logical calculi (propositional and predicate calculus) and recursion are also natural choices. Logic provides a deductive apparatus that we can use to reason about the descriptions provided by sets, relations, functions and sequences, while recursion is a powerful technique that can be used to describe the behaviour of software in an economic fashion.

The branch of mathematics that includes all of these topics is called *discrete mathematics*. The emphasis here is on the term 'discrete', by which we mean that our descriptions are in terms of clearly identifiable, stable and individual items of interest. Discrete mathematics is discussed in some detail in the next part of the book where we look at each topic in turn, illustrating its role in software engineering with examples and case studies familiar from everyday life.

4.6 SUMMARY

The argument presented in this chapter makes it self-evident that specification and verification are inextricably linked. That which is inadequately specified cannot be realized without potential defect (unless we are very lucky), while lack of a proper specification does not permit a (potentially defective) realization to be subjected to a process of verification. In this respect the specification is fundamental and forms the major concern of this book.

This chapter has tried to be even-handed when reviewing the various alternatives for a specification language. The advantages that natural language and soft formalisms have to offer have been highlighted. In terms of communication, comprehension, abstraction and range of problem they score highly, but the ability of these methods to support a deductive apparatus capable of revealing the properties of the specification in an objective fashion must be seriously questioned. Consequently, these techniques cannot be considered as a primary mechanism through which we can expect to develop proven correct code.

In contrast, mathematics has precise and well-defined meanings together with mechanisms that can be used to reason about its descriptions. Mathematics is universally constant throughout its user community and represents a stable communicable medium for the abstract description of the functionality of a wide range of complex systems. From the perspective of all of the requirements of a specification language then, mathematics has no peers. The bad press that mathematics tends to generate is unfortunate and in all honesty will probably always be with us, but where its practical usefulness has been demonstrated to the software engineering community the results have often been spectacular (for example Codd's relational database is built firmly on the mathematics of relations (Codd, 1970)). A proper understanding of discrete mathematics is essential for anyone wishing to study formal approaches to software development and requires a degree of commitment from the newcomer. However, the effort involved is well rewarded, as the following quote illustrates:

> *If you are faced by a difficulty or controversy in science, an ounce of algebra is worth a ton of verbal argument.*
>
> J. B. S. Haldane (1892–1964), British geneticist

PART THREE

Discrete Mathematics for the Software Engineer

An investment in knowledge pays the best interest...
Benjamin Franklin (1706–90), US scientist and statesman

INTRODUCTION

Part 2 tried to introduce readers to some of the ways in which software can be formally specified. Few practitioners would quarrel with the ultimate aim of such activities, namely that of developing proven compliant software, but the introduction of the various methods has been received by the general software engineering community with scepticism rather than enthusiasm. Indeed, it has become clear over the last few years that the root of the scepticism lies not with the sentiments of such methods but with their mathematics, which is frequently perceived as being too difficult to be practised by the community in general. To some extent this is understandable, for a perception based on a glance at even a modest formal specification can be a very sobering experience indeed!

'Mathsfear' is of course an (undesirable) characteristic of the population in general and consequently we should expect to find it within any contemporary software engineering community. However, this natural tendency has been compounded by the fact that many practising software engineers have become thoroughly used to the informal and semi-formalisms that have become accepted throughout the industry since the 1970s and often dismiss developments they see as preventing them from making a proper return on the intellectual effort they have expended in mastering the techniques (the inertia of change). One way to help counteract protective practice is to reassure practitioners of a continued role for semi-formalism as a major specification technique throughout the long term. Whereas this may reduce resistance to the introduction of more formal approaches, it does not further the understanding of their methods or their benefits. These objectives can only be addressed by expending some effort confronting the mathematical 'toolbox' and illustrating its role in areas of concern to software engineers. Promoting the case for formalism must therefore proceed by:

- Understanding its mathematics
- Understanding the use of the mathematics to specify events of interest to a software engineer
- Understanding the use of the mathematics within formal specification languages
- Understanding the use of the mathematics in guiding the construction of the software from the specification

The approach adopted in this book first introduces and familiarizes the reader with each of the major mathematical techniques contained in the toolbox. Subsequent parts of the book build on these foundations by examining the structure of different specification languages where theorems and proof mechanisms have a more relevant role. This text tries to avoid overwhelming the reader by avoiding the mathematics required actually to build the software. Formal specification is an activity in it own right; an activity upon which the success of all other development rests. This book tries to take the time to 'get it right'.

Thankfully, the toolbox presented in Part 3 is not too full and this must be encouraging for the existing software engineer new to formal methods, in that relatively few new techniques need be learned before beginning to appreciate and exercise these new skills. For students engaged on degree courses in software engineering or computer studies, the majority of the discrete mathematics will be familiar through first and second year studies. Discrete mathematics taught by mathematicians, however, may not be the same animal as discrete mathematics taught by a software engineer. Mathematicians are frequently more interested in the techniques *per se* and the relationships they hold to each other rather than in their application to the events of the real world. In Part 3, primary emphasis is on the ability to read and understand the intention and obligations embodied in a formal language rather than on developing an expertise in the logical manipulation of such descriptions. This part of the book introduces each area of discrete mathematics in turn, beginning with the fundamental topics of logical calculi, sets, relations and functions. These are essential requirements for anyone wishing to have some understanding of formal specification. The remaining topics, Sequences, Bags and Recursion introduce more sophistication. Hopefully, by segregating topics in this fashion the reader is free to travel as far as is necessary.

5

LOGIC

CHECKLIST OF OBJECTIVES

After reading this chapter you should be able to:

- Appreciate the fundamental role of logic in a specification language.
- Understand the nature and limitations of propositional calculus.
- Appreciate the additional expressive power of predicate calculus.
- Understand some of the logic used to simplify expressions in later chapters.

5.1 INTRODUCTION

By *logic* we mean the study of *inference*; of what *follows* from or what can be *deduced* from a given set of assumptions. Logic is important to us because a specification is really only a set of assumptions about an intended software module, e.g. 'program *P*1 must accept . . . and return a value that . . .', 'the input data will be in the range . . .'.

By applying logical *argument* to the specification we might be able to deduce its behavioural characteristics as a series of inferences which can then be compared to that which we intended. When these correspond we can be sure that the specification is accurate—in fact the process of logical reasoning provides us with a *proof* that this is so. But when inference(s) and intent are in conflict some redesign will be necessary.

Part 1 suggested that the primary vehicles for establishing correctness at the various stages of traditional software development were walkthroughs, prototyping and testing. Of these, walkthroughs and prototyping attempt to establish the correctness of the specification but the logic used here is largely that of everyday life conducted through the medium of a language such as English. The clumsy semantics of natural language, however, confounds a process of logical deduction as we must understand it—a process in which we have confidence that a formal logical argument leads to an inference that is universally correct or valid. The notion of logic we refer to therefore represents:

> A mathematical system for symbolically expressing statements about the properties of systems and for reasoning about them by manipulating the symbols in rigorous fashion.

In this respect the language of specification becomes the language of logic, for unless we express our properties in a logical fashion we cannot expect to reason logically about them. The symbolic statements representing properties of the system are referred to as *propositions* or sometimes *predicates*. Together with the apparatus used to manipulate these expressions they form a *calculus*. A logical calculus in which the truth or falsity of any expression can be determined is said to be *decidable*. Expressions written in propositional or predicate calculus are decidable and this chapter examines ways in which such logical expressions can be formed and their meaning deduced.

The ideas presented here are based on *classical two-valued logic* where logical expressions are considered to be either true or false, but not both. In this respect the logic here is largely that used by the specification language Z (see Parts 4 and 5). In the specification language of VDM, however (see Parts 6 and 7), a three-valued logic can be used where the truth value of an expression can be true, false or undefined—the last representing a situation corresponding to no information. This extra value is introduced to deal with situations which cannot be resolved in classical terms. For example, a program stuck in an infinite loop might (or might not) satisfy a specification if it terminated (recall the notion of 'partial correctness' introduced in Part 2). As it is, the truth of this statement is undefined. It can be argued of course that programs like this should not be written, but in real life they are and a way of modelling such events is needed. Despite this additional value we will try to avoid its use in what is, after all, an introductory text on the whole area of specification.

5.2 PROPOSITIONS AND CONNECTIVES

Propositions are simply statements which have a truth value (true or false) associated with them. Examples might be:

> Wales won the 1992 rugby World Cup. (false!)
> Cardiff is the capital city of Wales. (true)
> The earth is not flat. (true)
> $1000 < 99$ (false)

In the specification of software systems there will be a large number of such statements in a variety of forms. Indeed, the specification will probably involve quite complex combinations of propositions to describe the more difficult aspects of the system. This is a general observation reflecting the fact that very little is achievable with propositions alone. We therefore expect to find statements such as the following throughout an informal specification:

> The disk capacity is 40 Mb *and* the processor speed is 30 MHz.
> The processor is either . . . *or* . . .
> The input value is *not* in the range 1 . . . 500 *and if* the output exceeds 30 *then* it is stored.

In order to reason with such descriptions we have to express them in more manageable form. This involves the introduction of both a *symbolism* to represent the individual propositions together with *logical connectives* representing 'and', 'not', 'or', etc. These permit the combination of simple propositions into more complex expressions. The symbolism is quite easy to introduce; thus if P stands for 'the disk capacity is 40 Mb' and Q represents 'the processor speed is 30 MHz' then the expression:

> The disk capacity is 40 Mb *and* the processor speed is 30 MHz.

can be written *P and Q* (in this text the capital letters always stand for single, arbitrary propositions). The symbolism of course reduces the bulk of the logical expression but the value associated with such expressions can be deduced only if we can supply some meaning for the connective that operates upon the individual propositional truth values. In this example, the normal understanding we would expect of the expression is that it is true only when the two individual propositions are true. Any proposition whose principal connective is *and* is a 'conjunction' with the individual propositions either side of the operator termed 'conjuncts'. We can summarize the behaviour of the connective using Table 5.1. Such tables are *truth tables* and they can be constructed to show the effect of each of the logical connectives. Truth tables therefore summarize the role of the connective across any pair of propositions but they can also be used to determine the truth of any complex expression built from propositions and connectives. We examine this role once we have provided an interpretation for the remaining logical connectives.

Table 5.1   The *and* operator

P	Q	P and Q
true	true	true
true	false	false
false	false	false
false	false	false

5.2.1 Truth tables for the other common logical connectives

The remaining connectives are *or* and *not*—both of which largely correspond to their familiar everyday use—together with 'implication' and 'equivalence' which we need to explain in rather more detail. The truth tables for *or* and *not* are shown in Tables 5.2 and 5.3.

Table 5.2   The *or* operator

P	Q	P or Q
true	true	true
true	false	true
false	true	true
false	false	false

Table 5.3   The *not* operator

P	not P
true	false
false	true

The proposition *P or Q* is only false when both *P* and *Q* are false. Expressions whose principal connective is *or* are 'disjunctions' with the individual propositions either side of the operator termed 'disjuncts'. The *not* operator simply provides a truth value which is the opposite of that of the proposition to which it is applied. An expression whose principal operator is *not* is a 'negation'.

The remaining operators are implication and equivalence and these stand for the everyday English phrases 'if . . . then . . .' and 'if and only if . . . will . . .', respectively. There is a very subtle difference between these two operators which is best explained with an example. In the phrase '*if* it is raining *then* I wear a hat' we have an implication that suggests that if we know that it is raining then we can deduce that I will be seen wearing a hat. This implication will obviously be true if every time it is raining I am seen wearing a hat. If, however, it is raining and I am seen without my hat then the implication is clearly false. When it is not raining, however, we can make no inference about my tendency to wear a hat and in such circumstances the implication must be taken as true because there is no evidence to suggest otherwise. All of this can be summarized by realizing that the only way the implication can be shown to be false is to produce the case where I am without a hat when it is raining and the safest way to show that the implication is true is to establish that every time it rains I have my hat on. Implication arises quite often in formal methods and these two cases are often used in proofs. Difficulties in interpreting implications arise only in situations where there is no causal connection between P (the *antecedent*) and Q (the *consequent*); in this text such implications are avoided so that the expression is meant to reflect its intuitive meaning.

In contrast to the implication, the equivalence operator, if true, guarantees that if I am seen with my hat on then it will be raining. In other words '*if and only if* it is raining *will* I wear a hat'.

The behaviour of these operators is summarized in Tables 5.4 and 5.5.

Table 5.4   The implication operator *if . . . then*

P	Q	*if P then Q*
true	true	true
true	false	false
false	true	true
false	false	true

Table 5.5   The equivalence operator *if and only if P will Q*

P	Q	*if and only if P will Q*
true	true	true
true	false	false
false	true	false
false	false	true

5.2.2 Extending the symbolism

The use of the everyday English phrases 'if . . . then . . .', 'and', etc., is all very well on a small scale, but in large specifications the logical expressions can become somewhat unwieldy. Considering also that when reasoning with such expressions we often have to rewrite them over and over again, a more convenient symbolism is necessary. All the logical connectives are therefore subject to a shorthand notation which is gathered together in Table 5.6. From here on, the book uses these symbols exclusively.

Table 5.6   Logical connective symbols

English version	Symbolic version
P and Q	$P \wedge Q$
P or Q	$P \vee Q$
not P	$\neg P$
if P then Q	$P \Rightarrow Q$
if and only if P will Q	$P \Leftrightarrow Q$

SAQ 5.1   Which of the following statements are true?

(a) $12 < 33 \wedge 12 = 33$
(b) $12 < 33 \wedge 33 < 100 \Rightarrow 12 < 1000$
(c) $12 + 33 > 2 \Rightarrow 100 + 1000 > 4 \Rightarrow 12 = 12$

5.2.3 Logical operator precedence

By connecting propositions with the logical connectives more complex expressions can be built up, for example:

$$P \vee Q \wedge R \Rightarrow X \wedge \neg Y$$

To evaluate such expressions, however, we have to decide in which order to evaluate their individual parts. The rules are:

1. When the propositions in an expression are separated by the same binary operator then evaluation takes place from left to right.
2. When the expression is parenthesized the innermost parentheses are evaluated first, followed by the next innermost, and so on.
3. When the expression contains a mixture of operators whose evaluation is not dictated by parentheses the order of precedence among the operators follows the sequence $\Leftrightarrow$, $\Rightarrow$, $\vee$, $\wedge$, $\neg$, with the equivalence operator having the lowest precedence and negation the highest.

SAQ 5.2   Introduce parentheses to show the order of evaluation of the following expressions:

(a) $P \vee P \vee Q \vee R \wedge S \vee Q \wedge Q$
(b) $P \Rightarrow Q \Leftrightarrow S \Leftrightarrow R \Rightarrow Q \vee P \vee \neg P \wedge R$
(c) $(P \wedge Q \Rightarrow R) \Leftrightarrow P \wedge Q \vee R \Rightarrow S$

5.2.4 Tautologies and contradictions

Two interesting forms of proposition are the *tautology* and the *contradiction*. Tautologies are logical expressions which are always true irrespective of the truth values of their constituent propositions. Examples of simple tautologies are:

$$P \vee \neg P$$
$$P \Rightarrow P$$
$$P \Rightarrow Q \vee Q \Rightarrow P$$

The fact that an expression is a tautology can be shown by constructing a truth table. For example, the truth table for the expression $P \Rightarrow Q \vee Q \Rightarrow P$ is shown in Table 5.7.

Table 5.7 Truth table for $P \Rightarrow Q \vee Q \Rightarrow P$

P	Q	$P \Rightarrow Q$	$Q \Rightarrow P$	$P \Rightarrow Q \vee Q \Rightarrow P$
true	true	true	true	true
true	false	false	true	true
false	true	true	false	true
false	false	true	true	true

Tautologies are useful when expressing the various laws of propositional logic and in proving properties of certain logical expressions. We examine these shortly.

Contradictions are always false irrespective of the truth values of their constituent propositions. A classic (but trivial) contradiction is $P \wedge \neg P$. Contradictions are less useful than tautologies.

SAQ 5.3 Construct truth tables to show which of the following are tautologies:

(a) $(P \Rightarrow Q) \Rightarrow (P \Rightarrow Q)$
(b) $(P \Rightarrow Q) \vee (Q \Rightarrow R)$
(c) $((P \Rightarrow Q) \Rightarrow P) \Rightarrow P$

5.3 SEQUENTS AND TURNSTILES

The very essence of dabbling with logic means that we are forever constructing propositions of the form 'assuming . . . it is obvious that . . .' or 'assuming . . . then we can show that . . .'. Such a phrase is referred to as a *sequent* in that something follows quite naturally by assuming something else. That which is assumed is the *premise*, while that which is shown to follow is the *conclusion*; these two being separated in the expression of the sequent by a meta-symbol called the *turnstile*. (A meta-symbol is one which is not part of the language of propositional calculus itself but enables us to talk about expressions built with the language.)

There are two separate circumstances in which such sequents present themselves. In the first of these it is quite obvious that the conclusion follows from the set of premises; such sequents are written using the *double turnstile* ($\models$). In general the sequent is written:

$$\tau \models E$$

(where τ is a list of logical expressions) while an actual example might be:

$$P1 \wedge (P2 \vee P3) \models P1 \wedge P2 \vee P1 \wedge P3$$

Here the sequent may be read as 'it is obvious that . . .' or 'it is axiomatic that . . .'. Such sequents simply assert that whenever the expression to the left of the turnstile is true we can safely assume the truth of the expression to the right. There is no need to establish the sequents' validity; such expressions are simply used. If proof of validity is required then this can be established by truth tables, rigorous argument or formal derivation. We examine various proof mechanisms shortly. When truth tables are constructed for the expressions in τ, all rows in which the expression evaluates to false would be ignored; in the rows which remain E must evaluate to true.

SAQ 5.4   Draw the truth table to establish the validity of the sequent:

$$P1 \wedge (P2 \vee P3) \models P1 \wedge P2 \vee P1 \wedge P3$$

In the second case, the derivation of the conclusion from the premise(s) is less obvious and has to be established by a proof of some sort. Once this has been established the inference from sequent may be freely used. There is therefore a distinction between validity and provability and in the latter case the *single turnstile* is used:

$$\tau \vdash E$$

This second turnstile is simply a mechanism that records the fact that some proposition (E) is a consequence of (i.e. can be proved from) others (τ). An example of a valid sequent is:

$$P, P \Rightarrow Q \vdash Q$$

Tautologies can also be written in terms of the turnstile as:

$$\vdash P \vee \neg P$$

which suggests that nothing has to be assumed for its truth to be established so that it is 'universally true' for all values of its constituent propositions.

In certain cases, sequents may be formed where the inference can be made both ways, i.e. given the truth of the premise(s) the conclusion can be accepted as true. Additionally, if the conclusion is true then the truth of the premise(s) may also be assumed. In such circumstances the turnstiles are employed 'back to back', $\models\!\!\mid$ and $\dashv\vdash$. Some examples of such sequents are:

$$P \vee (Q \vee R) \models\!\!\mid (P \vee Q) \vee R$$
$$P \wedge (Q \wedge R) \models\!\!\mid (P \wedge Q) \wedge R \qquad \text{and}$$
$$(P \Rightarrow Q) \Rightarrow Q \dashv\vdash P \vee Q$$

5.4 SIMPLIFICATION AND PROOF FOR PROPOSITIONAL LOGIC

When dealing with propositional logic two problems often concern us:

1. How can we reduce complex propositions to simpler forms which have the same logical properties? (That is to say, whenever the complex expression is true the simpler expression is true and vice versa.)

2. Given the sequent $P1, P2, \ldots, Pn \vdash Q$ how can we prove the truth of the conclusion given the truth of the premises?

In ordinary algebra, simplification of expressions is aided by various laws which, when applied with precision and experience, transform complex expressions into simple ones. Simplification of propositions can be carried out in exactly the same way because we have an equivalent set of *propositional laws*. There are 12 such laws, and each is expressed as a tautology involving the equivalence operator. This simply means that the propositional expressions either side of the equivalence operator have the same logical properties and can be substituted for each other during the simplification process. These laws are presented shortly. The second problem—that of showing that a certain proposition holds given the validity of other propositions—is a vitally important process in the formal development of software. This process, above all others, permits us to reason about our descriptions to show that they are consistent or that they have properties that satisfy their specification. Because the process of logical reasoning ensures certainty, we have a major advantage over soft, quasi or informal argument, none of which can ever create certainty.

The problem of proof in logic requires us to establish that for a given sequent, the conclusion is true given the truth of certain premises. Here we have basically three ways of proceeding. First, we can take each individual proposition $P1, P2, \ldots, Pn, Q$ and draw a table containing every possible combination of truth values for these propositions. We then look along the table and check to see that every time all the Pis are true Q is true also. This method will always work but it is very long-winded indeed; recall that SAQ 5.4 used this technique to establish the truth of the sequent $P1 \wedge (P2 \vee P3) \models P1 \wedge P2 \vee P1 \wedge P3$. The second approach allows us to construct some rigorous argument, much as we do when proving theorems in geometry. In the case of the sequent in SAQ 5.4 this argument might proceed as follows: for a sequent to be false there must exist some situation where its hypothesis (premise(s)) is(are) true but its conclusion false. If $P1 \wedge (P2 \vee P3)$ is true then both $P1$ and at least $P2$ or $P3$ must be true. Therefore, either $P1 \wedge P2$ or $P1 \wedge P3$ (or both) must be true. We therefore cannot find a situation where the conclusion is false if the hypothesis is true.

The third approach depends on the fact that expressions such as:

$$P1, P2, \ldots, P_n \vdash Q$$

are really equivalent to:

$$P1 \wedge P2 \wedge \ldots, P_n \Rightarrow Q$$

Proving the sequent in this form requires us to write down the premises and then use the laws of propositional calculus together with various *rules of inference* (which are really only sequents themselves) to deduce other true formulae. From these and the originals we deduce further formulae and so on until we (hopefully) derive the conclusion. This is a *chain of inference* and is the method most commonly used for mathematical proofs. In this respect, remember that for an implication, if the antecedent is true and the implication is true then the consequent is always true. Alternatively, the implication is proved true if, given the truth of the premise(s), we can show the truth of the conclusion.

In formal specification, the turnstile is frequently used in the expression of theorems which establish that the specification has particular logical properties. Theorems are really only propositions that are known to be true. We will examine some simplifications and proofs once we have established the laws of propositional calculus and the rules of inference.

5.5 THE LAWS OF PROPOSITIONAL CALCULUS

The 12 laws presented here are fundamental to the understanding and use of propositional logic. They are used frequently in the rest of the book, often with reference to the names which introduce them here, e.g. 'by De Morgan'. Although some of the laws may be quite obvious, others are not. Readers might like to attempt proofs as exercises using the techniques presented in the following section but really these laws are simply best accepted and used.

1 Associative laws

These laws can be used to introduce or eliminate parentheses in propositional expressions involving the operators $\wedge$ and $\vee$:

$$P \wedge (Q \wedge R) \Leftrightarrow (P \wedge Q) \wedge R \Leftrightarrow P \wedge Q \wedge R \qquad \text{(Assoc } \wedge\text{)}$$
$$P \vee (Q \vee R) \Leftrightarrow (P \vee Q) \vee R \Leftrightarrow P \vee Q \vee R \qquad \text{(Assoc } \vee\text{)}$$

2 Commutative laws

These laws allow us to interchange operands in expressions involving the operators $\wedge$, $\vee$ and $\Leftrightarrow$. These laws may seem quite obvious but there are a number of operators in the discrete mathematics in the following chapters which are not commutative. It is well worth watching out for them:

$$(P \wedge Q) \Leftrightarrow (Q \wedge P) \qquad \text{(Comm } \wedge\text{)}$$
$$(P \vee Q) \Leftrightarrow (Q \vee P) \qquad \text{(Comm } \vee\text{)}$$
$$(P \Leftrightarrow Q) \Leftrightarrow (Q \Leftrightarrow P) \qquad \text{(Comm } \Leftrightarrow\text{)}$$

3 Distributive laws

These laws involve $\wedge$ and $\vee$ and are used to factor out or to expand propositional expressions:

$$P \vee (Q \wedge R) \Leftrightarrow (P \vee Q) \wedge (P \vee R) \qquad \text{(Dist } \vee \wedge\text{)}$$
$$P \wedge (Q \vee R) \Leftrightarrow (P \wedge Q) \vee (P \wedge R) \qquad \text{(Dist } \wedge \vee\text{)}$$

4 De Morgan's laws

Augustus De Morgan was a nineteenth-century British mathematician. His laws allow us to apply negation to simple expressions involving the $\wedge$ and $\vee$ operators:

$$\neg(P \wedge Q) \Leftrightarrow \neg P \vee \neg Q \qquad \text{(DeM } \wedge\text{)}$$
$$\neg(P \vee Q) \Leftrightarrow \neg P \wedge \neg Q \qquad \text{(DeM } \vee\text{)}$$

5 The law of negation

This law simply states that the negation of a negated proposition is the proposition itself. The law is written quite simply as:

$$\neg\neg P \Leftrightarrow P \qquad \text{(Neg)}$$

6 The law of the excluded middle

This law simply says that either the predicate is true or the negation of the predicate is true. In other words, a proposition has to be either true or false:

$$P \vee \neg P \Leftrightarrow \text{true} \qquad \text{(Ex Mid)}$$

7 The law of contradiction

It follows from Law 6 that a proposition cannot be true and false at the same time. This is the law of contradiction, expressed as:

$$P \wedge \neg P \Leftrightarrow \text{false} \qquad \text{(Contr)}$$

8 The law of implication

This is a very useful law in that it allows implication to be removed from an expression and replaced by disjunction and negation. This is often used in proofs for it permits the subsequent use of De Morgan's laws.

$$P \Rightarrow Q \Leftrightarrow \neg P \vee Q \qquad \text{(Impl)}$$

9 The law of equality

This law expresses equivalence in terms of implication. The link with the previous law is therefore obvious.

$$(P \Leftrightarrow Q) \Leftrightarrow (P \Rightarrow Q) \wedge (Q \Rightarrow P) \qquad \text{(Equal)}$$

10 The laws of *and* simplification

These laws permit certain propositions containing *true, false* or $\wedge$ to be simplified. The laws are written:

$$P \wedge P \Leftrightarrow P \qquad \text{(and1)}$$
$$P \wedge \textit{true} \Leftrightarrow P \qquad \text{(and2)}$$
$$P \wedge \textit{false} \Leftrightarrow \textit{false} \qquad \text{(and3)}$$
$$P \wedge (P \vee Q) \Leftrightarrow P \qquad \text{(and4)}$$

11 The laws of *or* simplification

These laws permit certain propositions containing true, false or $\vee$ to be simplified. The laws are written:

$$P \vee P \Leftrightarrow P \qquad \text{(or1)}$$
$$P \vee \textit{true} \Leftrightarrow \textit{true} \qquad \text{(or2)}$$
$$P \vee \textit{false} \Leftrightarrow P \qquad \text{(or3)}$$
$$P \vee (P \wedge Q) \Leftrightarrow P \qquad \text{(or4)}$$

12   The *exclusive or* law

The *exclusive or* operator, $\vee_e$, is a binary operator that returns *true* when only one of the propositions to which it is applied is *true*. The law is expressed as:

$$P1 \vee_e P2 \Leftrightarrow P1 \wedge \neg P2 \vee \neg P1 \wedge P2 \qquad \text{(exor)}$$

Thus, when both $P1$ and $P2$ are *true*, the operator returns *false*. The law as expressed above shows the relationship between the *exclusive or* operator and the normal *or* operator.

5.6 THE RULES OF INFERENCE

Although proofs can be conducted by building truth tables this is impossibly inconvenient. Most proofs are conducted using a method by means of which the truth of one proposition can be safely inferred (deduced) from the truth of others. This is known as *logical inference* and, using the propositional laws together with a series of inference rules, successive transformations on a series of assumptions hopefully leads to the expression we wish to prove. A rule of inference is simply a statement that asserts that if one proposition is *true* then we can safely assume that another proposition is *true*. The mechanism we adopt to indicate what can be inferred from what involves separating the two by a line. All our rules of inference are therefore written in the following style:

$$\frac{\text{If we know this to be true}}{\text{It can be replaced by this}}$$

which is really only another way of writing a sequent. The first rule of inference we look at is the *and elimination rule* (or simply $\wedge$ elim). We write the rule in the general form as follows, where $1 \leq i \leq n$:

$$\frac{P1 \wedge P2 \wedge \ldots \wedge Pn}{Pi} \qquad (\wedge \text{ elim})$$

This rule follows from the truth table of the $\wedge$ operator in that, given that the conjunction of the predicates is true, each individual Pi must also be true. Consequently, whenever we have such a conjunction the expression can be replaced by any one of the individual propositions.

The second rule is the *or introduction rule* (or simply $\vee$ intro). Again in general form the rule becomes:

$$\frac{Pi}{P1 \vee P2 \vee \ldots \vee Pn} \qquad (\vee \text{ intro})$$

assuming $1 \leq i \leq n$. This rule follows directly from the truth table for the $\vee$ operator. If any proposition Pi is true, then the proposition formed by *or*-ing the propositions $P1$ to Pn would also be true.

The next rule is the *and introduction rule* ($\wedge$ intro):

$$\frac{P1; P2; \ldots; Pn}{P1 \wedge P2 \wedge \ldots \wedge Pn} \qquad (\wedge \text{ intro})$$

The justification for this rule is that if all of the propositions $P1$ to Pn are true then the conjunction of the propositions must also be true. Notice that, in the general form, the individual propositions on the top line are separated by semi-colons rather than commas as in ordinary sequents. This reflects the fact that in a rule of inference a premise may itself be a sequent. This convention is followed in the remaining rules.

Three other useful rules are *equivalence introduction* ($\Leftrightarrow$ intro), *equivalence elimination* ($\Leftrightarrow$ elim) and *implication elimination* ($\Rightarrow$ elim):

$$\frac{P1 \Rightarrow P2;\ P2 \Rightarrow P1}{P1 \Leftrightarrow P2} \qquad (\Leftrightarrow \text{intro})$$

$$\frac{P1 \Leftrightarrow P2}{P1 \Rightarrow P2;\ P2 \Rightarrow P1} \qquad (\Leftrightarrow \text{elim})$$

$$\frac{P1 \Rightarrow P2;\ P1}{P2} \qquad (\Rightarrow \text{elim})$$

The $\Leftrightarrow$ intro rule states that if $P1$ implies $P2$ and $P2$ implies $P1$ then the two propositions are equivalent. They can therefore replace each other where convenient. The $\Leftrightarrow$ elim rule is really the reverse of this process such that an equivalence can be replaced by the individual implications. Finally, the $\Rightarrow$ elim rule states that if $P1$ implies $P2$ and $P1$ is true, then the implication can be replaced by $P2$. There are many other rules of inference available which follow the general form presented in these examples. As far as this text is concerned, if additional rules are required we should now be able to introduce them locally as and when they are required. However, interested readers are referred to Jones (1991) which covers the additional rules quite comprehensively.

Finally, for the sake of completion, it should also be pointed out that many of the laws referred to earlier can be expressed as rules of inference rather than as tautologies involving equivalence. An example is $\vee$ ass:

$$\frac{(P \vee Q) \vee R}{P \vee (Q \vee R)} \qquad (\vee \text{ass})$$

where the double line represents that fact that it is safe to conduct the inference in either direction, i.e. given $(P \vee Q) \vee R$ then $P \vee (Q \vee R)$ or given $P \vee (Q \vee R)$ then $(P \vee Q) \vee R$. This notation is equivalent to the use of the $\dashv\vDash$ turnstile with the same sequent discussed earlier.

5.6.1 Some examples of simplification and proof

All these rules are important but they can be put into perspective only by using them. In this respect this section illustrates the use of the rules both in simplification of propositional expressions and in the conduct of formal proofs. A proof 'template' that is used in later parts of the book is also introduced (see the chapters on VDM in Parts 6 and 7). However, I am of the opinion that although proof presented in this format may be acceptable to the community at large, any proof is better than none so that truth tables and rigorous argument all have a place. This is especially so in an introductory text. We begin by considering the simplification of the following expression:

$$\neg\neg(\neg((P \vee Q) \wedge P))$$

The simplification is as follows, where each step in the process refers to the various propositional laws that have been used.

$$
\begin{array}{ll}
\neg\neg(\neg(P \wedge (P \vee Q))) & \text{(Comm } \wedge) \\
\neg\neg(\neg(P \wedge P \vee P \wedge Q)) & \text{(Dist } \wedge\vee) \\
\neg\neg(\neg(P \vee P \wedge Q)) & \text{(and1)} \\
\neg\neg(\neg(P)) & \text{(or4)} \\
\neg P & \text{(Neg)}
\end{array}
$$

The simplification therefore provides us with an equivalent logical expression; whatever the value of P and Q, $\neg P$ has the same value as $\neg\neg(\neg(P \wedge (P \vee Q)))$.

SAQ 5.5 Simplify the following expressions and state the laws used in the process:

(a) $(P \wedge \neg Q) \wedge P$
(b) $\neg(P \vee Q) \wedge P$
(c) $(P \vee Q) \wedge (\text{true} \vee Q)$

As an example of a proof—and the style in which it may be conducted—we examine the proof of the sequent:

$$P \wedge (Q \wedge R) \vdash (P \wedge Q) \wedge R$$

which represents the associativity of 'and'. The proof is as follows:

$$\texttt{from } P \wedge (Q \wedge R)$$

1. P		$\wedge$ elim(h)
2. $Q \wedge R$		$\wedge$ elim(h)
3. Q		$\wedge$ elim(2)
4. R		$\wedge$ elim(2)
5. $P \wedge Q$		$\wedge$ intro(1,3)
$\texttt{infer } (P \wedge Q) \wedge R$		$\wedge$ intro(5,4)

This style is referred to as the *natural deduction style* and shows the dependency of the proof on various hypotheses (premise(s)) at the head of the 'box'. These are introduced with the keyword `from` and are taken as true. The overall goal of the proof closes the box with the keyword `infer` and claims the establishment of the conclusion from the premise(s) through the logical argument within the box. Each stage in this argument is referenced with a line number and the annotation to the extreme right of the line presents the justification for the statement in terms of the laws of inference that have been used. For example, line 1 is true because of the use of the *and* elimination rule on the original hypothesis (h), i.e. $\wedge$ elim(h). Here P is the individual proposition that can replace the whole conjunction. In line 2 the same rule is applied again this time choosing $(Q \wedge R)$ as the individual proposition. Two further applications of the rule with line 2 ($\wedge$ elim(2)) establish the truth of Q and R on lines 3 and 4. The *and* introduction rule in line 5 ($\wedge$ intro(1,3)) establishes that $P \wedge Q$ is true based on lines 1 and 3, while the conclusion is established in the final line because of the *and* introduction rule applied to the results in lines 5 and 4.

Not all proofs need be conducted in natural deduction style, but it is somewhat more concise than the clumsy explanation that follows the proof and appears frequently in texts on the specification language VDM. Later chapters of the book study this language in some detail and proofs in this format will be discussed again. Because any proof is better than none, rigorous argument well explained is perfectly acceptable and will be used frequently in later chapters.

SAQ 5.6 Conduct natural deduction proofs on the following sequents which have two hypotheses:

$$P \wedge Q, P \Rightarrow R \vdash R \vee (Q \Rightarrow R)$$
$$P \vee Q, \neg Q \vdash P$$

SAQ 5.7 The sequent:

$$P \wedge (Q \wedge R) \vdash (P \wedge Q) \wedge R$$

can be written:

$$P \wedge (Q \wedge R) \Rightarrow (P \wedge Q) \wedge R$$

and ultimately as:

$$\neg(P \wedge (Q \wedge R)) \vee ((P \wedge Q) \wedge R)$$

Use the natural deduction style to prove the sequent in this form.

5.7 PREDICATES AND PREDICATE CALCULUS

In the introduction to this chapter it was suggested that specifications can be regarded as a collection of propositions concerning the behaviour of an intended software module. In a sense this statement is still quite true, but unfortunately the propositions are often in a form which makes treatment by propositional calculus very difficult. For example, a specification might demand that:

all parts supplied by the company cost less than £50; the company supplies part P30

Intuitively we would deduce that P30 certainly costs less than £50 but, using propositional calculus, it is impossible to come to that conclusion unless the first proposition is expressed in a form that applies to part P30 specifically. Thus, if the following implication below is true:

if the company supplies P30 *then* P30 costs less than £50

by assuming the truth of:

the company supplies part P30

we can deduce 'P30 costs less than £50' because when the implication is true and the antecedent is true the consequent must also be true.

Clearly, statements such as 'all parts supplied by the company cost less than £50' embody implications about every single product that the company supplies, and reasoning with such statements demands that we write an individual implication for every single part. When such expressions involve large numbers of items this is impossible; what is needed is some way of dealing with whole classes, sets or groups of objects without recourse to enumerating their individual propositions. In this sense we need to *parametrize* propositions so that they involve *variables* whose values are allowed to range over the items in the groups. When the variables are *instantiated* these expressions provide individual (customized) instances of propositions. For our particular example, this mechanism requires the following compound proposition:

> the company supplies P1 $\Rightarrow$ P1 costs less than £50 $\wedge$
> the company supplies P2 $\Rightarrow$ P2 costs less than £50 $\wedge$
> $\vdots$
> the company supplies Pn $\Rightarrow$ Pn costs less than £50

to be replaced by a *generalized truth-valued statement* such as:

> for all parts p, *the-company-supplies*(p) $\Rightarrow$ *cost*(p) < 50

Here, *the-company-supplies*(p) and *cost*(p) are *parametrized propositions*. If at some time we have $p = $ P30, then the expression:

> *the-company-supplies*(P30) $\Rightarrow$ *cost*(P30) < 50

provides an instance of a proposition which is exactly equivalent to:

> the company supplies P30 $\Rightarrow$ P30 costs less than £50

In this way we can generate any proposition we wish; control over the parametrization process is provided by phrases such as 'for all parts X' which suggests that we are building a conjunction of propositions for every part the company supplies. When the whole statement 'for all parts p . . .' is true we understand that every individual proposition is true. Thus we capture logical properties of whole groups of objects in a compact and convenient fashion.

Parametrized propositions are *predicates*. Predicates are subject to the laws and rules of inference discussed earlier because they only represent instances of particular propositions. These laws, together with the various statements that control which propositions are generated, constitute *predicate calculus*. The remaining parts of this chapter discuss the notation of the predicate calculus used in Parts 3–7.

5.8 QUANTIFIERS

The phrases that control the instantiation of the predicates in a generalized truth-valued statement are written using *quantifiers*. Quantifiers are introduced into a predicate calculus expression using a special notation and a number of different quantifiers exist. In this book we require only three:

- $\forall$ the universal quantifier
- $\exists$ the existential quantifier
- $\exists!$ the unique existential quantifier, sometimes written $\exists_1$

The universal quantifier is used to demand that every object in a collection has a particular property. The quantifier is written as an inverted capital A ($\forall$) and is read 'for all' or sometimes 'for every'. Using this quantifier we can write a predicate calculus expression corresponding to the requirement that: 'all parts supplied by the company cost less than £50'. Thus:

$$\forall p : Parts \bullet the\text{-}company\text{-}supplies(p) \Rightarrow cost(p) < 50$$

Here the predicate is said to be 'quantified'. The expression consists of two parts: the *signature* and the *predicate*—separated by a bullet (•). The expression is read as:

> for all *p*s that are *Parts* ($\forall p : Parts$) the following is true (•) if the company supplies *p* then *p* costs less than £50

The signature introduces the quantifier ($\forall$) and the variable (p) used in the quantification process. The notation $p : Parts$ is meant to indicate that the value p accepts belongs to the set (see Chapter 6) or collection called *Part* which in turn represents (the names of) all the parts the company might supply. All variables introduced into an expression in this way are *bound* and are subject to scoping rules similar to those in programming languages. Thus p is a variable whose existence is known about only within the sphere of influence of the quantifier that introduced it. Any variable which is present in such expression that has not been introduced by a quantifier is *free*. We shall see shortly that it is possible to have free and bound variables in the same expression sharing the same name; they are, however, different variables.

The use of the universal quantifier is equivalent to creating separate propositions by instantiating the predicate with every value in the set of *Parts* and then demanding that the conjunction of all these is true, that is:

$$\forall p : Parts \bullet the\text{-}company\text{-}supplies(p) \Rightarrow cost(p) < 50 \Leftrightarrow$$
$$the\text{-}company\text{-}supplies(\text{P}1) \Rightarrow cost(\text{P}1) < 50 \wedge$$
$$the\text{-}company\text{-}supplies(\text{P}2) \Rightarrow cost(\text{P}2) < 50 \wedge$$
$$\vdots$$
$$the\text{-}company\text{-}supplies(\text{P}n) \Rightarrow cost(\text{P}n) < 50$$

In circumstances where we require *at least one* but possibly more members of a set of objects to possess a particular property we can use the existential quantifier. To modify our earlier example we might demand that: 'at least one of the parts that the company supplies will cost less than £50'. Such a requirement can be written in calculus as:

$$\exists p : Parts \bullet the\text{-}company\text{-}supplies(p) \wedge cost(p) < 50$$

which reads as:

> There exists at least one part *p* ($\exists p : Parts$) where (or such that) the following is true (•) the company supplies *p* and *p* costs less than £50.

This expression is really equivalent to our constructing individual propositions by instantiating the predicate with every single value in *Part* and then building a compound proposition which is the *disjunction* of them all:

$$the\text{-}company\text{-}supplies(\text{P}1) \wedge cost(\text{P}1) < 50 \vee$$
$$the\text{-}company\text{-}supplies(\text{P}1) \wedge cost(\text{P}1) < 50 \vee$$
$$\vdots$$
$$the\text{-}company\text{-}supplies(\text{P}1) \wedge cost(\text{P}1) < 50$$

Because this is a disjunction, the whole expression is true if one or more of the individual propositions are true.

SAQ 5.8 Does the following quantified predicate conform to the requirement that: 'at least one of the parts that the company supplies will cost less than £50'?

$$\exists p: Parts \bullet \textit{the-company-supplies}(p) \Rightarrow cost(p) < 50$$

Finally, if we were to demand that 'the company supplies *one part only* that costs less than £50, we can use the unique existential quantifier:

$$\exists! \, p: Parts \bullet \textit{the-company-supplies}(p) \wedge cost(p) < 50 \qquad \text{or}$$
$$\exists_1 p: Parts \bullet \textit{the-company-supplies}(p) \wedge cost(p) < 50$$

which reads as:

> There exists *exactly one part p* ($\exists! p: Parts$) where (or such that) the following is true ($\bullet$) the company supplies p and p costs less than £50.

This expression can be written in terms of the other quantifiers and therefore ultimately in terms of conjunctions and disjunctions. We return to this point shortly.

Many of the quantifiers used in this book involve variables belonging to collections of numbers such as the integers ($\mathbb{Z}$), the natural numbers($\mathbb{N}$) or the strictly positive natural numbers($\mathbb{N}_1$). To consolidate our understanding of quantifiers and to introduce some 'variations on a theme' this section ends by examining some predicate calculus expressions involving members of these sets.

The expression:

$$\forall x, y: \mathbb{N} \bullet x \neq y \Rightarrow x > y \vee x < y$$

simply says that for any two natural numbers x and y, if x is not equal to y then x is either greater than y or less than y. Notice here that the signature involves two variables—both bound by the quantifier. In general, predicate calculus expressions can involve as many variables as you wish. Notice also that $\forall x, y: \mathbb{N} \bullet$ is really only a more convenient form of $\forall x: \mathbb{N} \bullet \forall y: \mathbb{N} \bullet$.

The expression:

$$\exists x: \mathbb{N} \bullet 10 \leq x \wedge x \leq 50$$

says that there exists at least one natural number that lies in the range 10 to 50 inclusive, while the expression:

$$\exists x, y: \mathbb{N} \bullet 1 \leq x \wedge x \leq 8 \wedge 10 \leq y \wedge y \leq 100 \wedge x * y = 81$$

says that there exists at least one value of x in the range 1 to 8 and one value of y in the range 10 to 100 where the product $x * y$ equals 81. This expression is true because $x = 3$ and $y = 27$ satisfy this condition. Expressions such as these are often written rather more conveniently using a form of *restricted quantifier* (which applies equally well to $\exists$, $\forall$ or $\exists!$) together with some additional set notation, which we develop further in the next chapter. Thus we could rewrite the expression as:

$$\exists x, y: \mathbb{N} \,|\, x \in \{1 \ldots 8\} \wedge y \in \{10 \ldots 100\} \bullet x * y = 81$$

where the vertical bar is read 'such that'. Notation such as $x \subset \{1 \ldots 8\}$ demands that x is a member of ($\in$) the set containing the numbers 1 to 8 inclusive, while the whole expression can be read 'there exists at least one value of x and one value of y such that x lies in the range 1 to 8 and y lies in the range 10 to 100 where $x * y = 81$'. We meet a number of restricted quantifications later in the book.

Quite often we need to build up predicates that involve a number of different quantifiers. For example, the familiar 'is less than' relationship between integers can be expressed as follows:

$$\forall i, j : \mathbb{Z} \bullet i < j \Rightarrow \exists k : \mathbb{N}_1 \bullet i + k = j$$

while the 'is less than or equal to' relationship is expressed as:

$$\forall i, j : \mathbb{Z} \bullet i \leq j \Rightarrow \exists k : \mathbb{N} \bullet i + k = j$$

In the first of these the universal quantifier introduces two bound variables (i and j), while the existential quantifier introduces the bound variable k, a strictly positive natural number. Here the scope of i and j covers the whole implication—they can be used in expressions on both sides—but k is known only on the consequent side. Notice also that the variables range over different sets ($\mathbb{Z}$ and $\mathbb{N}_1$). The whole expression is read as: 'for all pairs of is and js that are integers, if i is less than j then there must exist at least one number greater than 0 such that if it is added to i we produce j'. Thus, 3 is less than 5 because we can find a value for k (2) which when added to 3 gives 5. In the second expression k becomes a natural number because the relationship is now 'less than or *equal* to'.

Another example of mixed quantification occurs in the definition of the unique existential quantifier $\exists!$. In general, the following quantified predicate:

$$\exists! x : X \bullet p(x)$$

can be written as:

$$\exists x : X \bullet p(x) \land \forall y : X \bullet p(y) \Rightarrow x = y$$

This expression can be read as: 'there exists at least one value of x belonging to X which satisfies the predicate and for all values that belong to X if a value satisfies the predicate it must be equal to x'. Because sets cannot contain duplicates there can be only one value that satisfies $p(x)$. We meet a large number of expressions involving mixed quantifiers in later parts of the book.

5.8.1 The relationship between $\forall$ and $\exists$

An important relationship exists between the universal and the existential quantifiers. Universal quantification expresses the fact that *all* objects in some collection have a particular property, while existential quantification demands that there exists *at least one* object that has the property. Consequently, an assertion that *not all* objects in a collection have the property is really the same as saying that *at least one does not* have the property. In general then:

$$\neg \forall x : X \bullet p(x) \Leftrightarrow \exists x : X \bullet \neg p(x)$$

Similarly, if we assert that there does not exist a single object that has the property then we are really saying that all objects do not have the property. In general then:

$$\neg \exists x : X \bullet p(x) \Leftrightarrow \forall x : X \bullet \neg p(x)$$

These equivalences are intuitively true but we can show the equivalence rather more formally if we consider the real nature of each quantifier. Assuming some predicate $p(x)$, we argued earlier that:

$$\forall x : X \bullet p(x) \Leftrightarrow P1 \wedge P2 \wedge P3 \wedge \ldots \wedge Pn$$

and

$$\exists x : X \bullet p(x) \Leftrightarrow P1 \vee P2 \vee P3 \vee \ldots \vee Pn$$

Clearly, if:

$$\forall x : X \bullet p(x) \Leftrightarrow P1 \wedge P2 \wedge P3 \wedge \ldots \wedge Pn$$

then:

$$\neg \forall x : X \bullet p(x) \Leftrightarrow \neg (P1 \wedge P2 \wedge P3 \wedge \ldots \wedge Pn)$$

Now by De Morgan:

$$\neg (P1 \wedge P2 \wedge P3 \wedge \ldots \wedge Pn) \Leftrightarrow \neg P1 \vee \neg P2 \vee \neg P3 \vee \ldots \vee \neg Pn$$

but:

$$\neg P1 \vee \neg P2 \vee \neg P3 \vee \ldots \vee \neg Pn \Leftrightarrow \exists x : X \bullet \neg p(x)$$

so that finally:

$$\neg \forall x : X \bullet p(x) \Leftrightarrow \exists x : X \bullet \neg p(x)$$

In later parts of the book we have many other opportunities to reason with expressions involving quantifiers.

SAQ 5.9   By a similar argument show that:

$$\neg \exists x : X \bullet p(x) \Leftrightarrow \forall x : X \bullet \neg p(x)$$

SAQ 5.10   Given that we have now established:

$$\neg \forall x : X \bullet p(x) \Leftrightarrow \exists x : X \bullet \neg p(x)$$

and

$$\neg \exists x : X \bullet p(x) \Leftrightarrow \forall x : X \bullet \neg p(x)$$

what are $\forall x : X \bullet p(x)$ and $\exists x : X \bullet p(x)$ equivalent to? Express your conclusions in simple natural language. Clearly, the quantifiers provide a very powerful expressive medium. Consequently, quantified predicates form a very important part of the formal specification of software systems. The remaining chapters use quantification freely— usually accompanied by an informal English explanation.

5.9 VALID SEQUENTS INVOLVING QUANTIFIERS

There are a very large number of valid sequents involving expressions in predicate calculus and many of these are useful in simplifying some of the logical expressions generated in later parts of the book. Interested readers might like to refer to Diller (1990) or Potter *et al.* (1991) for a comprehensive list, but this text concentrates only on those which are used later. In this respect the following sequents (proofs largely assumed) are important. Notice that in most cases, the inference can be conducted in both directions.

$$\exists x : X \bullet P_y \dashv\vdash P_y$$
$$\exists x : X \bullet P_y \land Q_x \dashv\vdash P_y \land \exists x : X \bullet Q_x$$
$$P_y \dashv\vdash \exists x : X \bullet x = y \land P_x$$
$$\exists a,b : X \bullet P_a \land P_b \vdash \exists a : X \bullet P_a \land \exists b : X \bullet P_b$$

The first of the sequents allows us to drop (or insert) vacuous quantification. If an expression is quantified with a variable that does not appear in the predicate, then the quantification can be removed. In the sequent, P_y is meant to represent a predicate involving y and this notation is used in the remaining examples.

In the second example the quantification is applied to the conjunction of two predicates but only in the second (Q_x) does the variable introduced by the quantification appear. The quantification for the first predicate is therefore vacuous and can be dropped.

In the third example, because $x = y$ we can replace every occurrence of x in P_x with y. This leaves the expression with a vacuous quantification which can then be dropped.

The final example illustrates how quantification can be split into component parts which can then be treated individually. Because the signature $\exists a,b : X \bullet$ is shorthand for $\exists a : X \bullet \exists b : X \bullet$, this sequent can be demonstrated quite simply as:

$$\exists a,b : X \bullet P_a \land P_b$$
$$\exists a : X \bullet \exists b : X \bullet P_a \land P_b$$

which by the second sequent above can be written as:

$$\exists a : X \bullet P_a \land \exists b : X \bullet P_b$$

The argument can be extended to expressions of the type $\exists a,b,c,\dots : X \bullet P_a \land P_b \land P_c \land \dots$ which can be written $\exists a : X \bullet P_a \land \exists b : X \bullet P_b \land \exists c : X \bullet P_c \land \dots$.

5.10 MORE ABOUT THE USE OF LOGIC IN SPECIFICATION LANGUAGES AND PROOFS

In the introduction to this chapter the point was made that our treatment of logic is largely that used by the specification language Z, covered in Parts 4 and 5. The specification language VDM (Parts 6 and 7) differs from Z in that it uses a three-valued logic and has a different notational convention for signatures. Thus, the shorthand $a : X$ appears (more correctly) as $a \in X$ in VDM so that the Z expressions:

$$\neg\forall x : X \bullet p(x) \Leftrightarrow \exists x : X \bullet \neg p(x)$$
$$\neg\exists x : X \bullet p(x) \Leftrightarrow \forall x : X \bullet \neg p(x)$$

become:

$$\neg\forall x \in X \bullet p(x) \Leftrightarrow \exists x \in X \bullet \neg p(x)$$
$$\neg\exists x \in X \bullet p(x) \Leftrightarrow \forall x \in X \bullet \neg p(x)$$

Apart from this convention, the laws, rules of inference, sequents and general logic notation remain the same.

Proofs in Z are expressed as sequents with general form:

$$\text{Declarations} \mid \text{Predicate(s)} \vdash \text{Conclusion}$$

which is really only a form of implication. In order to prove the theorem we must establish the truth of the consequent given the truth of the antecedent or vice versa. In VDM, theorems are conventionally expressed as implications of the form:

$$\forall x \in X \bullet A \Rightarrow B$$

which is really the same thing, but with the added consideration that proof also shows that neither A nor B can be undefined in VDM's three-valued logic.

6

SET THEORY

CHECKLIST OF OBJECTIVES

After reading this chapter you should be able to:

- Understand what is meant by a 'typed set theory'.
- Use enumeration or set comprehension to construct simple sets of interest to you.
- Use the operators of set theory to manipulate sets.
- Use enumeration or set comprehension to construct sets of tuples.
- Understand how set theory can be used to describe interesting events in a formal fashion.

6.1 INTRODUCTION

Set theory represents the foundation stone upon which many of the aspects of formal approaches to the specification and verification of software are built. The most frequent description of sets employed is that of a *typed set theory*. This corresponds to the natural way in which we think about systems, i.e. as collections of like objects. Additionally, restricting sets to contain elements of the same type has advantages in that certain mathematical paradoxes are avoided, while consistency checking among specifications is supported in the same ways that a compiler benefits from the strong typing in a programming language. The important aspects of typed set theory are that:

- A set is completely defined by the members it contains.
- An item is either a member or not; it cannot be repeated within a set neither can it fractionally occur.
- There is no intrinsic order among members of a set.
- All members are of the same type or sort.
- An item cannot belong to more than one type.

A further property of typed sets is that they are either *finite* or *infinite*. In a finite set there exists some upper limit to the population. This may be large or small but in all such cases the population is countable. An infinite set, however, as the name implies, has an immeasurably large population and some important examples are:

- $\mathbb{Z}$ The set of integers which is perceived to extend throughout the range $-\infty .. 0 .. +\infty$

- ℕ   The set of natural numbers which corresponds to integers in the range $0 .. + \infty$
- ℕ₁   The set of strictly positive natural numbers corresponding to integers in the range $1 .. + \infty$

where the special symbols represent a widely accepted shorthand for each set. In most cases when we use mathematics to describe events of interest we tend to use definitions that involve infinite sets, simply because this avoids our having to deal with situations where sets become full as operations are performed upon them. Such detail is seen as a problem for the implementation, which is where the choice of real sets has to be addressed. On occasions, however, finite set populations are required and these carry the corresponding obligation that their members be countable. An example of a frequently used finite set is the set that represents the English-language characters {a,b,c, .. A,B,C, ..}. This set is frequently referred to as char or *CHAR*.

In this chapter we lay the foundations for much of what follows by describing the fundamental operations that can be carried out upon sets. In a few cases an operation may be defined only for certain types of set, typically having to draw a distinction between finite and infinite sets or ensuring that when two or more sets are involved in an operation they are all of the same type (whatever that may be). Apart from these exceptions, the operators can be applied to sets of any type. Our definitions are therefore *generic*, that is to say they have a definition that uses *type parameters* such as A, B, T_1 or T_2. When we use such constants later in a specification, actual named sets are used to replace the type parameters thereby providing a proper context for the operation.

6.2 DEFINING (MAKING) AND DECLARING SETS

Because a set is completely defined by the members it contains, the definition of a set corresponds to the identification of its members. This can be achieved by *enumeration* (often called *explicit construction*) or by *set comprehension*. To construct a set explicitly, its members are simply listed (in some arbitrary order) separated by commas and enclosed in set braces { }. Possible examples are {1,8,12,36} and {1,4,9,16}. Repeating members or writing them in a different order has no effect. Each of the following enumerations (where the symbol $==$ may be read as 'is defined by' or 'is a name for') therefore represents the same set:

$$S == \{16,9,4,1\}$$
$$S == \{1,1,16,9,4\}$$
$$S == \{9,4,1,16\}$$
$$S == \{16,16,1,9,16,9,4,1\}$$

The fact that a particular element x is a member of some set S is written $x \in S$, where the symbol $\in$ represents the *set inclusion* operator. The expression $x \in S$ is therefore read 'x is a member of the set S' and is a predicate evaluating to true or false. The fact that x is not a member of the set is determined by the truth of $\neg(x \in S)$ or $(x \notin S)$.

Explicit set definition is simple enough but it suffers from certain disadvantages. First, many of the sets of interest to software engineers are very large indeed, for example, the set of all possible telephone numbers in the United Kingdom or the set of all possible employees in a multinational company. Indeed, as we have seen, certain common sets are infinite. Secondly, the explicit list does not make clear the relationship the members have to each other that declare them to be of the same type and qualify them for membership of the set. For example, is the set $\{1,3,5,7\}$ just an arbitrary set of four integers or natural numbers? Does the set represent the first four odd natural numbers? Could they be the set of positive square roots of the set $\{1,9,25,49\}$? To overcome these difficulties we have developed a notation that defines the members succinctly and unambiguously.

Set comprehension defines a set by stating the *properties* of its members. The properties of interest are their type, the rule admitting members to the set and the form of expression of each member in the set. The general form of comprehensive specification is:

$\{$*declaration list* (or signature)$\,|\,$*predicate* (or constraint) $\bullet$ *expression* (or term)$\}$

In all the previous examples the members of the sets have been implicitly assumed to be either integers or natural numbers. In general, however, sets can be constructed from interesting objects of any type. The declaration list or signature of the set specification provides details of the type of its members, while the expression or term dictates how individual member elements should be written. For example $x,y:P$ declares identifiers x and y to belong to some set P, while the declaration a, b, $c:\mathbb{N}$ declares a, b and c to be natural numbers. Declaration lists or signatures are therefore shorthand notation for such as $x \in P$, $y \in P$. There is no restriction on the number and type of each identifier. As an illustration, consider the declaration list for the following (incomplete) specification:

$\{p,q,r:A;\,\textit{file\_1}:User;\,\textit{file\_2}:Sys\,|\,\text{constraint} \bullet (p,q,r,\textit{file\_1},\textit{file\_2})\}$

The list introduces three identifiers, p, q and r, that are members of some set A, an identifier *file_1* which is a member of the set *User* and an identifier *file_2* which belongs to the set *Sys*. Each declaration of a different type is separated by a semi-colon. Notice that individual members of the set are discrete collections of $(p,q,r,\textit{file\_1},\textit{file\_2})$ units. Although there is a mixture of types within the units, the set consists of a collection of such units where *each unit is of the same type* and therefore conforms to strict typed set theory. (See Sec. 6.5 for an explanation of the type of such sets.)

The remaining part of the specification makes use of the identifiers to construct the rules for set membership. Thus:

$$\{x:\mathbb{N}\,|\,x^2 > 10 \bullet x\}$$

defines a set of natural numbers *such that* ($|$) their squares are greater than 10, while individual members are expressed in terms of $\{4,5,6,7,..\}$. With the specification:

$$\{x:\mathbb{N}\,|\,x^2 > 10 \bullet x^2\}$$

however, the set must be expressed as $\{16,25,36,49,..\}$ which makes it clear that it is the value of the term that is put into the set. Notice also that, in the definitions, the variables used are bound within the set definition and local to its scope. This point applies to any set defined by comprehension.

SAQ 6.1 Write typical members of the sets specified by the following comprehensive notation and describe the definition of the sets in informal English:

(a) $\{x:\mathbb{N}\,|\,x > 10 \wedge x < 100 \bullet x\}$
(b) $\{x,y:\mathbb{N}\,|\,x + y = 100 \bullet (y,x)\}$

SAQ 6.2 Devise some comprehensive specifications for the following sets:

(a) The set of files that are both system files and user files.
(b) The set of system files that can be accessed by user *Thomas*. (*Hint*: assume we have a parametrized proposition *Thomas* (*f*) where *f* is a file name.)

It is quite common to omit the expression or term in a comprehensive specification if it involves simple elements such as *n*, *x* or (*a*,*b*). In such cases we get the form:

$$\{declaration\ list\,|\,predicate\} \qquad \text{or} \qquad \{\texttt{signature}\,|\,\texttt{constraint}\}$$

SAQ 6.1(a) is therefore equally well understood as $\{x:\mathbb{N}\,|\,x > 10 \wedge x < 100\}$. In cases where there is more than one variable, the shape of a typical set member is represented by the order in the declaration list. This is sometimes called the *characteristic tuple* (see Sec. 6.5 on tuples).

Finally, on occasions the constraint may be omitted and we get the form:

$$\{declaration\ list \bullet expression\} \qquad \text{or} \qquad \{\texttt{signature} \bullet \texttt{term}\}$$

or even:

$$\{declaration\ list\} \qquad \text{or} \qquad \{\texttt{signature}\}$$

Here the only constraint on members is the implicit set membership of their type, while for the final example the characteristic tuple again provides the shape of the terms. Some typical examples of these specifications might be:

The set of all possible pairs of natural numbers $\{x,y:\mathbb{N} \bullet (x,y)\}$ or $\{x,y:\mathbb{N}\}$

A very common declaration which appears to omit both constraint and term is that of the set which forms a subrange or *segment* of the integers. Written $\{m..n\}$, where $m \leq n$, some examples of its use are:

$$\{1..3\} == \{1,2,3\}$$
$$\{-5..1\} == \{-5,-4,-3,-2,-1,0,1\}$$
$$\{2..2\} == \{2\}$$

whilst in cases where $m > n$ the set is *empty* and contains no members (see later). The $m..n$ notation therefore declares a set in which we have a continuous unbroken sequence of integers from *m* through to *n*. This is really only shorthand for the more complete definition:

$$\{k:\mathbb{Z}\,|\,\forall k \bullet m \leq k \wedge k \leq n \bullet k\}$$

which may be read as 'the set of integers such that, for every integer *k* in the set, *m* is less than or equal to *k* and *k* is less than or equal to *n*' and indicates that the shorthand notation simply hides the existence of the underlying `constraint` and `term`. Typed set theory makes wide use of such abbreviations to make declarations more manageable and readable.

6.3 THE SET OPERATORS

Set theory is endowed with a number of operators that can be used to describe the events of interest to software engineers. Each operator is described both formally and informally below. In these descriptions pay particular attention to the use of the mathematics to capture their precise meaning and the emphasis on the importance of the underlying types of the sets involved in the operation. The introduction indicated what is meant by the type of a set; the notion of an underlying type is a generalization which is more fully explained later in the chapter. For the moment simply treat 'type' and 'underlying type' as equivalent and interchangeable terms. Notice also that the set inclusion operator $\in$ has been used as a *primitive* as all other operators are defined in terms of it using predicate calculus.

6.3.1 Set equality

A set is completely determined by its members. Therefore, two sets are equal if and only if they have the same members exactly. In typed set theory the predicate $A = B$ is true if sets A and B are equal otherwise it is false, while the predicate $\neg(A = B)$ is true if sets A and B are not equal otherwise it is false. For either of the predicates to make sense, both A and B must be of the same underlying type. Set equality can be defined in terms of set membership and predicate calculus as follows:

$$(A = B) \Leftrightarrow \forall a : A \bullet a \in B \land \forall b : B \bullet b \in A$$

In this and subsequent definitions used throughout the book, we regard A and B as *type parameters* which are replaced by the names of actual sets (both of the same underlying type) when the equality operator is used in practice. In this way the operator is generic and defined for any sets we wish to use in a specification. The definition itself may be read as:

> Two sets A and B of the same underlying type are equal if and only if all elements of A are members of B and all members of B are members of A.

6.3.2 Subsets

A subset of some set S is any set of elements, each of which is a member of S. By this definition a set is regarded as a subset of itself and consequently two different subsets are recognized—the *subset* and the *proper subset*.

The predicate $A \subseteq B$ (A is a subset of B) is true if A is any subset of B including being equal to B. A formal definition of this predicate is given by:

$$A \subseteq B \Leftrightarrow (\forall a : A \bullet a \in B)$$

which can be read as: 'A is a subset of B if and only if all elements of A are members of B'.

The predicate $A \subset B$ (A is a proper subset of B) is true if A is a subset of B *but not equal* to B. A formal definition of this predicate is given by:

$$A \subset B \Leftrightarrow (\forall a : A \bullet a \in B \land \neg(A = B))$$

which may be read as: 'A is a proper subset of B if and only if all elements of A are members of B and A is not equal to B'.

This is clearly equivalent to the use of the subset operator:

$$A \subset B \Leftrightarrow A \subseteq B \wedge \neg(A = B)$$

An important observation concerning subsets is that if A is a subset of B and B is a subset of A then A and B are equal.

SAQ 6.3   Determine the truth of the following:

(a) $\{1,2,3,4\} \subseteq \{4,3,2,1\}$
(b) $\{1,4\} \subset \{4,3,2,1\}$
(c) $\{a\} \subseteq \{b,c,d\}$
(d) $\{d,c,b\} \subset \{b,c,d\}$

6.3.3 The empty or null set

The comprehensive specification $\{n : \mathbb{N} \mid \forall n \bullet n > 20 \wedge n < 5\}$ or equivalent abbreviation $\{20..5\}$ embodies a predicate that cannot be satisfied by any natural number. Consequently there are no members in this set and the set is *empty* or *null*. In this book the empty set is denoted by $\{\}$ (or sometimes $\emptyset$) . It is a curious property of set theory that the empty set is a subset of every set. We can prove this quite easily with the knowledge of sets and logic that we have already:

1. Let S be any set.
2. $\neg(\{\} \subset S)$ assume the empty set is not a subset of S. Therefore,
3. $\exists a : \{\} \bullet \neg(a \in S)$ there must exist at least one member of $\{\}$ that is not a member of S.
4. $\neg(a \in S) \wedge a \in \{\}$ a is not a member of S but it is a member of $\{\}$, consequently
5. $a \in \{\}$ there is an element in $\{\}$.

This reasoning leads to a contradiction because by definition an empty set cannot have a member. Therefore the original assumption at line 2 must be incorrect and the empty set *is* a subset of any set.

This observation raises an interesting question for typed set theory: do we need to distinguish between (say) an empty set of *Books* and an empty set of *Cars*? Strictly speaking we do, but in typed set theory the symbol $\{\}$ is defined as a generic constant and therefore can be safely used to represent empty sets of any underlying type. Thus:

$$\{\} == \{x : X \mid x \neq x\}$$

In this expression, $\{\}$ is defined to be a set of elements of arbitrary underlying type X. The predicate dictates the contents of this set and shows that it contains elements x of X such that no element is equal to itself. There is of course no x that satisfies $x \neq x$ and so the set is empty.

6.3.4 ∪   Set union

The union of two sets is written $A \cup B$ and is the set of elements that are members of A or B or both. The effect of the union operator is to combine the members of two sets, eliminating repetitions. With typed set theory, the two sets must of course be of the same underlying type for the operation to be defined. If we denote this type by T then the union may be expressed as:

$$A \cup B == \{t : T \mid (t \in A) \vee (t \in B)\}$$

which may be read as: 'the union of two sets A and B of the same underlying type T is that set of elements t of type T such that t is a member of A or t is a member of B'.

The set union operator is commutative and associative, that is:

$$A \cup B = B \cup A \qquad \text{and} \qquad A \cup (B \cup C) = (A \cup B) \cup C$$

Notice here (and in many other examples later) the use of $=$ rather than $==$. At this stage we are not defining anything but simply recording the fact that the right-hand side of the expression describes the same set as the left-hand side. Typed set theory also supports a *distributed union* operator that forms the union across a number of sets. For example, if S represents a *set of sets* such that:

$$S == \{\{1,2,3\}, \{2,3,4\}, \{3,4,5\}\}$$

then the distributed union of S (written $\cup S$) is given by:

$$\cup S = \{1,2,3,4,5\}$$

6.3.5 ∩ Set intersection

Set intersection of two sets is written $A \cap B$. It is the set of elements that are members of both A and B. Intersection therefore produces a set of common members with repetitions again eliminated. Once again for typed set theory, the two sets must be of the same underlying type. If we again denote this type by T then the union may be expressed as:

$$A \cap B == \{t : T \mid (t \in A) \wedge (t \in B)\}$$

which may be read as: 'the intersection of two sets A and B of the same underlying type T is that set of elements t of type T such that t is a member of A and t is a member of B'.

The set intersection operator is commutative and associative, that is:

$$A \cap B = B \cap A \qquad \text{and} \qquad A \cap (B \cap C) = (A \cap B) \cap C$$

Finally, typed set theory supports a *distributed intersection* which can be applied across a set of sets. Given the set:

$$S == \{\{1,2,3\}, \{2,3,4\}, \{3,4,5\}\}$$

then the distributed intersection of S (written $\cap S$) is given by:

$$\cap S = \{3\}$$

6.3.6 \ Set difference

The set difference between two sets is written $A \setminus B$. It is the set that contains those elements that are members of A but are not members of B. For typed set theory, the two sets must be of the same underlying type. If we denote this type by T then the difference of two sets A and B may be expressed as:

$$A \setminus B == \{t : T \mid (t \in A) \wedge \neg(t \in B)\}$$

which may be read as: 'the difference of two sets A and B of the same underlying type T is that set of elements t of type T such that t is a member of A and t is not a member of B'.

In general, set difference is not commutative, i.e. $A \setminus B \neq B \setminus A$.

SAQ 6.4   Given the following sets:

$$A == \{2,4,6,8,23,45\}$$
$$B == \{19,4,34,45,27,101,2\}$$

write down the results you would expect from $A \cup B$, $A \cap B$ and $A \setminus B$.

6.3.7 #   Set cardinality

The number of distinct members in some finite set S is its *cardinality*, written $\#S$. Given the sets A and B in SAQ 6.4, $\#A = 6$ and $\#B = 7$, while for the empty set, $\#\{\} = 0$. The formal definition of this operator requires the use of functions. Interested readers familiar with functions may care to move directly to Chapter 8 where a definition appears.

6.3.8 $\mathbb{P}$ Power set

The power set of some set S is the set of all possible subsets of S. It is written $\mathbb{P}S$. For example, if $S == \{3,5,7\}$ then $\mathbb{P}S$ is a set with eight members, each one a set in its own right:

$$\mathbb{P}S == \{\{3,5,7\}, \{3,5\}, \{3,7\}, \{5,7\}, \{3\}, \{5\}, \{7\}, \{\}\}$$

The power set $\mathbb{P}S$ of a set with $\#S = n$ therefore contains 2^n elements including the set itself and the empty set $\{\}$. There is therefore a clear distinction between the declarations $x : \mathbb{N}$ and $x : \mathbb{P}\mathbb{N}$ such that in the former case x is a natural number, while in the latter it is a *set* of natural numbers. This notation makes possible the notion of *sets of sets*.

In most cases the operator $\mathbb{P}S$ conveys the writer's intent well enough. However, there are three further power set operators available:

$\mathbb{P}_1 S$ Declares the set of all possible subsets of S excluding the empty set $\{\}$
$\mathbb{F}S$ Declares the set of all possible finite subsets of S
$\mathbb{F}_1 S$ Declares the set of all possible finite subsets of S excluding the empty set $\{\}$

Power sets are useful in modelling dynamic situations where populations or characteristics are liable to change from time to time. Consider the set *File_Access* which describes possible user privileges within some computer filing system:

$$File\_Access == \{Read, Delete, Write, Create, Copy\}$$

System users could have a combination of privileges ranging from none to all five. In such cases the declaration:

$$User1\_Access : \mathbb{P} \; File\_Access$$

declares *User1_Access* to be any member of the set:

{{*Read,Delete, Write, Create, Copy*}, {*Read, Delete, Write, Create*},
{*Read, Delete, Write*}, {*Read, Delete*}, {*Read*}, {*Read, Delete, Write, Copy*},...,{ }}

such that the condition of *User1_Access* at any point in time models the current status of a particular user's privileges.

6.3.9 *max* and *min*   Set maximum and set minimum

These are two useful operators that determine the maximum and minimum in a finite set of numbers. For example, in set A given for SAQ 6.4, $min\ A = 2$, while $max\ A = 45$. Like cardinality, these two operators are again best defined as functions. Interested readers familiar with functions may care to move directly to Chapter 8 where a definition of these operators appears.

6.4 THE TYPE OF A SET

In the introduction to set theory it was made clear that the descriptions dealt with *typed* sets, and from the general definition of the power set it is equally clear that $S \subset \mathbb{P}S$. The declaration list for comprehensive set specification employs the notation $s : S$ which is meant to convey that s is a member of the set S, i.e. it is of type S. However, since S is itself a member of $\mathbb{P}S$, the underlying type of a set must be the power set of the type of its elements, $\mathbb{P}S$.

The concept of an underlying type is important in typed set theory because it preserves consistency in the use of the objects of a specification. As an illustration, consider two variables $a : \mathbb{N}$ and $b : \mathbb{Z}$, signifying that a is a natural number and b is an integer. Given the two comprehensive set specifications:

$$A == \{a : \mathbb{N} \mid a < 100 \wedge a > 10\}$$
$$B == \{b : \mathbb{Z} \mid b < 50\}$$

the operations $A \cup B$, $A \cap B$ and $A \setminus B$ are all defined because, although the elements of A and B *appear* to be of different types, the underlying type of both is $\mathbb{Z}$ since $\mathbb{N} \subset \mathbb{Z}$ and $\mathbb{Z} \subset \mathbb{P}\mathbb{Z}$. A similar argument applies to the subrange type $m..n$, which has underlying type integer, while a set declared as $s : \mathbb{F}S$ again apparently gives s a type. However, since $\mathbb{F}S \subset \mathbb{P}S$ we deduce that the underlying type is, in fact, $\mathbb{P}S$.

The notion of an underlying type allows us to use definitions of sets that have already been introduced. This in turn provides a more concise and readable specification.

6.5 TUPLES

A *tuple* is an ordered collection of elements. The term 'tuple' is used as a generalization for pair, triple, quartuple, quintuple, sextuple, etc. To define a tuple explicitly the elements are listed, separated by commas and enclosed in tuple braces. In this book tuples are enclosed by ordinary parentheses ( ). For example, with the following declarations:

$$x, y : \mathbb{N}$$
$$z : \mathbb{Z}$$
$$a, b, c : \text{char}$$

we can construct a number of different tuples, each of which is an ordered collection of elements drawn from the sets $\mathbb{N}$, $\mathbb{Z}$ and char. Examples might be:

$$(x,y,y)$$
$$(y,y,x)$$
$$(x,y,z)$$
$$(a,b,c)$$
$$(a,x,c,z)$$

If the individual members of a tuple are all of the same underlying type the tuple is *homogeneous* otherwise it is *heterogeneous*. The first four examples are therefore homogeneous while the last is not.

It is important to realize that order is significant in a tuple. For example, the tuples (x,y,y) and (y,y,x) are not the same. Similarly, $(1,3,4,7)$ and $(3,1,4,7)$ are different. Remember that an individual tuple is not a set so that whereas $\{1,3,4,7\}$ and $\{3,1,4,7\}$ are equal, $(1,3,4,7)$ and $(3,1,4,7)$ are not. However, we can construct sets whose individual elements are tuples of some type. The following set consists of 'triples' and of course each member of the set is different:

$$\{(1,5,9),\ (5,9,1),\ (9,1,5)\}$$

A 2-tuple is called an *ordered pair*. Sets of ordered pairs are of particular significance because they are used to define relations and functions which in turn describe operations useful in software engineering. These are described in detail in the next chapter.

6.6 CHARACTERISTIC TUPLES AND SET COMPREHENSION TERMS

The notation we use for the construction of sets by comprehension charges the declaration list with the responsibility for introducing local variables. A sequence of declarations that introduces two or more variables is said to have a *characteristic tuple*. Its components are the variables in the order they appear in the declaration list. For example, a declaration used earlier was:

$$\{p,q,r:A\,;file\_1:User\,;file\_2:Sys\,|\,\texttt{constraint}\bullet(p,q,r,file\_1,file\_2)\}$$

so that the characteristic tuple is given by $(p,q,r,file\_1,file\_2)$. In this example the term and the characteristic tuple are the same. This need not always be the case. If the definition had been:

$$\{p,q,r:A\,;file\_1:User\,;file\_2:Sys\,|\,..\bullet(p,r,q,file\_2,file\_1)\}$$

then the characteristic tuple remains the same but the individual tuples that compose the set would have their collection of items expressed in a different order. At this stage in our studies there seems little purpose in such a definition however (certain formal definitions of relations in the next chapter use such 'tricks'). It would be much simpler to make a further adjustment and define the set as:

$$\{p,r,q:A\,;file\_2:User\,;file\_1:Sys\,|\,...\}$$

To generalize, the following notation (where P is some predicate and each x_i is of type T_i):

$$\{x_1 : T_1, x_2 : T_2, x_3 : T_3, \ldots, x_n : T_n \mid P\}$$

represents the set of n-tuples $(x_1, x_2, x_3, \ldots, x_n)$ such that P is true.

6.7 × THE CARTESIAN (CROSS) PRODUCT

The Cartesian product of two sets A and B is the set of all ordered pairs of the form (a,b) where a is a member of A and b is a member of B. It is written as $A \times B$. If the sets are the same underlying type the tuples of the product are homogeneous. If not they are heterogeneous. As an example of a Cartesian product take the following sets of men and women:

$$Men == \{Joe, Bill, Fred\}; \quad Women == \{Mary, Sue\}$$

the Cartesian product $Men \times Women$ is therefore the set of all possible combinations of men and women, i.e. mixed couples. The set is:

$$\{(Joe, Mary), (Joe, Sue), (Bill, Mary), (Bill, Sue), (Fred, Mary), (Fred, Sue)\}$$

Formally, the Cartesian product over two sets can be defined as:

$$A \times B == \{a : A; \, b : B \bullet (a,b)\}$$

which has no predicate to control the admission of members and can be read as: 'the Cartesian product over two sets A and B is the set of all possible ordered pairs (a,b) such that a is drawn from set A and b is drawn from set B'.

A Cartesian product, however, can be *extended* or *distributed* and applied across a number of sets just like union and intersection:

$$T_1 \times T_2 \times T_3 \times \ldots \times T_n = \{x_1 : T_1, x_2 : T_2, x_3 : T_3, \ldots, x_n : T_n \bullet (x_1, x_2, x_3, \ldots, x_n)\}$$

If the underlying type of these sets is the same then the Cartesian product across n sets can be described with the following shorthand notation:

$$T^n = T \times T \times T \times \ldots \times T$$

If the sets are different then:

$$\times_{i=1}^{n} T_i = T_1 \times T_2 \times T_3 \times \ldots \times T_n$$

Finally, notice that a Cartesian product is neither commutative nor associative:

$$A \times B \neq B \times A \quad \text{and} \quad (A \times B) \times C \neq A \times (B \times C)$$

An obvious and frequent use of a Cartesian product is in describing the state space for a program. At any point during its execution, the state of the program is described by some combination of values of its variables which in turn is modelled by a tuple within their Cartesian product. The tuple therefore captures a 'snapshot' of the program as it moves from one discrete state to another. This is an important observation, because changes in the condition of tuples within the Cartesian product can be used to express the effect of a single operation or even a complete program. The introduction to the formal aspects of software engineering (Sec. 4.5) made use of a program that sums the series for a given natural number and showed how changes in the state space occur as execution of the program proceeds. The program is reproduced here:

```
var i,n,sum:Natural;
begin
    input(n);
    sum:= 0;
    i:= 1;
    while (i<=n) do
        sum := sum + i;
        i:= i + 1
    end;
    write(sum);
end.
```

The program state space consists of all possible combinations of the three natural numbers that compose the program's variables (i,n,sum). The Cartesian product $\mathbb{N} \times \mathbb{N} \times \mathbb{N}$ can therefore be used to model the state space which clearly consists of a set of 3-tuples (triples). At any point during the execution of the program (at the beginning, at the end or somewhere in between) the state of the program will be described by a member of this set.

Tuples resulting from some kind of extended (or distributed) Cartesian product like this are also frequently required to express the state space for individual variables. Programming languages realize the abstract concept of a tuple by representing and implementing them in a variety of different ways, for example:

- An array of integers simply represents a member of $\mathbb{Z}^n$.
- A 'record' contains a fixed arrangement of fields of different kinds.

A tuple is an ideal model for the latter structure in that a record definition can be described by $\times_{i=1}^{n} T_i$ where n is the number of fields in the record and T_i represents the set of values which can be taken by the ith field, i.e. its type.

6.7.1 The type of a tuple

The type of a tuple is the Cartesian product of the underlying type of its elements. For example the type of the tuple (x,y) where x and y are natural numbers, is $\mathbb{Z} \times \mathbb{Z}$ because the underlying type of natural numbers is integer.

6.8 TWO SPECIAL OPERATORS

One particular sort of tuple that occurs over and over again in specifications is the ordered pair, which takes the general form (a,b). It is frequently necessary to split ordered pairs into their individual components and two operators are available—*first* and *second*—to achieve this for us. Thus:

$$first(a,b) = a$$
$$second(a,b) = b \quad \text{and}$$
$$(first(a,b), second(a,b)) = (a,b)$$

6.9 SUMMARY

Sets describe collections of items of some sort (or type) that are of interest to us. The operators that characterize sets can bring about permanent changes in the condition of these structures. Therefore sets can act as persistent objects whose condition at any time reflects a history of events carried out upon them. Simple sets can be constructed using a variety of techniques. With the power set and Cartesian product more complex sets can be built. These properties make sets a fundamental component of all formal specifications. Sets are subject to a number of laws that we have not discussed in this chapter. Laws are used in proofs and these are examined later. However, the various set operators and the laws in which they participate are gathered together in Spivey (1992). The notation used is explained fully in Parts 4 and 5.

7

CASE STUDY: A SPECIFICATION USING SIMPLE SET THEORY

7.1 INTRODUCTION

This chapter describes a system that keeps track of students who have handed in a particular piece of homework. A number of sets combine to describe the sorts of data in which we are interested:

- The set of all possible students (*Student*)
- The set of students in the class (*Class*)
- The set of students who have handed in their homework (*Handed_in*)
- The set of students who have not handed in their homework (*Not_handed_in*)

Each of the various groups, *Class*, *Handed_in*, *Not_handed_in* represents persistent objects and each has an existence independent of any operation upon it. The groups may also have changing student populations and so the most instinctive way to model them is as variables of type $\mathbb{P}Student$. The three variables in combination provide us with a description of the *abstract state space* for the problem and, as we have seen, such combinations are described as tuples. The state of the system at any point in time is therefore modelled by the condition of the tuple describing the Cartesian product of the variables:

$$\{Class, \ Handed\_in, \ Not\_handed\_in : \mathbb{P}Student\}$$

The declaration of the abstract state is a useful starting point for a formal description of the *Homework* problem, but as it stands the tuple describes all sorts of combinations of students, many of which are unrealistic (e.g. combinations are possible where students appear in both the *Handed_in* and the *Not_handed_in* groups) The declaration must therefore be predicated to restrict student combinations to those which are meaningful within the context of this problem. This common sense observation in turn suggests a mechanism for the definition of operators using typed set theory: operations upon the abstract state are described in terms of sets of tuples whose individual elements are related in correspondence with the intended meaning of the operation. The individual elements of the tuple must include:

- The input(s) to the operator (if any)
- The output(s) from the operator (if any)
- The state that the persistent object(s) must exist in before the operation
- The state that the persistent object(s) must exist in after the operation

while the relationships between these elements are expressed as predicates that convey both the static (*invariant*) properties that apply to the problem as a whole, together with the conditions local to a particular operation.

In the discussion that follows, we use the prime (′) to indicate the condition of a set after the operation upon it, while an undecorated set represents the set before the operation. Similarly, an input to an operation is decorated with a question mark (?). This latter notation is consistent with the observation that in computing we are never quite sure (?) what we are about to receive!

7.2 THE STATE DATA

We begin our understanding of operator descriptions by examining the static properties of the problem:

1. The combination of the set of students that has handed in together with the set that has not handed in must always equal the set of students in the class.
2. Because a student cannot simultaneously have handed in and not handed in the homework, the student can never appear in both sets at the same time.

These properties represent an invariant on the abstract state space, i.e. a particular combination of variables (tuple) describing the state of the *Homework* system can be regarded as legal only if it reflects these properties. The formal expression of the state invariant is given below. Notice that in this expression, the conjunction (∧) of the two clauses can be true only if (1) and (2) are simultaneously true:

1. *Handed_in* ∪ *Not_handed_in* = *Class* ∧
2. *Handed_in* ∩ *Not_handed_in* = { }

To describe the *Homework* problem properly, the invariant must be applied to the abstract state space to restrict it to tuples containing sensible combinations of variables and we do this simply by including it as a predicate on the earlier declaration. The resulting tuple is then regarded as describing the *state data* for the problem, i.e. it describes the persistent objects that comprise the state and the rule(s) governing their legal combination. The state data for the *Homework* problem is as follows:

$$Homework ==$$
$$\{Class, Handed\_in, Not\_handed\_in: \ Student \,|$$
$$Handed\_in \cup Not\_handed\_in = Class \ \wedge$$
$$Handed\_in \cap Not\_handed\_in = \{ \}\}$$

7.3 CHANGES IN THE STATE DATA

Strictly speaking, *Homework* describes the state data only as it exists before an operation. Once an operation has been performed the objects will persist in some after state (which may or may not be different from before). It is important of course that operations preserve the type of the objects and ensure that the relationship(s) between the after objects still satisfy the state invariant. The state data as it exists after an operation is therefore described by:

$$Homework' ==$$
$$\{Class', Handed\_in', Not\_handed\_in' : \mathbb{P}Student \mid$$
$$Handed\_in' \cup Not\_handed\_in' = Class' \wedge$$
$$Handed\_in' \cap Not\_handed\_in' = \{\}\}$$

Because an operation must begin and terminate in a legal state then any operation that brings about a change in the state data must (in part) be described by the tuple:

$$\{Class, Handed\_in, Not\_handed\_in : \mathbb{P}Student ;$$
$$Class', Handed\_in', Not\_handed\_in' : \mathbb{P}Student \mid$$
$$Handed\_in \cup Not\_handed\_in = Class \wedge$$
$$Handed\_in \cap Not\_handed\_in = \{\} \wedge$$
$$Handed\_in' \cup Not\_handed\_in' = Class' \wedge$$
$$Handed\_in' \cap Not\_handed\_in' = \{\}\}$$

This description is clearly derived from *Homework* and *Homework'* by simply *merging* the declarations of each and *conjoining* their predicates. Unfortunately there is no operator available in typed set theory that can achieve the construction of this more complex tuple from the definitions of the others. However, if we use the operator '∧' to convey the merging and conjunction between two tuples then the change in state data could be conveniently described as:

$$Homework \wedge Homework' =$$
$$\{Class, Handed\_in, Not\_handed\_in : \mathbb{P}Student ;$$
$$Class', Handed\_in', Not\_handed\_in' : \mathbb{P}Student \mid$$
$$Handed\_in \cup Not\_handed\_in = Class \wedge$$
$$Handed\_in \cap Not\_handed\_in = \{\} \wedge$$
$$Handed\_in' \cup Not\text{-}handed\_in' = Class' \wedge$$
$$Handed\_in' \cap Not\_handed\_in' = \{\}\}$$

The context in which ∧ is used here clearly distinguishes it from its normal Boolean role (as in the predicates for example) because its arguments are tuples rather than propositions. In this sense we are 'overloading' the operator, allowing it to assume different effects with different objects.

7.4 OPERATIONS ON THE STATE DATA

Any operation that brings about a change in the state space must include the declarations and predicates equivalent to *Homework* ∧ *Homework'* in its definition. In complex systems the inclusion can produce a somewhat unwieldy description. We would therefore benefit from a shorthand notation such that if:

$$\Delta Homework = Homework \wedge Homework'$$

(where Δ universally denotes a change) then the appearance of Δ*Homework* in the definition of an operator not only alerts us to the fact that it brings about a change of state but also does so in an economic fashion.

Each individual operation, however, has a specific task to perform over and above its obligation to maintain the state invariant. The behaviour of a particular operation is characterized by describing its input(s) and output(s) (if any) together with additional predicates that relate these to the persistent objects in such a way that they describe just what the operation achieves. As an example of this more complete description, consider the event *Submit* which describes the changes that occur when a student hands in a piece of homework. The following tuple definition characterizes this operation:

$$Submit ==$$
$$\{Class, Handed\_in, Not\_handed\_in : \mathbb{P}\,Student;$$
$$Class', Handed\_in', Not\_handed\_in' : \mathbb{P}\,Student;$$
$$Stud? : Student \mid$$
$$Handed\_in \cup Not\_handed\_in = Class \wedge$$
$$Handed\_in \cap Not\_handed\_in = \{\,\} \wedge$$
$$Handed\_in' \cup Not\_handed\_in' = Class' \wedge$$
$$Handed\_in' \cap Not\_handed\_in' = \{\,\} \wedge$$
$$Stud? \subset Not\_handed\_in \wedge$$
$$Not\_handed\_in' = Not\_handed\_in \setminus \{Stud?\} \wedge$$
$$Handed\_in' = Handed\_in \cup \{Stud?\} \wedge$$
$$Class' = Class\}$$

This takes a more compact (but equivalent) form if we make use of the shorthand notation such that:

$$Submit ==$$
$$\{\Delta Homework;$$
$$Stud? : Student \mid$$
$$Stud? \in Not\_handed\_in \wedge$$
$$Not\_handed\_in' = Not\_handed\_in \setminus \{Stud?\} \wedge$$
$$Handed\_in' = Handed\_in \cup \{Stud?\} \wedge$$
$$Class' = Class\}$$

Here the inclusion of $\Delta Homework$ implies merging the before and after state declaration lists with those of the operator and conjoining the invariant on these states with the characteristic predicates of the operator. The additional declarations and predicates 'customize' the *Submit* operation towards a particular behaviour, and a further advantage of the shorthand version is that these are shown free from the clutter of the more general state requirements. The *Submit* operator clearly:

- Describes the state data and maintains the invariant on the before and after states (through $\Delta Homework$)
- Accepts a submitting student as input (*Stud? : Student*)
- Insists that he or she belongs to the group that have not handed in (*Stud? ∈ Not_handed_in*) and, because of the invariant, also to the *Class*
- Removes the student from the group that have not handed in (*Not_handed_in' = Not_handed_in \ {Stud?}*)
- Adds them to the group that have handed in (*Handed_in' = Handed_in ∪ {Stud?}*)
- And finally insists that the population of the class remains unchanged, $Class' = Class$

This final item is particularly important. The inclusion of $\Delta Homework$ describes the relationship between before and after states, but operations that produce a change in state need not change all persistent objects. The presence of $\Delta Homework$, together with the qualification that *Class* remains unchanged, therefore allow us to deduce that *Submit* changes only *Handed_in* and *Not_handed_in*. This technique is widely used throughout later parts of the book.

We can write an equivalent informal English description of the event, a possible attempt being:

> The class, together with the groups that have handed in and not handed in their homework, must always be some combination of the current student population, while the student to whom this operation applies must also be a member of this population. The class is composed of those students who have handed in homework and those who have not. This relationship holds true before and after any operation on the class. Similarly, those who are members of one group cannot be members of the other and this relationship also holds before and after any operation. The student wishing to submit homework must be a member of the group who has not handed in and therefore by implication be a member of the class. After the submission, the student is removed from the group that has not handed in and included in the group that has. Finally, this operation does not change the population of the class which remains as before.

Notice that the narrative requires all of these conditions to be simultaneously true and this is reflected in the conjunction ($\wedge$) of the clauses in the formal description. Surely the formal approach—especially the shorthand version—is far more concise, unambiguous and elegant.

As a final point, a word of warning on the use of the Δ notation that 'simplifies' the description by separating the state invariant predicates from the characteristic predicates of the operation. In the shorthand version of *Submit*, a first glance at the clauses in the predicate part might suggest that they can be divided into two groups such that $Stud? \in Not\_handed\_in$ represents a precondition, while the remaining predicates compose a postcondition. In Chapter 4 we saw that preconditions describe the relationships that must exist before an operator can be legally applied, while postconditions describe the relationships that must exist if the application of the operator has been successful. This is an interesting—and to some extent valid—observation. But we must remember that the characteristic predicates are local to a particular operation. They are also clauses that form part of pre- and postconditions 'hidden' in the $\Delta Homework$ notation, namely those clauses that affect the persistent state, and these are active for *all* operations. The deduction of pre- and postconditions is therefore not always as straightforward as it may seem. Pre- and postconditions of course describe 'normal' behaviour. If any of the conditions fail then the operation will be flawed, and this in turn raises the question of exception handling, error reports and alternative actions. We return to both these points later in the book when we examine in more detail the specification language Z, which is based largely on the approach taken in this case study.

SAQ 7.1 Other operations that involve a change in the state data are *Remove*, which describes the removal of a student from the class, and *Enrol*, which describes the addition of a new student to the class. Write descriptions of *Remove* and *Enrol* using set theory.

Submit, Remove and *Enrol* illustrate events that cause changes in the state data. There are of course many operations that leave the state data unchanged, such as simply enquiring whether a student has yet submitted homework. In later chapters we see how typed set theory approaches the formal description of these cases.

8

RELATIONS AND FUNCTIONS

CHECKLIST OF OBJECTIVES

After reading this chapter you should be able to:

- Understand how mathematical relations model relationships between the elements of two sets.
- Understand and apply the operators of the theory of relations.
- Appreciate that functions are simply special kinds of relations.
- Appreciate the characteristics of the various functions that can be derived from relations.
- Apply lambda abstraction to the definition of certain functions.
- Understand how relations can be classified according to the various properties they possess.

8.1 INTRODUCTION

Relations and functions are mathematical structures used to model events of interest to us in the real world. The fundamental structure is the relation from which functions can be defined. Relations in turn are dependent upon set theory and tuples, so that the whole concept rests on an essentially simple base. Relations are sets and each element or member of the set is an ordered pair. As the name implies, the pairs are members of the relation because there exists some kind of relationship between the two. A simple example will make this property clear. The following set is meant to capture the relationship between departments and their employees. In the set of pairs, the department name appears first and the employee name is second:

{(*Systems, Thomas*), (*Systems, Sheppard*), (*Operations, Sheppard*), (*Design, Evans*),
(*Accounts, Read*), (*Accounts, Loveday*), (*Accounts, Eyres*), (*Stock, Stock*),
(*Admin, Dodds*), (*Finance, Phillips*), (*Programming, Jones*), (*Programming, Coles*)}

Each member of the relation is in fact a 2-tuple and within a tuple order is significant. In most cases we could see which name corresponds to departments and which to employees even if the pairs were arbitrarily organized, e.g. in the pairs (*Systems, Thomas*) and (*Thomas, Systems*) it is fairly clear that *Thomas* is the employee and *Systems* the department. However, this is true only because of our intuitive understanding of the data. In the case of (*Stock, Stock*), if the order were arbitrary then which is the department, *Stock* or *Stock*? We must resolve such conflict, for employees and departments are of different types, the notion of order is therefore crucial and it is imposed so that there can be no ambiguity in the correspondence between the two sets from which elements are drawn to compose a pair. In the example, the first element of the pair is drawn from the set of departments and the second from the set of employees. The elements from the two sets that are currently members of the relation are therefore easily recognized:

{*Systems, Operations, Design, Accounts, Stock, Admin, Programming, Finance*} and {*Thomas, Sheppard, Evans, Read, Loveday, Eyres, Stock, Dodds, Phillips, Jones, Coles*}

(*Note*: the set of departments and employees may contain elements that are not currently involved in the relation, i.e. departments may exist without employees and some employees may not be associated with a department.) These are clearly subsets of departments and employees respectively, while a formal definition of the relation as a set of pairs would take the general form:

$$\{d\text{: }departments;\ e\text{: }employees \mid P(d,e) \bullet (d,e)\}$$

Here the predicate $P(d,e)$ governs those pairs that can be included as members of the relation, e.g. $P(Systems, Sheppard) = true$, $P(Programming, Loveday) = false$, while the requirements for an ordered pair can be summarized as:

$$((p,q) = (r,s) \Leftrightarrow (p = r) \wedge (q = s))$$

which reads as: 'two ordered pairs (p,q) and (r,s) are equal if and only if p is equal to r and q is equal to s'.

The two sets involved in forming the relation are often called the *from-set* and the *to-set*. This description is meant to convey the notion of a *mapping* of elements from one set to the other (see Fig. 8.1). In our example, departments represents the *from-set* and employees the *to-set*.

We have seen in earlier parts of the book that software engineers have made considerable efforts to capture the relationships between data items because it is relationships that provide the semantic content of our data descriptions. They tell us what the data means and therefore what operations upon that data make sense. In contemporary software engineering our descriptions of relationships correspond to E–R diagrams and normalized entities. Operations on these entities are described by data flow diagrams and entity life histories. Whether an operation is meaningful is left to the judgement of the designer. The theory of relations, however, provides a set of operators designed to deal specifically with these structures. Events that manipulate the relationship can be expressed in terms of the operators, and the semantics of the mathematics ensures that the meaning of the operation can be unambiguously deduced. Relations and their derivatives are therefore powerful tools for the specification of processes and their data.

8.2 RELATIONS

Mathematical relations are designed to model relationships between data. In our example we illustrated a possible relationship between departments and employees.

There are many more relationships that are equally well disposed to such treatment, for example:

> 'is greater than'   a relation between two sets of numbers
> 'is an anagram of'   a relation between two sets of words
> 'is a student on'   a relation between students and courses
> 'has a road to'   a relation between two towns on a map
> 'is a phone number of'   a relation between phone numbers and names
> 'is on queue'   a relation between programs and stream queues

The characteristics of relations can be listed as:

- An element of the *from-set* may correspond (map) to any number of elements in the *to-set*.
- There may be members of the *from-set* that do not map to any member of the *to-set*.
- Those members of the *from-set* that do have a corresponding member in the *to-set* are the *domain* of the relation, i.e. *domain* ⊆ *from-set*.
- An element of *to-set* may correspond to any number of elements in the *from-set*.
- There may be members of the *to-set* that do not correspond to any member of the *from-set*.
- Those members of the *to-set* that do have a corresponding member in the *from-set* are the *range* of the relation, i.e. *range* ⊆ *to-set*.

These features are illustrated graphically in Fig. 8.1.

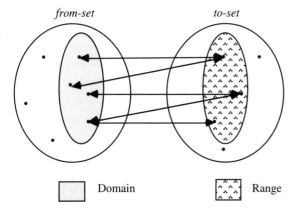

Figure 8.1   The mapping nature of a relation.

8.3 THE MEMBERS OF A RELATION

Each member of a relation is an ordered pair where the first element of the pair belongs to the *from-set* and the second belongs to the *to-set*. The relation itself is a set of such pairs. Assuming *Alpha* and *Beta* correspond to the *from-set* and *to-set*, respectively, then a relation is simply a subset of the Cartesian product *Alpha* × *Beta*. If we place no constraints at all on the members then the relation consists of all the members of the product. However, in practice, the characteristics of a relation are conveyed by a predicate that admits members, and this often restricts the population. As an example, any member (a,b) of the relation 'is greater than' must satisfy $a > b$. We can illustrate these issues if we define:

$$Alpha == \{2,4,6,8\}$$
$$Beta == \{3,5,7,9\} \qquad \text{such that}$$
$$is\_greater\_than == \{(4,3), (6,3), (6,5), (8,3), (8,5), (8,7)\}$$

the domain of the relation is $\{4,6,8\}$ while the range is $\{3,5,7\}$. The Cartesian product describes $4 \times 4 = 16$ pairs (i.e. $\#(Alpha \times Beta) = 16$) while $\#(is\_greater\_than) = 6$. (Notice that cardinality determines how many pairs are present in the relation and not how many distinct values. The cardinality is therefore 6 and not 12.) Consequently the relation has been confined to a subset of the product because of its predicate.

Relations are normally named. A name is therefore equivalent to the set of pairs that currently define the relation. The fact that a particular ordered pair (a,b) is a member of some relation R can be conveyed in a number of ways:

$$(a,b) \in R \qquad \text{or} \qquad R(a,b) \qquad \text{or} \qquad aRb$$

Because relations are subsets of some Cartesian product we usually refer to them through phrases such as 'relation R is over $A \times B$'.

8.3.1 Maplet notation

Because a relation is a set of ordered pairs, we can refer to one of its members using the normal tuple notation (a,b). However, this does not convey the essential mapping nature of the relation, so many authors prefer to use the *maplet* notation $a \mapsto b$. As an example, the whole of our 'is greater than' relation could be enumerated as:

$$is\_greater\_than == \{(4 \mapsto 3), (6 \mapsto 3), (6 \mapsto 5), (8 \mapsto 3), (8 \mapsto 5), (8 \mapsto 7)\}$$

8.4 DECLARING AND DEFINING A RELATION

To declare a relation we must first define the underlying relation type. In Chapter 6 we showed that the type of any set is the power set of its members. If R is a relation over sets A and B—both of which have been previously defined—then the members of R are ordered pairs of the form (a,b). If the underlying type of A is T_A and the underlying type of set B is T_B then the type of an individual element of R is $(T_A \times T_B)$. Because R is a set of such elements, the type of the whole relation must be $\mathbb{P}(T_A \times T_B)$, which describes the set of all possible relations that can be formed from the two sets. Relations form the bedrock of specification using typed set theory and so it is important to understand this typing mechanism fully. This is best achieved by considering the Cartesian product and power set applied to two small sets:

$$A == \{p,q\} \qquad \text{and} \qquad B == \{r,s\}$$

Assuming the underlying types of these sets are T_A and T_B, respectively, the Cartesian product is:

$$A \times B == \{(p,r), (p,s), (q,r), (q,s)\}$$

with each individual element of type $T_A \times T_B$.

The power set is the set of all possible subsets of $A \times B$ (including $\{\}$), thus:

$$\mathbb{P}(T_A \times T_B) == \{\{\}, \{(p,r)\}, \{(p,s)\}, \ldots, \{(p,r), (p,s)\}, \{(p,r), (q,r)\}, \ldots,$$
$$\{(p,r), (p,s), (q,r)\}, \ldots, \{(p,r), (p,s), (q,r), (q,s)\}\}$$

and any relation over $A \times B$ will therefore be a member of this set which consequently acts as a type. A double-headed arrow ($\leftrightarrow$), is often used to introduce a type which is a relation, e.g. $A \leftrightarrow B$ describes the set of all possible relations that can be formed over A and B and is a shorthand for $\mathbb{P}(T_A \times T_B)$. The symbol conveys the notion of a two-way correspondence, in that elements of the *from-set* may correspond to many in the *to-set* and vice versa. A relation is declared by simply making it a member of this set. Thus:

$$R : A \leftrightarrow B$$

Some typical examples of relations in everyday life are:

> $Road : Town \leftrightarrow Town$ a relation between two towns
> $Line : Point \leftrightarrow Point$ a relation between two points
> $Auth : Book \leftrightarrow Author$ a relation between authors and their books

The declaration of a relation does not define its members, but because a relation is a set we can describe its content either by enumeration—using maplet or tuple notation—or by comprehension. This latter method corresponds to an implicit definition in that members are not listed but their properties are. Therefore using sets *Alpha* and *Beta* defined earlier, we have:

> $is\_greater\_than == \{(4 \mapsto 3), (6 \mapsto 3), (6 \mapsto 5), (8 \mapsto 3), (8 \mapsto 5), (8 \mapsto 7)\}$ (maplet)
> $is\_greater\_than == \{(4,3), (6,3), (6,5), (8,3), (8,5), (8,7)\}$ (tuple)

Comprehensive specification follows directly from sets, for example:

> $is\_greater\_than ==$
> $\{a : Alpha; b : Beta \mid \forall a : Alpha; b : Beta \bullet (a,b) \in is\_greater\_than \Leftrightarrow a > b \bullet (a,b)\}$

which states: '*is_greater_than* is a relation over two sets A and B such that for all elements a that are members of A and all elements b that are members of B the ordered pair (a,b) is a member of the relation if and only if a is greater than b'.

SAQ 8.1   Assuming $\mathbb{N}$ represents the set of natural numbers, enumerate the members of the relations defined by the following comprehensive specification:

$$\{a,b : \mathbb{N} \mid a + b = 4 \bullet (a,b)\}$$
$$\{x,y : \mathbb{N} \mid x = y \wedge x < 4 \bullet (x,y)\}$$

If $\mathbb{N}_1$ corresponds to the set of strictly positive natural numbers what does the following comprehensive set specification define?

$$\{a,b:\mathbb{N} \mid \exists k:\mathbb{N}_1 \bullet a + k = b \bullet (a,b)\}$$

What are the types of each of these relations and what is the type of *is_greater_than*?

8.4.1 The identity relation

The remainder of this chapter concerns the relational operators. The identity relation is an important relation used in the specification of some relational operators. The identity relation on some arbitrary set A, is written id A and is simply the set of ordered pairs formed from the elements of A. Thus:

$$\text{id } \{5,10,15,20\} = \{(5,5), (10,10), (15,15), (20,20)\}$$

Formally we have:

$$\text{id } A == \{a:A \bullet (u,u)\}$$

We shall find more practical uses for this relation later.

8.5 OPERATIONS ON RELATIONS

Just as the operators of set theory permit operations on the members of sets, relational operators permit manipulation on the members of relations. The remaining parts of this chapter discuss the mechanics of these operations and their formal specifications. Parts of this discussion are understandably rather technical, however we must realize that when relations involve meaningful predicates over useful sets, the concept provides a powerful mechanism for the description of information and its consequent interrogation. This is the major point to appreciate when reading the next few pages. To this end, all the operations are illustrated with respect to a simple situation of interest so that the results of the operations can be seen as fulfilling some practical task. Because relations are sets, however, we should never forget that *all* the previous set operators apply with equal validity.

The relation we shall study is that between the possible users of some computer filing system and the file access privileges they are permitted. These two sets can be defined by enumeration as:

$$Users == \{Sheppard, Hanlon, McPhee, Eyres, Ellis, Willis, Read\}$$
$$Access == \{Read, Write, Delete, Archive, Purge\}$$

The relation is a relation over $Users \times Access$ and of type $\mathbb{P}(Users \times Access)$ such that:

$$User\_Access ==$$
$$\{a:Users; b:Access \mid \forall a:Users, b:Access \bullet (a,b) \in User\_Access \Leftrightarrow P(a,b) \bullet (a,b)\}$$

The informal English description of this definition follows a similar pattern to the earlier definition of *is_greater_than*. However, the predicate $P(a,b)$ is not so easy to describe, and this is a general observation for many of those relations that model the real world. For now we shall assume the following applications apply for the initial state of the relation:

$$
\begin{aligned}
P(Sheppard,\ Read)\ &=\ true\\
P(Sheppard,\ Write)\ &=\ true\\
P(Sheppard,\ Delete)\ &=\ true\\
P(Sheppard,\ Archive)\ &=\ true\\
P(Sheppard,\ Purge)\ &=\ true\\
P(Hanlon,\ Read)\ &=\ true\\
P(Hanlon,\ Archive)\ &=\ true\\
P(Hanlon,\ Purge)\ &=\ true\\
P(McPhee,\ Read)\ &=\ true\\
P(Eyres,\ Read)\ &=\ true\\
P(Eyres,\ Write)\ &=\ true\\
P(Ellis,\ Purge)\ &=\ true
\end{aligned}
$$

The initial state of the relation can then be defined by tuple enumeration as:

User_Access ==
{(*Sheppard, Read*), (*Sheppard, Write*), (*Sheppard, Delete*), (*Sheppard, Archive*),
(*Sheppard, Purge*), (*Hanlon, Read*), (*Hanlon, Archive*), (*Hanlon,* Purge),
(*McPhee,* Read), (*Eyres, Read*), (*Eyres, Write*), (*Ellis, Purge*)}

(In a practical context, this abstract initialization process is the equivalent of the initial file loading of a 'database' with records we know to be valid.)

The major relational operators we consider are:

> Domain
> Range
> Inverse relation
> Composition
> Domain restriction
> Range restriction
> Domain subtraction
> Range subtraction
> Override
> Set image

In the formal definitions of the operators that follow we use the terminology R or R_i for general relations and T_i, t_i to represent the types and corresponding elements of the *from* and *to* sets.

8.5.1 Domain

The *domain* of some relation R is written dom R. It accepts one operand, a relation, and returns the set whose members are the left-hand elements of the ordered pairs in the relation. This set is the set of all the elements of the *from-set* that have corresponding members in the *to-set*. With the initial state of *User_Access* we have:

dom *User_Access* = {*Sheppard, Hanlon, McPhee, Eyres, Ellis*} which clearly details those users that currently have some access privileges. The operator can be formally defined as:

$$\text{dom } R == \{t_1 : T_1 \mid \exists t_2 : T_2 \bullet t_1 \, R t_2\}$$

'the domain of a relation R over two arbitrary sets T_1 and T_2 is a set of elements drawn from T_1 such that for each element there exists at least one element t_2 of type T_2 with which it forms an ordered pair that is member of the relation'.

8.5.2 Range

The *range* of some relation R is written $\text{ran } R$. It accepts one operand, a relation, and returns the set whose members are the right-hand elements of the ordered pairs in the relation. This set is the set of all the elements of the *to-set* that have corresponding members in the *from-set*. With the initial state of *User_Access* we have:

$$\text{ran } User\_Access = \{Read, Write, Delete, Archive, Purge\}$$

which clearly lists the set of file access privileges currently in use with users. The operator is formally defined as:

$$\text{ran } R == \{t_2 : T_2 \mid \exists t_1 : T_1 \bullet t_1 \, R t_2\}$$

and has an informal definition which follows directly from that of domain. Notice that with the current state of the relation *User_Access* the range is the complete set of user privileges, while the domain is only a subset of the possible users. (*Willis* and *Read*, for example, currently do not have any access privileges at all. Notice also that there is no conflict between the user name *Read* and the access privilege *Read*.) The operators described later can change the members of the relation and consequently many other conditions are possible during its lifetime. The important point to realize is that at any instant it always records which users have access to the filing system and the privileges they currently enjoy.

8.5.3 Inverse relation

The inverse of a relation R is written $R^{\sim}$. It is a relation in which the order of all pairs in R is reversed. If R has been declared as $R : T_1 \leftrightarrow T_2$ then $R^{\sim}$ is a relation in the set $T_2 \leftrightarrow T_1$. We may define the operator formally and informally as:

$$R^{\sim} == \{t_1 : T_1, t_2 : T_2 \mid (t_1,t_2) \in R \bullet (t_2,t_1)\}$$

'the inverse of some relation R over two arbitrary sets T_1 and T_2 is the set of ordered pairs (t_2,t_1) such that the pairs (t_1,t_2) are members of the original relation R'.

Notice in this definition the term (t_2,t_1) has been used to reverse the order of the elements, thereby overriding the characteristic tuple. This 'trick' was mentioned earlier in the discussion of comprehensive specification in set theory (see Chapter 6).

The inverse relation is useful to define 'reverse' behaviour. For example in the case of *is_greater_than* we can define:

$$is\_less\_than = (is\_greater\_than)^{\sim}$$

Enumeration of tuples in the relation and its inverse confirm this:

$$is\_greater\_than == \{(4,3), (6,3), (6,5), (8,3), (8,5), (8,7)\}$$
$$(is\_greater\_than)^\sim = \{(3,4), (3,6), (5,6), (3,8), (5,8), (7,8)\}$$

8.5.4 Composition

Composition is a mechanism by means of which certain aspects of relations can be combined to create a new relation. Given two relations:

$$R_1 : T_1 \leftrightarrow T_2 \quad \text{and}$$
$$R_2 : T_2 \leftrightarrow T_3$$

relational composition is written $R_1; R_2$ and produces a relation $R_3 : T_1 \leftrightarrow T_3$ where members of the domain of R_1 are mapped first to elements of T_2 and thence *through* the relation R_2 to elements of T_3. The effect of this operator is therefore to 'join' elements in T_1 to elements in T_3 through common elements identified from the intersection of the range of R_1 with the domain of R_2. Figure 8.2 illustrates the mechanism very clearly.

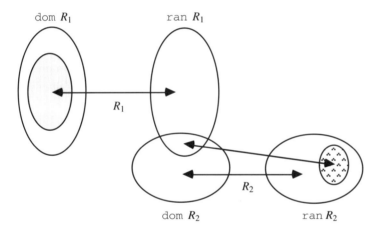

Figure 8.2   **The mechanism of relational composition.**

For composition to be defined, the type of the range of R_1 must obviously correspond to the type of the domain of R_2. Thus if R_1 is over $T_1 \times T_2$ and R_2 is over $T_2 \times T_3$ then the composition is possible. If R_2 were over $T_3 \times T_2$, however, and $T_2 \neq T_3$, then composition is not possible. It is also possible to compose a relation with itself but because of the general restriction above, the type of its domain must match the type of its range. Such relations are homogeneous. In fact, given such a relation ($R_4 : T_1 \leftrightarrow T_1$) the composition can be *extended* or *distributed*:

$$R_4; R_4; R_4; \ldots; R_4 = (R_4)^n$$

All this sounds a little technical but the mechanism is really quite straightforward. To illustrate composition, consider the new relation:

$$Process\_Queue == \{(Read, Q_1), (Write, Q_2), (Delete, Q_3), (Archive, Q_4), (Purge, Q_5)\}$$

which expresses the fact that requests to read or write to files, delete files, archive old files or purge the file system are entered in one of five separate queues, Q_1, Q_2, Q_3, Q_4 and Q_5, respectively. Because the type of the range of *User_Access* matches the type of the domain of *Process_Queue*, composition is possible:

$$
\begin{array}{lll}
(Sheppard,\ Read) & \longrightarrow (Read, & Q_1) \longrightarrow (Sheppard, Q_1) \\
(Sheppard,\ Write) & \longrightarrow (Write, & Q_2) \longrightarrow (Sheppard, Q_2) \\
(Sheppard,\ Delete) & \longrightarrow (Delete, & Q_3) \longrightarrow (Sheppard, Q_3) \\
(Sheppard,\ Archive) & \longrightarrow (Archive, & Q_4) \longrightarrow (Sheppard, Q_4) \\
(Sheppard,\ Purge) & \longrightarrow (Purge, & Q_5) \longrightarrow (Sheppard, Q_5) \\
(Hanlon,\ Read) & \dashrightarrow & (Hanlon, \quad Q_1) \\
(Hanlon,\ Archive) & \dashrightarrow & (Hanlon, \quad Q_4) \\
(Hanlon,\ Purge) & \dashrightarrow & (Hanlon, \quad Q_5) \\
(McPhee,\ Read) & \dashrightarrow & (McPhee, \quad Q_1) \\
(Eyres,\ Read) & \dashrightarrow & (Eyres, \quad Q_1) \\
(Eyres,\ Write) & \dashrightarrow & (Eyres, \quad Q_2) \\
(Ellis,\ Purge) & \dashrightarrow & (Ellis, \quad Q_5) \\
\end{array}
$$

Clearly the new relation is formed by pairing elements in the domain of *User_Access* with elements in the range of *Process_Queue* for each occasion an element in the range of *User_Access* matches an element in the domain of *Process_Queue*. The final relation provides information as to which users could be present in each of the system's process queues. The composition operator is useful therefore because it joins information present in two different relations. Such a mechanism has obvious implications for the manipulation of data (especially when the data is fragmented). The operator is defined formally as:

$$R_1;\ R_2 == \{t_1 : T_1;\ t_3 : T_3 \mid \exists t_2 : T_2 \bullet (t_1, t_2) \in R_1 \land (t_2, t_3) \in R_2 \bullet (t_1, t_3)\}$$

This is probably the most complex definition we have met so far and the literal English translation is very cumbersome indeed: 'the composition of two relations R_1 and R_2 is the set of ordered pairs (t_1, t_3) (where t_1 is of type T_1 and t_3 of type T_3), such that for each element t_2 of type T_2 there exists at least one pair (t_1, t_2) that is a member of R_1 and correspondingly one pair (t_2, t_3) that is a member of the relation R_2 and, on each occasion where this condition is true, we form the pair (t_1, t_3)'.

The example, however, nicely illustrates the general relationship between formal and informal descriptions—that as the degree of complexity increases, formal descriptions become more and more advantageous in terms of brevity and clarity. There is an obvious inference to be drawn when very large systems are being specified.

8.5.5 Restriction and subtraction

There are frequent occasions when the domain or range of a relation has to be limited to certain values only. For example, in the relation *User_Access*, we may want to determine the current privileges of a user or determine which users currently have permission to read files. The two operators:

$$\lhd\ (domain\ restriction) \qquad \text{and} \qquad \rhd\ (range\ restriction)$$

permit such restrictions on a relation. Both operators accept two operands, a set S and a relation $R : T_1 \leftrightarrow T_2$. For domain restriction, the set must of the same type as the domain of the relation. This means that we select only pairs $(t_1, t_2) \in R$ where $t_1 \in S$. For the range restriction, the set must be of the same type as the range of the relation. In this case we select those pairs $(t_1, t_2) \in R$ where $t_2 \in S$.

To illustrate domain restriction consider *File_Access* once again. With {*Hanlon, McPhee*} as the set, the result of the operator is defined by:

$$\{Hanlon, McPhee\} \lhd User\_Access =$$
$$\{(Hanlon, Read), (Hanlon, Archive), (Hanlon, Purge), (McPhee, Read)\}$$

while with {*Sheppard*} as the set:

$$\{Sheppard\} \lhd User\_Access =$$
$$\{(Sheppard, Read), (Sheppard, Write), (Sheppard, Delete), (Sheppard, Archive),$$
$$(Sheppard, Purge)\}$$

By applying `ran` to the result of the second operation we can further modify the output:

$$\texttt{ran}\ (\{Sheppard\} \lhd User\_Access) = \{Read, Write, Delete, Archive, Purge\}$$

These two operations can be regarded as expressing *queries* on the relation in that the first can be interpreted as 'get all the access privileges for Hanlon and McPhee', while the second is clearly equivalent to 'get the access privileges of Sheppard'. The sets {*Hanlon, McPhee*} and {*Sheppard*} correspond to the arguments for the restriction operator. These are important observations that we can exploit to express the functionality of software. Looked at in this way, the relational operators provide the formal expression of the intended behaviour of the software that provides such functionality.

Range restriction behaves in a similar manner, except now the operator uses the set arguments to restrict the range. An example might be:

$$User\_Access \rhd \{Write\} = \{(Sheppard, Write), (Eyres, Write)\}$$

which can be operated upon further:

$$\texttt{dom}\ (File\_Access \rhd \{Write\}) = \{Sheppard, Eyres\}$$

and is clearly equivalent to the query 'get the names of the users with Write privileges'.

Both of these restriction operators can be expressed in terms of the operators we have previously introduced, consequently they are not primitives. We leave it to the reader to confirm that:

- Domain restriction with P $P \lhd R = (\texttt{id}\ P); R$ or $R \cap (P \times T_2)$
- Range restriction with Q $R \rhd Q = R;(\texttt{id}\ Q)$ or $R \cap (T_1 \times Q)$

where P is a subset of T_1 (the domain of R), while Q is a subset of T_2 (the range of R). These definitions also provide some justification for the identity operator `id` and illustrate the point we made earlier that standard set operators (in this case $\cap$) are equally valid applied to relations.

Two further restriction operators are available, very closely related to the previous two:

$\lhd$ *domain subtraction* (or *anti-restriction*) and $\rhd$ *range subtraction* (or *anti-restriction*)

$S \lhd R$ is similar to $\lhd$ in that it acts on the domain, but it now returns those members of the relation $(t_1, t_2) \in R$ where $\neg(t_1 \in S)$. In other words those members where t_1 is not a member of S. For example, with the previous sets, domain subtraction gives:

> $\{Hanlon, McPhee\} \lhd User\_Access =$
> $\{(Sheppard, Read), (Sheppard, Write), (Sheppard, Delete), (Sheppard, Archive),$
> $(Sheppard, Purge), (Eyres, Read), (Eyres, Write), (Ellis, Purge)\}$

and

> $\{Sheppard\} \lhd User\_Access =$
> $\{(Hanlon, Read), (Hanlon, Archive), (Hanlon, Purge), (McPhee, Read), (Eyres, Read),$
> $(Eyres, Write), (Ellis, Purge)\}$

These operations are clearly equivalent to expressions of the queries 'get all the users and their privileges except for Hanlon and McPhee' and 'get all the users and their privileges except for Sheppard'.

Range subtraction $R \rhd S$ is defined in a similar fashion so that with $(t_1, t_2) \in R$ we return those members of R where $\neg(t_2 \in S)$. With the set $\{Write\}$ as an argument we get:

> $File\_Access \rhd \{Write\} =$
> $\{(Sheppard, Read), (Sheppard, Delete), (Sheppard, Archive), (Sheppard, Purge),$
> $(Hanlon, Read), (Hanlon, Archive), (Hanlon, Purge), (McPhee, Read), (Eyres, Read),$
> $(Ellis, Purge)\}$

These restrictions can again be expressed in terms of other operators. Assuming once more that $R : T_1 \leftrightarrow T_2$, we have:

- Domain subtraction with P $P \lhd R = (T_1 \setminus P) \lhd R$ *or* $R \setminus (P \times T_2)$
- Range subtraction with Q $R \rhd Q = R \rhd (T_2 \setminus Q)$ *or* $R \setminus (T_1 \times Q)$

where P is a subset of T_1 (the domain of R), while Q is a subset of T_2 (the range of R). Figure 8.3 illustrates the restriction and subtraction operators.

8.5.6 Override $\oplus$

The override operator $\oplus$ accepts two relations of the same type as operands (e.g. R_1 and R_2 where $R_1 : T_1 \leftrightarrow T_2$ and $R_2 : T_1 \leftrightarrow T_2$) and combines the elements of both to produce a third relation R_1' such that:

$$R_1' = R_1 \oplus R_2$$

The operator achieves this effect in two ways:

1. Those pairs in R_1 whose first elements are also in the domain of R_2 are removed and *replaced* by the elements of R_2.
2. Those elements in R_2 that are not already in R_1 are *added* to R_1.

The operator therefore *updates* R_1 to R_1' by removing certain entries and adding others. Once again we may define the operator formally in terms of others such that:

$$R_1 \oplus R_2 = (\text{dom } R_2 \lhd R_1) \cup R_2$$

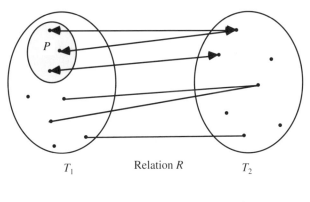

Domain restriction   Domain subtraction

(a)

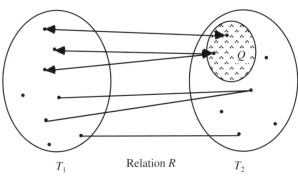

Range restriction   Range subtraction

(b)

Figure 8.3 (a) Domain restriction and subtraction. (b) Range restriction and subtraction.

Great care must be taken when using this operator with relations, for it can be very dangerous if misinterpreted. To illustrate the danger consider *User_Access* once again, which is enumerated here for convenience:

$User\_Access == \{(Sheppard, Read), (Sheppard, Write), (Sheppard, Delete),$
$(Sheppard, Archive), (Sheppard, Purge), (Hanlon, Read), (Hanlon, Archive),$
$(Hanlon, Purge), (McPhee, Read), (Eyres, Read), (Eyres, Write), (Ellis, Purge)\}$

We may wish to update the relation by giving *Hanlon* additional privileges, e.g. *(Hanlon, Write)* and attempt the update with the statement:

$$User\_Access' = User\_Access \oplus \{(Hanlon, Write)\}$$

However, look at the formal definition of override. First, we perform a domain sub-traction on *User_Access* with dom $\{(Hanlon, Write)\}$. Domain subtraction with $\{Hanlon\}$ of course eliminates *all* pairs from *User_Access* that have *Hanlon* as the first item. This gives:

> *User_Access'* =
> $\{(Sheppard, Read), (Sheppard, Write), (Sheppard, Delete), (Sheppard, Archive),$
> $(Sheppard, Purge), (McPhee, Read), (Eyres, Read), (Eyres, Write), (Ellis, Purge)\}$

while subsequent union with $\{(Hanlon, Write)\}$ gives:

> *User_Access'* =
> $\{(Sheppard, Read), (Sheppard, Write), (Sheppard, Delete), (Sheppard, Archive),$
> $(Sheppard, Purge), (McPhee, Read), (Eyres, Read), (Eyres, Write), (Ellis, Purge),$
> $(Hanlon, Write)\}$

This was clearly not the intention because we have lost all of *Hanlon*'s previous privileges! The operator is therefore dangerous because it can simultaneously add, delete and amend pairs in the relation. To bring about the desired effect of giving *additional* privileges to *Hanlon*, while leaving his original privileges intact, we should have used:

User_Access' =
User_Access $\oplus \{(Hanlon, Read), (Hanlon, Archive), (Hanlon, Purge), (Hanlon, Write)\}$

which can be written in more general form as:

$$User\_Access' = User\_Access \oplus \{\{\{Hanlon\} \lhd User\_Access\} \cup \{(Hanlon, Write)\}\}$$

Indeed, in this particular case we should have written:

$$User\_Access' = User\_Access \cup \{(Hanlon, Write)\}$$

which is far simpler than using override. To illustrate an addition, amendment and deletion all in one override, consider:

User_Access' =
User_Access $\oplus \{(Sheppard, Read), (Willis, Read), (Willis, Write), (Ellis, Read)\}$

which returns:

> *User_Access'* =
> $\{(Sheppard, Read), (Hanlon, Read), (Hanlon, Archive), (Hanlon, Purge),$
> $(McPhee, Read), (Willis, Read), (Willis, Write), (Eyres, Read), (Eyres, Write),$
> $(Ellis, Read)\}$

The greatest of care should be taken when using this operator to ensure that it properly conveys your intent. Simultaneous addition, deletion and amendment is neither a desirable nor common activity and needs careful management. The updating of a relation is therefore best achieved using the simple set operators union and difference. In fact, although we have introduced the operator with regard to relations in general, it is best suited to a particular type of relation—the function. The reasons for this will be made clear later.

8.5.7 Set image

The final operator we shall consider is *set image*. The image of a set S through a relation R is the set of elements which are second elements of pairs contained in R whose first elements are in S. Formally, the set image operator $(\!|\ |\!)$ is defined as:

$$R (\!| S |\!) = \{t_2 : T_2 \mid \exists t_1 : S \bullet t_1 \, R t_2\}$$

where $R : T_1 \leftrightarrow T_2$ and S is a subset of T_1. The behaviour of the operator is best conveyed with some examples and so, returning once again to the definition of *User_Access*, we could have:

$User\_Access\,(\!|\,\{Willis\}\,|\!) = \{\ \}$
$User\_Access\,(\!|\,\{Sheppard\}\,|\!) = \{Read, Write, Delete, Archive, Purge\}$
$User\_Access\,(\!|\,\{McPhee, Eyres\}\,|\!) = \{Read, Write\}$

Figure 8.4 summarizes its effect, while the informal version of the definition reads: 'the image of a set S through some relation R is a set of elements t_2 of type T_2 such that each time a pair (t_1,t_2) exists in the relation (where t_1 is also member of S) the value of t_2 is added to the image'.

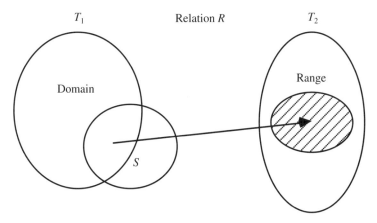

Figure 8.4   Relational set image.

8.6 FUNCTIONS

A function is a relation which bears the restriction that each member of the *from-set* maps to at most one member of the *to-set*. Therefore, given a member of the domain we can determine the single member of the range to which it maps. (It is possible, however, that several (different) members of the domain map to the same member of the range.) Functions are particularly valuable constructs to ensure that when we provide a name, product code or identifier of some sort we get a single corresponding value as a result. There are very many examples where this constraint must apply, for example: a symbol table is a correspondence between a variable name and a single address in memory; a sales catalogue is a correspondence between a product code and an item price; a programmer personnel file is a correspondence between a programmer number and a name.

If each relationship is defined as a function then we can be sure that when we 'look up' the variable name, the product code or the programmer number, a single value is returned. This definition of a function also ensures that the variable names, product codes, programmer numbers, etc., are all unique.

The restriction on a relation $R : T_1 \leftrightarrow T_2$ that transforms it to a function can be expressed formally as:

$$\forall a : T_1; \ \forall p,q : T_2 \bullet ((a,p) \in R \wedge (a,q) \in R \Rightarrow p = q)$$

which states that: 'for every element a of type T_1, p and q of type T_2, if the pair (a,p) is a member of the relation and the pair (a,q) is a member of the relation then p and q are equal and therefore the same element'. This preserves the 'uniqueness' property that each member of the domain maps to just one member of the range.

8.7 TYPES OF FUNCTION

A number of variations on this basic definition of a function are possible, each one corresponding to data relationships in the real world. Probably the most common of these variations is the distinction between a *partial function* and a *total function*. For example, the set of personal identifier numbers in a programmer personnel file will be a subset of all possible employee personal identifier numbers. Some employees are not programmers however, and so the function that maps employee numbers to programmer names is often defined for only part of the total set of numbers available. In general then, a common use for a function is where the complete *from-set* may contain members that are not necessarily currently in the domain. Such a function is a partial function and is characterized by the fact that its domain is a subset of the *from-set*. Figure 8.5 illustrates the mapping nature of a partial function.

In contrast, a total function is one whose domain is the whole of the *from-set*. Figure 8.6 illustrates a total function. In such cases every member of the *from-set* is (always) mapped to a member of the *to-set*. A simple example might occur within a manufacturing company where a total function maps current product code numbers to their corresponding stock levels. Every product will have a stock level even if it is zero!

Total functions frequently appear in specifications but it is probably more common to meet a partial function. This is primarily because functions are often used to model dynamic processes where elements in the domain are frequently changing. Consider again the function that maps employee numbers to programmer names. During the lifetime of this relationship, new programmers will arrive and some programmers leave thereby respectively mapping and releasing employee numbers in the *from-set*. The set of employee numbers which form the domain of the function will therefore change in correspondence with these events. In such circumstances the permanent and static domain offered by a total function is unrealistic. All that can be said of the domain of a partial function is that it will always be a subset ($\subseteq$) of the *from-set*. In our example, the domain at any time will be a subset of all possible employee numbers. This property, however, does not preclude occasions during the life history of the relationship where

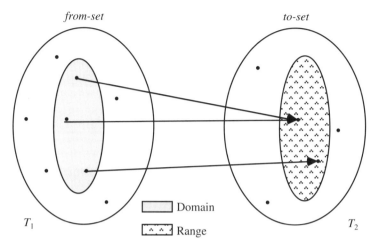

Figure 8.5 A partial function.

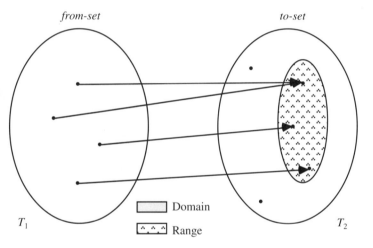

Figure 8.6 A total function.

the function uses all (or none) of the employee numbers. Such conditions correspond to everyone being a programmer and no one being a programmer, respectively. These are possible real-life situations which can be modelled by the partial function along with the more common situation where only certain of the employees are programmers.

SAQ 8.2 Decide whether the following functions are partial or total:

(a) A function called *halve* that maps integers to integers, e.g. $\{..(4,2),..,(10,5)..\}$.
(b) A function called *passport* that maps people to a passport number, e.g.
   $passport == \{..(Sheppard, 156790)..\}$
(c) A function called *square* that maps integers to integers, e.g. $\{(1,1),(2,4),..,(5,25)\}$

Functions are very useful constructs for the software engineer, but there are many different ways in which the elements of a domain can be related to the elements of a range. Each of these reflects a relationship that can exist between data items in the real world. Consequently there are further function types that can be recognized, each being sub-classified as partial or total. These special functions are created by placing various additional constraints on the mapping between the two sets. The following are currently recognized:

- Injective functions
- Surjective functions
- Bijective functions

An *injection* is a one-to-one function, that is, distinct elements of the domain map to distinct elements of the range. Because of this property, an injective function will have an inverse that is also a function. Figure 8.7 illustrates the nature of partial and total injections.

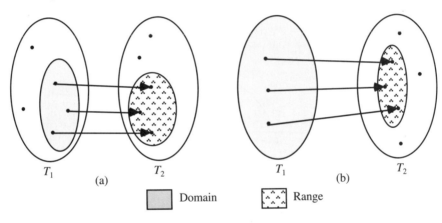

Figure 8.7   (a) Partial and (b) total injections.

A *surjection* is a function whose range is the whole of the *to-set*, that is it 'fills' the *to-set*. Figure 8.8 illustrates partial and total surjections.

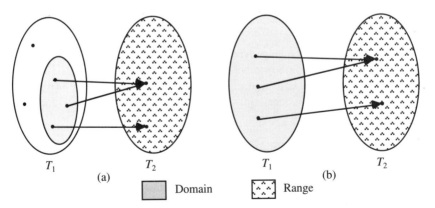

Figure 8.8   (a) Partial and (b) total surjections.

A *bijection* is a function that is a total one-to-one correspondence between the *from-set* and the *to-set*. A bijection is both a total injection and a total surjection. That is, each member of the *from-set* maps to one and only one member of the *to-set* and every member of the *to-set* is associated with a member of the *from-set*. Figure 8.9 illustrates the nature of a bijection.

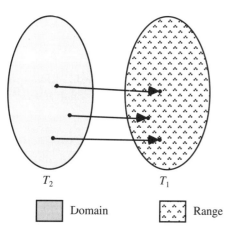

T_2 T_1

▢ Domain   ▨ Range

Figure 8.9 A bijection.

SAQ 8.3 Show that each of the following relationships can be modelled as a special function of some sort:

(a) The relationship between all the countries of the world and their capital cities.
(b) The relationship between the European countries and their capital cities.
(c) The relationship between countries and their reigning monarchs.
(d) The relationship between countries and their currencies.
(e) The relationship between a month and its predecessor.
(f) The relationship between a month and its successor.
(g) The relationship between national flags and the countries to which they belong.

8.8 THE APPLICATION OF A FUNCTION

If F is a function from T_1 to T_2 and $t_1 \in T_1$, then $F(t_1)$ or Ft_1 denotes the *application* of the function to the value t_1, i.e. it is the element t_2 of set T_2 that corresponds to t_1. For example, a function called *Programmer* that maps programmer numbers to programmer names can be defined by enumeration as:

$$Programmer == \{(P1, Jack), (P2, Jill), (P3, Julie), (P4, Jenny), (P5, Jack)\}$$

An application of the function such as *Programmer*(P4) will return *Jenny*. If, however, the application proceeds with a value not in dom *Programmer*, e.g. *Dave*, then the function is not defined and a meaning for *Programmer*(*Dave*) cannot be determined.

8.9 DECLARING A FUNCTION

8.9.1 Partial and total functions

Before we can declare a variable to be a function we have to provide the function with a type. If a function F is a function over a *from-set* and a *to-set* of underlying types T_1 and T_2, respectively, then the underlying type of the function is:

$$F : \mathbb{P}(T_1 \times T_2)$$

Although a function is a relation, we cannot declare it as $F : T_1 \leftrightarrow T_2$ for this loses the uniqueness property that an element of T_1 maps to at most one in T_2; the definition of a function must therefore include this restriction. The set of all possible functions that can be formed over these two sets can be deduced from the set of relations such that:

$$\{R : T_1 \leftrightarrow T_2 \mid \forall a : T_2; \ \forall p,q : T_2 \bullet ((a,p) \in R \wedge (a,q) \in R \Rightarrow p = q)\}$$

For any sets and T_1 and T_2 the set of partial functions from T_1 to T_2 are all those relations which map elements of the domain uniquely and are partial because the implication ($\Rightarrow$) places no obligation on element a to be a member of a function, only a member of the *from-set*. Declaring some function F_p to be a partial function from T_1 to T_2 therefore simply requires that it be made a member of this set of relations which acts as a type. This declaration would clearly benefit from some notational shorthand such that if:

$$T_1 \nrightarrow T_2 == \{R : T_1 \leftrightarrow T_2 \mid \forall a : T_1; \ \forall p,q : T_2 \bullet ((a,p) \in R \wedge (a,q) \in R \Rightarrow p = q)\}$$

the corresponding declaration can be made as:

$$F_p : T_1 \nrightarrow T_2$$

where the $\nrightarrow$ arrow is shorthand notation for the comprehensive declaration and shows that F_p is a partial function from T_1 to T_2. Total functions are best defined in terms of partial functions. This observation stems from the fact that there is nothing to prevent the domain of a partial function filling the whole of the *from-set* on occasions. A total function is therefore simply a partial function whose domain always equals the *from-set*. The set of all total functions from T_1 to T_2 can be expressed as:

$$T_1 \rightarrow T_2 == \{F_p : T_1 \nrightarrow T_2 \mid \mathrm{dom}\,(F_p = T_1\}$$

and again benefits from a notational shorthand such that:

$$F_t : T_1 \rightarrow T_2$$

declares F_t to be a total function from T_1 to T_2 with the $\rightarrow$ arrow again acting as the shorthand notation for the comprehensive declaration.

8.9.2 Special functions

The definitions of the more specialized functions are based largely on those of the partial and total functions and again a shorthand notation provides a more convenient mechanism to declare types for such functions within a specification.

Injections

A partial injection can be defined as:

$$A \rightarrowtail B == \{F_p : A \nrightarrow B \,|\, \forall a_1, a_2 : \text{dom}\,(F_p) \bullet F_p(a_1) = F_p(a_2) \Rightarrow a_1 = a_2\}$$

This says that partial injective functions have the property that if a_1 and a_2 are mapped to the same value then a_1 and a_2 must in fact be the same element. $A \rightarrowtail B$ is shorthand for the set of partial injections from A to B, while the declaration of such a function takes the form:

$$p_i : A \rightarrowtail B$$

declaring p_i to be a partial injection from A to B.

Total injective functions can be defined in a similar fashion except that now they are regarded as forming a subset of the total functions:

$$A \rightarrowtail B == \{F_t : A \rightarrow B \,|\, \forall a_1\, a_2 : \text{dom}\,(F_t) \bullet F_t(a_1) = F_t(a_2) \Rightarrow a_1 = a_2\}$$

By comparison with partial injections we can say that $A \rightarrowtail B$ is shorthand for the set of total injections from A to B while:

$$t_i : A \rightarrowtail B$$

declares t_i to be a total injection from A to B.

Surjections

A partial surjection can be defined as:

$$A \nrightarrow\!\!\!\twoheadrightarrow B == \{F_p : A \nrightarrow B \,|\, \text{r\,an}\,(F_p) = B\}$$

This says that partial surjective functions have the property that (at all times) the range of the function fills the *to-set*. $A \nrightarrow\!\!\!\twoheadrightarrow B$ is shorthand for the set of partial surjections from A to B, while the declaration of such a function takes the form:

$$p_s : A \nrightarrow\!\!\!\twoheadrightarrow B$$

declaring p_s to be a partial surjection from A to B.

The definition of a total surjection follows directly but is regarded as a subset of the set of total functions. Thus:

$$A \twoheadrightarrow B == \{F_t : A \rightarrow B \,|\, \text{r\,an}\,(F_t) = B\}$$

$A \twoheadrightarrow B$ is shorthand for the set of total surjections from A to B, while the declaration of such a function takes the form:

$$t_s : A \twoheadrightarrow B$$

declaring t_s to be a total surjection from A to B.

Bijections

Because a bijection is both a total injection and a total surjection, it is most naturally defined in terms of the set of total injections and the set of total surjections. Therefore, assuming a final shorthand notation of $A \rightarrowtail\!\!\!\twoheadrightarrow B$ which represents the set of all total bijections from A to B, we formally define this set as the intersection:

$$A \rightarrowtail\!\!\!\twoheadrightarrow B == (A \rightarrowtail B) \cap (A \twoheadrightarrow B)$$

giving the set common to both and therefore totally bijective. The declaration of such a function takes the form:

$$t_b : A \rightarrowtail\!\!\!\twoheadrightarrow B$$

which declares t_b to be a total bijection from A to B.

8.10 DEFINING A FUNCTION

Declaring a function does not define its members. Definition may require extra predicates over and above those applied to the relation to convert it to a function of a particular flavour. Functions can be defined by explicit construction as we have seen for sets and relations. However, a more convenient mechanism employs the set comprehension used for both sets and relations. To illustrate the various techniques, consider the definition of a function *abs* that determines the 'absolute value' of an integer. The function will be over integers ($\mathbb{Z}$) and natural numbers ($\mathbb{N}$) and is total because every integer has an absolute value equivalent. The function is therefore just one of the sets included in the type $\mathbb{Z} \rightarrow \mathbb{Z}$ (because the underlying type of natural numbers is integer), but a declaration such as $abs : \mathbb{Z} \rightarrow \mathbb{Z}$ does not tell us which one. We can achieve an explicit definition of the function by enumeration:

$$abs == \{\ldots, (-2,2), (-1,1), (0,0), (1,1), (2,2), \ldots\}$$

but as usual this is tiresome. The implicit definition of the function, however, proceeds in terms of the relationship that elements of the *from-set* bear to those of the *to-set*:

$$abs == \{i:\mathbb{Z}; \; r:\mathbb{N} \mid \forall i:\mathbb{Z}; \; r:\mathbb{N} \bullet ((i,r) \in abs \Leftrightarrow (r = i) \vee (r = -i)) \bullet (i,r)\}$$

An alternative approach could define the function in terms of its application. For example:

$$abs == \{i:\mathbb{Z} \mid \forall i:\mathbb{Z} \bullet (i \geq 0 \Rightarrow abs(i) = i) \wedge (i < 0 \Rightarrow abs(i) = -i) \bullet (i,abs(i))\}$$

8.10.1 Lambda abstraction

Each of these techniques is equally valid, widely used and, applied with discretion, provides a most appropriate description. There is, however, another way of writing (defining) functions which we shall use later in the book called *lambda abstraction*. There is little advantage in burdening the reader with further notation unless there is some justification for its use and, in the case of functions, lambda expressions often prove to be shorter and more convenient than the forms of definition we have met so far.

A lambda expression, like set comprehension, takes the now familiar form of *declaration*, *predicate* and *term*, thus for some function *f*:

$$f == \lambda \, declaration \mid predicate \bullet term$$

The use of the Greek letter lambda (λ) distinguishes this form of expression from normal set comprehension and alerts us to the pending definition of a function. Such an expression takes arguments moulded by the form of *declaration* | *predicate* and maps them to a value defined by *term*. The expression therefore describes a set of pairs of general form:

$$(declaration \mid predicate, term)$$

As a simple example, f could be defined by the expression:

$$f == \lambda n : \mathbb{N} \mid 0 \le n < 5 \bullet n^2$$

The construction $n : \mathbb{N} \mid 0 \le n < 5$ confines our interest in the complete set of integers to the subrange $0 .. 4$ and maps each of these to their squares. It therefore defines the set of pairs:

$$f == \{(0,0), (1,1), (2,4), (3,9), (4,16)\}$$

with legal applications $f(0) = 0$ through to $f(4) = 16$. The function is of course equally well described by:

$$f == \{n : \mathbb{N} \mid 0 \le n < 5 \bullet (n,n^2)\} \quad \text{or} \quad \{n : \mathbb{N} \mid 0 \le n < 5 \bullet n \mapsto n^2\}$$

so that in general there exists an equivalence between the lambda expression and the corresponding set comprehension such that:

$$f == \lambda x : T \mid pred \bullet term = \{x : T \mid pred \bullet x \mapsto term\} \quad \text{or} \quad \{x : T \mid pred \bullet (x,term)\}$$

Because the lambda expression describes a function (by definition), the mapping is implicit and can be omitted along with the set braces.

There is of course no obligation to constrain (the domain) of a function by a predicate. The lambda expression:

$$Double == \lambda n : \mathbb{N} \bullet 2n$$

therefore describes the infinite set that maps each integer to its double. The absence of a predicate represents one way to distinguish the total function from the partial function, while by including predicates of a particular flavour we can describe each of the special functions as lambda expressions.

This notation does not appear to be much of an advantage in the examples we have examined so far, but when there is more than one entry in the declaration list the lambda expression is rather more economical. As an example, consider a function $Total_{m<n}$ that accepts two integers m and n (where $m < n$), and maps the pair to their sum $m + n$, i.e. it describes the set:

$$Total_{m<n} == \{\ldots, ((1,2),3), ((1,3),4), ((1,4),5), \ldots\}$$

Set comprehension provides the following definitions:

$$Total_{m<n} == \{m,n : \mathbb{N} \mid m < n \bullet ((m,n), m + n)\} \quad \text{or}$$
$$\{m,n : \mathbb{N} \mid m < n \bullet ((m,n) \mapsto m + n)\}$$

while the corresponding lambda expression is rather more compact:

$$Total_{m<n} == \lambda m,n : \mathbb{N} \mid m < n \bullet m + n$$

Economy of notation is, of course, a useful feature of a lambda expression and this becomes an even more important aspect of its use when the complexity of the function we are trying to describe increases. This is particularly so when the arguments and/or term for the lambda expression are themselves functions. To illustrate this final point consider the lambda expression *Sum* that describes a function that accepts two total functions as arguments (*f* and *g*) and has as its result another total function that maps an integer *x* to the sum of the applications *fx* and *gx*.

$$Sum == \lambda f,g : \mathbb{N} \to \mathbb{N} \bullet (\lambda x : \mathbb{N} \bullet fx + gx)$$

The first point to appreciate is that a lambda expression can appear at any (legal) point within another lambda expression and so the economy of notation is compounded. (To appreciate this point try writing the definition in comprehensive notation!) But there is a more important point to be made in favour of the notation. Assume we have two functions *Square* and *Negate* which are total functions $\mathbb{N} \to \mathbb{N}$ and defined as:

$$Square == \lambda x : \mathbb{N} \bullet x^2$$
$$Negate == \lambda x : \mathbb{N} \bullet - x$$

Both of these functions can act as arguments to *Sum* for they are both of the correct type. Consequently we can define a whole series of applications of general form *Sum* (*fx*, *gx*)*x* such as:

$$Sum \ (Square, \ Square) \ x$$
$$Sum \ (Square, \ Negate) \ x$$
$$Sum \ (Negate, \ Square) \ x$$
$$Sum \ (Negate, \ Negate) \ x$$

Each of these variants behaves differently depending upon the functions that it receives as arguments, and so the notation not only acts as a convenient shorthand but also permits the *dynamic definition* of new functions from others as and when required. This aspect of the notation extends to a complete lambda calculus, however, in speci- fications, it is principally the shorthand aspect that is most heavily used. We cannot complete this section satisfactorily, of course, until we have seen how the above are evaluated, so for example consider one particular application, *Sum* (*Square, Square*) 5. We take the expression in parts, first introducing the functions as parameters:

$$Sum \ (Square, \ Square) = (\lambda f,g : \mathbb{N} \to \mathbb{N} \bullet (\lambda x : \mathbb{N} \bullet fx + gx) \ (Square, Square)$$
$$= \lambda x : \mathbb{N} \bullet Square \ x + Square \ x$$

we can now introduce the integer parameter 5 such that:

$$Sum \ (Square, \ Square) \ 5 = (\lambda x : \mathbb{N} \bullet Square \ x + Square \ x) \ 5$$
$$= 25 + 25 = 50$$

SAQ 8.4   What are the results of the remaining applications?

(a) *Sum* (*Square, Negate*) 5
(b) *Sum* (*Negate, Square*) 5
(c) *Sum* (*Negate, Negate*) 5

8.11 FINITE FUNCTIONS

Occasionally, when using mathematics to model events of interest in the real world, we need to restrict the sets with which we work to those which have a finite (countable) number of entries. An example of this occurs when we need to draw elements from the subrange of integers $m..n$. This requirement extends quite naturally to the domain of a function which on occasions needs to be similarly restricted to model the event adequately. We therefore recognize the need for a set of *finite functions* with the desired properties. In practice the most common are the set of finite partial functions and the set of finite partial injections for which special (shorthand) notation has developed. The definitions and notation are:

$$A \nrightarrow B == \{f : A \nrightarrow B \mid \operatorname{dom} f \in \mathbb{F}A\}$$
$$A \rightarrowtail\mkern-14mu\rightarrow B == (A \nrightarrow B) \cap (A \rightarrowtail B)$$

where $A \nrightarrow B$ represents the set of finite partial functions and $A \rightarrowtail\mkern-14mu\rightarrow B$ the set of finite partial injections.

8.12 OPERATIONS ON FUNCTIONS

Because a function is a relation, all the relational (and set) operators we examined in the previous sections can be applied to functions. Some of the operators, however, may produce a result that is no longer a function, and in cases where the functional quality must be retained it is as well to be aware of certain restrictions.

The relational inverse when applied to a function may not produce a function. Take for example the explicit definition of *Programmer*:

$$Programmer == \{(P1, Jack), (P2, Jill), (P3, Julie), (P4, Jenny), (P5, Jack)\}$$

such that:

$$(Programmer) \sim = \{(Jack, P1), (Jill, P2), (Julie, P3), (Jenny, P4), (Jack, P5)\}$$

The inverse is clearly a relation not a function because *Jack* is mapped to both *P1* and *P5*. Moreover, set intersection and set difference when applied to functions, produce functions, but set union will, in general, produce a relation that is *not* a function. To illustrate this point further, consider *Programmer* once more. If we employ the prime (') notation to indicate the state of a set after an operation upon it, we see that the union:

$$Programmer' = Programmer \cup \{(P5, William)\}$$

is perfectly legal but *Programmer'* is now a relation and not a function, that is:

$$Programmer' = \{(P1, Jack), (P2, Jill), (P3, Julie), (P4, Jenny), (P5, Jack), (P5, William)\}$$

In such cases the override operator $\oplus$ should be used to preserve the property of a function:

$$Programmer' = Programmer \oplus \{(P5, William)\}$$

gives:

$$Programmer' == \{(P1, Jack), (P2, Jill), (P3, Julie), (P4, Jenny), (P5, William)\}$$

The function override operator is defined as for relations, and the domain subtraction inherent in the definition removes all entries in *Programmer* that are currently in the domain of the set used as the argument. Consequently, if *Programmer* and the set argument are functions, override guarantees a new function. Override therefore combines two functions and produces a third, and although we introduced it with respect to relations it is really of more use with functions. It is always safer to 'update' a function with override rather than union. For relations, override sometimes has added complications and union is simpler.

8.13 SOME FAMILIAR FUNCTIONS: *MAX, MIN* AND *CARDINALITY*

Functions are clearly powerful vehicles for the expression of relationships of interest and this chapter is concluded by illustrating their role in the definition of the operators *max*, *min* and *cardinality*. In this way we complete our definitions of the fundamental operators of set theory and illustrate the creation of more complex functions from simpler sets and functions.

Recall that *max* and *min* accept a set of numbers and return their maximum and minimum elements respectively. Their definitions are:

$$min == \{S : \mathbb{P}\mathbb{N} >; m : \mathbb{N} \mid S \neq \{\} \wedge m \in S \wedge (\forall i : S \bullet m \leq i) \bullet (S,m)\}$$

and:

$$max == \{S : \mathbb{P}\mathbb{N}; m' : \mathbb{N} \mid S \neq \{\} \wedge m' \in S \wedge (\forall i : S \bullet m' \geq i) \bullet (S,m')\}$$

These definitions show that *max* and *min* are regarded as partial functions that map from a set containing sets of natural numbers ($\mathbb{P}\mathbb{N}$) to elements in the set of natural numbers. The type of these functions is therefore $max, min : \mathbb{P}\mathbb{N} \nrightarrow \mathbb{N}$, while the application proceeds:

$$min\,S = m \quad \text{or} \quad min(S) = m \quad \text{and} \quad max\,S = m' \quad \text{or} \quad max(S) = m'$$

where in each case S is one of the sets of natural numbers and m and m' are the natural numbers that correspond to the minimum and maximum elements of S respectively. In each definition, the predicates and terms combine to describe *min* and *max* as sets of ordered pairs and these sets are in turn constrained by the predicates:

$$S \neq \{\} \wedge m \in S \wedge (\forall i : S \bullet m \leq i) \quad \text{and} \quad S \neq \{\} \wedge m' \in S \wedge (\forall i : S \bullet m' \geq i)$$

respectively, which state (for example) that we cannot apply *min* to an empty set, the minimum value of a set must be included in the set, and the minimum value is that element which is less than or equal to all the members of the set (including of course itself). A similar predicate describes the pairs that compose *max*. Some examples of the pairs present in *max* and *min* might therefore be:

$$min = \{((\{1\},1), (\{1,2\},1), (\{1,2,3\},1), \ldots, (\{2\},2), \ldots\}$$
$$max = \{((\{1\},1), (\{1,2\},2), (\{1,2,3\},3), \ldots, (\{2\},2), \ldots\}$$

with actual applications of the functions such as:

$$min\,\{1,2,3\} = 1 \quad \text{and} \quad max\,\{1,2,3\} = 3 \ldots$$

Some of the sets in the *from-set* will, of course, be infinite and have no determinable maximum element. Such sets will therefore not correspond to an element in the *to-set* and will not be mapped in *max*. Similarly, if we cannot determine the maximum of a set we cannot infer the minimum value (for the latter is deduced by comparison) and the same sets will not be mapped in *min*. The functions are therefore partial for this reason.

The cardinality operator (#) when applied to a finite set yields a natural number that represents the number of elements in the set. A finite set is therefore one whose elements are countable. The distinction between sets and finite sets was made in earlier parts of the book, and the first step in devising a definition for cardinality is to clarify the definition of *finiteness*. We do this by first describing the set of all possible finite sets to which, of course, any individual finite set must belong.

A set is *finite* if it is possible to find some total bijection (f say) between an initial segment of the natural numbers $1..n$ and the set. We know that $1..n$ is finite (it has n elements) and because the bijection is a total one-to-one correspondence between the members of $1..n$ and the members of the set, the set itself must also be finite. If such a relationship exists then $f(1)$ provides the first element of the set, $f(2)$ the second element and $f(n)$ the last. With this observation we can provide a definition of the *finite power set* of some set X which was previously introduced in Chapter 6:

$$\mathbb{F}X == \{S:\mathbb{P}X \mid \exists n:\mathbb{N}; f:1..n \rightarrowtail\!\!\!\rightarrow S \bullet true\}$$

Here the finite power set of X is taken as a subset of the power set of X predicated in such a way that members of the power set are finite if there simply exists some natural number, n, and a corresponding total bijection, f, that maps each individual member of the subrange $1..n$ to an individual member of the set. In this definition, the number n represents what we know more familiarly as the cardinality of the set and a consequence of this observation is that only finite sets can have a cardinality. Using the notion of $\mathbb{F}X$ we can finally see that cardinality can be regarded as a total function from the finite power set of some set X to the set of natural numbers (i.e. $\#:\mathbb{F}X \rightarrow \mathbb{N}$), the function being total because every set in a finite power set will (by definition) have a countable population. A formal definition is:

$$\forall S:\mathbb{F}X \bullet \exists f:1..\#S \rightarrowtail\!\!\!\rightarrow S \bullet true$$

where the predicate demands that for all sets S that are members of the finite power set of X there must exist a total bijection from the segment $1..n$ to the elements of S and that the cardinality of S ($\#S$) is simply the value of n.

8.14 GENERAL PROPERTIES OF RELATIONS

In this chapter we have examined a number of relations chosen deliberately to illustrate their usefulness when describing aspects of everyday life. There are, however, important properties of relations *per se*; properties that permit the classification of relations. In particular, relations that relate the elements of some arbitrary set X to one another reveal a number of interesting and useful properties. We have formed such relations on many occasions, e.g. *is_greater_than* over the set of natural numbers or *Road* over the set of *Towns*. By now you should be familiar with the description of the set of all possible relations on some set X as $\mathbb{P}(X \times X)$ or $X \leftrightarrow X$ and if $R : X \leftrightarrow X$ then R is simply a relation that relates elements of X to one another.

Probably the most common examples of such homogeneous relations are $=, \neq, <, >, \leq$ and $\geq$ over the natural numbers and relations such as these may be described variously as:

1. *Reflexive* (r) if $\forall x \in X \bullet xRx$. Here every member of X is in relation R to itself. The relations $=, \leq$ and $\geq$ are all reflexive because $x = x$, $x \leq x$ and $x \geq x$.
2. *Symmetric* (s) if $\forall x, y \in X \bullet xRy \Rightarrow yRx$. Here, whenever (x,y) is a member of the relation so also is (y,x). The relations $=$ and $\neq$ are symmetric because $x = y \Rightarrow y = x$ and $x \neq y \Rightarrow y \neq x$.
3. *Transitive* (t) if $\forall x, y, z \in X \bullet xRy \wedge yRz \Rightarrow xRz$ so that if (x,y) and (y,z) are members of the relation then so too is (x,z). The relations $=, <, >, \leq$ and $\geq$ are all transitive because:

$$x = y \wedge y = z \Rightarrow x = z$$
$$x < y \wedge y < z \Rightarrow x < z$$
$$x > y \wedge y > z \Rightarrow x > z$$
$$x \leq y \wedge y \leq z \Rightarrow x \leq z$$
$$x \geq y \wedge y \geq z \Rightarrow x \geq z$$

4. *Antisymmetric* ($anti$) if $\forall x,y \in X \bullet xRy \wedge yRx \Rightarrow x = y$ which prevents R relating two distinct elements of X to each other in both directions. The relations $\leq$ and $\geq$ are antisymmetric because:

$$x \leq y \wedge y \leq x \Rightarrow x = y$$
$$x \geq y \wedge y \geq x \Rightarrow x = y$$

(Irreflexive and asymmetric relations can also be described but these are less useful.) These properties can be used to classify homogeneous relations. Important examples are relations which are simultaneously *reflexive*, *transitive* and *symmetric* and those which are simultaneously *reflexive*, *transitive* and *antisymmetric*. The first of these are called *equivalence relations* where the concept is meant to capture the notion of sameness or similarity. With our examples of relations over the integers, only $=$ is an equivalence relation and the equivalence it conveys is a familiar one. The notion extends beyond integers to relations over any type, an example being *Has_the_same_salary_as* over a set of employees. If we consider the set of employees as:

$$Employees == \{John, David, William\}$$

then the following relation shows who currently earns the same salary as whom:

$$Has\_the\_same\_salary\_as == \{(John, John), (David, David), (William, William),$$
$$(John, David), (David, John)\}$$

Clearly this relation is *reflexive* because every employee earns the same salary as themselves. (*John* earns the same as *John*, *David* earns the same as *David*, etc.). The relation is *symmetric* because for all such cases, if *David* earns the same as *John* then *John* earns the same as *David*, and the relation is *transitive* for if *John* earns the same as *David* and *David* earns the same as *John* then *John* earns the same as *John*. The reader might like to experiment with more employees and more salary equivalences to show that these properties are always a characteristic of this type of relation.

Equivalence relations abound in specifications and represent a useful model for certain aspects of real life. Relations that are simultaneously *reflexive*, *transitive* and *antisymmetric* are *partial orders*. These are examined in more detail in Chapter 12.

8.15 SUMMARY

Whereas the set is the atomic mathematical object in typed set theory, the relation represents the fundamental complex object. Consequently, relations and functions form the cornerstone of our specifications and the operators and definitions introduced here reappear constantly throughout the book. There are certain operators that our discussion has omitted however. The interested reader is referred to Spivey (1992). This chapter has also omitted certain laws to which these operators are subject. The laws are often required in proofs which are considered later in the book. For those who are interested all the laws are presented in Spivey (1992). The notation used is explained in Parts 4 and 5.

9

CASE STUDY: A SPECIFICATION USING RELATIONS AND FUNCTIONS

9.1 INTRODUCTION

To describe the usefulness of functions, relations and their operators we return to examine certain aspects of the *Project–Programmer* scenario used in earlier parts of the book. In doing so, we follow and build upon the pattern that emerged from the *Homework* example used to illustrate the role of set theory. Our treatment therefore proceeds in discrete stages:

1. Identify the sorts of data required to describe the *Project–Programmer* problem.
2. Use these to describe the abstract state space.
3. Identify the state invariant and consequently the state data.
4. Identify the operators that characterize the *Project–Programmer* object and describe the changes in the state data that can occur.
5. Formally describe the operators and provide informal explanations of their behaviour.

Readers unfamiliar with either the *Homework* or *Project–Programmer* details should ideally review these sections before proceeding (see Chapters 7 and 2, respectively).

9.2 THE SORTS OF DATA REQUIRED

The *Project–Programmer* example assumes that our programmers can be identified by programmer numbers, which in turn determine programmer names. Likewise, project codes identify particular project names, while assignments are determined by a combination of programmer number and project code. These tell us which programmers are engaged on which projects. Each of the relationships of interest, *Programmer*, *Project* and *Assignment* can be modelled either as a function or as a relation because the information they hold can be represented as a set of ordered pairs. However, each should be investigated further to determine which of the two possible structures is the more appropriate model.

It is important that a programmer number is associated with a single name so that we can uniquely reference our programmers. There may well be a very large number of possible programmer numbers and only some of these will correspond to actual programmers at any one time. This relationship is therefore best modelled as a partial function. A function provides the mapping we require and the fact that it is partial models the dynamic nature of this association in real life.

Similarly, project codes must uniquely identify project names and, for the same reasons, a partial function would seem appropriate. However, whereas we can rightly expect duplicate programmer names within the programmer population, duplicate project names would be singularly unhelpful, even though they could be distinguished by their individual project codes. The relationship between codes and names is therefore best modelled as a partial injection which permits the one-to-one correspondence we need and allows projects to come and go.

For the assignments, however, it is possible that a programmer may be engaged on a number of different projects so that a programmer number identifies several different projects. Similarly, a project code could be associated with several programmers and consequently a relation is a more appropriate model. In typed set theory we regard relations and functions as mappings between two sets, and the first step in constructing appropriate mathematical models is to identify the sets that participate in the relationships. The sorts of data that interest us are therefore:

- The set of all possible programmer numbers: (*Prog_Num*)
- The set of all possible programmer names: (*Prog_Name*)
- The set of all possible project codes: (*Proj_Code*)
- The set of all possible project names: (*Proj_Name*)

so that the following declarations model the corresponding relationships:

$$Programmer: Prog\_Num \nrightarrow Prog\_Name$$
$$Project: Proj\_Code \rightarrowtail Proj\_Name$$
$$Assignment: Prog\_Num \leftrightarrow Proj\_Code$$

Notice that here, as in the *Homework* problem, we make no comment as to the nature of the items that compose each of these sets. Such detail will have to be addressed by a program implementing the system, but at the specification level it represents an unnecessary complication.

9.3 THE ABSTRACT STATE SPACE

The various mathematical structures *Programmer*, *Project* and *Assignment* represent persistent objects in that each has an existence independent of any operation upon it. They may also have varying populations during the lifetime of the system because programmers, projects and assignments come and go. Each can therefore be regarded as a variable whose condition at any time reflects the state of a particular relationship. The state of the whole system will therefore belong to the set of tuples which describes the Cartesian product across all three variables and this in turn determines the abstract state space for the problem, i.e. it is a description of every possible condition in which the system could conceivably exist. The abstract state space is therefore represented by the set of tuples:

$$\{Programmer: Prog\_Num \nrightarrow Prog\_Name;$$
$$Project: Proj\_Code \rightarrowtail Proj\_Name;$$
$$Assignment: Prog\_Num \leftrightarrow Proj\_Code\}$$

9.4 THE STATE INVARIANT AND STATE DATA

The identification of an abstract state space is a useful starting point for a formal description of this problem, but as it stands the set of tuples it describes permits all sorts of combinations of the variables, many of which are unrealistic. The declaration must therefore be predicated to restrict membership to those tuples which are meaningful within the context of the relationships that exist in the scenario.

The predicates that admit member tuples to the set can be divided into two groups: those that always apply to the system as a whole and those that describe only the change(s) brought about by a particular operation upon the system. The former provides the invariant on the abstract state space, i.e. it dictates the relationship(s) that must exist among the persistent objects of the system if that state is to be regarded as a legal state of the system. Because all operations are obliged to begin and terminate in a legal state, the state invariant applies to each one. The state invariant for the *Project–Programmer* problem has the following properties:

1. Each programmer number that appears in the *Assignment* relation must be mapped to a name through the *Programmer* function. This ensures that only known programmers are assigned to projects.
2. Each project code that appears in the *Assignment* relation must be mapped to a project name through the *Project* function. This ensures that programmers are assigned to known projects.

Taken together, these ensure that only known programmers are assigned to known projects. The formal expression of this state invariant is given below and follows directly from our understanding of the operators of relations and functions. Notice also that in this expression the conjunction of the two clauses ensures that the whole invariant can be true only if (1) and (2) are simultaneously true:

1. $\mathrm{dom}(Assignment) \subseteq \mathrm{dom}(Programmer) \wedge$
2. $\mathrm{ran}(Assignment) \subseteq \mathrm{dom}(Project)$

To describe the *Project–Programmer* problem properly then, the state invariant must be applied to the description of the abstract state space, and we do this simply by including it as a predicate on the earlier declaration. The resulting set is then regarded as the state data for the problem, i.e. it describes the nature of each of the persistent objects and the rule(s) governing their legal combination. The state data for the *Project–Programmer* problem is consequently defined as:

$$Project\_Programmer ==$$
$$\{Programmer : Prog\_Num \nrightarrow Prog\_Name;$$
$$Project : Proj\_Code \nrightarrow Proj\_Name;$$
$$Assignment : Prog\_Num \leftrightarrow Proj\_Code \mid$$

$$\mathrm{dom}(Assignment) \subseteq \mathrm{dom}(Programmer) \wedge$$
$$\mathrm{ran}(Assignment) \subseteq \mathrm{dom}(Project)\}$$

9.5 THE OPERATORS AND CHANGES IN THE STATE DATA

A number of operators will be required by the *Project–Programmer* system and some natural candidates are:

1. Add a new programmer to the system.*
2. Assign a programmer to a project.*
3. Remove a programmer from a given project.*
4. Amend a programmer's name.*
5. Add a new project to the system.
6. Amend a project name.
7. List the names of the programmers on a particular project.*
8. List the names of the projects assigned to a particular programmer.
9. List the names of projects with no programmers.*
10. List the names of programmers with no projects.
11. Remove a programmer from the system.*
12. Remove a project when completed.

Many of these operators clearly bring about changes in the state data, e.g. adding a new programmer to the system. The tuple defined by *Project_Programmer* however, only describes the abstract state as it exists *before* an operation occurs. Once the operation has been performed the objects will persist in some *after* state (which may or may not be the same as before). It is important of course that the operation preserves the type of the object (a function must not be allowed to degrade to a relation for example) and that the relationships between the after objects still satisfy the invariant. The state data as it exists after an operation is described by:

$$
\begin{aligned}
&Project\_Programmer' == \\
&\{Programmer' : Prog\_Num \twoheadrightarrow Prog\_Name; \\
&\quad Project' : Proj\_Code \rightarrowtail\!\!\!\twoheadrightarrow Proj\_Name; \\
&\quad Assignment' : Prog\_Num \leftrightarrow Proj\_Code \mid \\
&\quad\quad \mathrm{dom}\,(Assignment') \subseteq \mathrm{dom}\,(Programmer') \wedge \\
&\quad\quad \mathrm{ran}\,(Assignment') \subseteq \mathrm{dom}\,(Project')\}
\end{aligned}
$$

so that any operation that brings about a change in the state data must be described (at least in part) by the tuple:

$$
\begin{aligned}
&\{Programmer, Programmer' : Prog\_Num \twoheadrightarrow Prog\_Name; \\
&\quad Project, Project' : Proj\_Code \rightarrowtail\!\!\!\twoheadrightarrow Proj\_Name; \\
&\quad Assignment, Assignment' : Prog\_Num \leftrightarrow Proj\_Code \mid \\
&\quad\quad \mathrm{dom}\,(Assignment) \subseteq \mathrm{dom}\,(Programmer) \wedge \\
&\quad\quad \mathrm{ran}\,(Assignment) \subseteq \mathrm{dom}\,(Project) \wedge \\
&\quad\quad \mathrm{dom}\,(Assignment') \subseteq \mathrm{dom}\,(Programmer') \wedge \\
&\quad\quad \mathrm{ran}\,(Assignment') \subseteq \mathrm{dom}\,(Project')\}
\end{aligned}
$$

As we saw in the *Homework* problem, this definition is formed by merging the declaration lists of *Project_Programmer* and *Project_Programmer'* and conjoining their predicates. If we now reintroduce the operator that achieves this effect for us ($\wedge$) we can express the whole process succinctly as:

$$\Delta Project\_Programmer = Project\_Programmer' \wedge Project\_Programmer$$

where:

$$\Delta Project\_Programmer ==$$
$$\{Programmer, Programmer' : Prog\_Num \nrightarrow Prog\_Name;$$
$$Project, Project : Proj\_Code \nrightarrow Proj\_Name;$$
$$Assignment, Assignment' : Prog\_Num \leftrightarrow Proj\_Code \mid$$

$$\mathrm{dom}\,(Assignment) \subseteq \mathrm{dom}\,(Programmer) \wedge$$
$$\mathrm{ran}\,(Assignment) \subseteq \mathrm{dom}\,(Project) \wedge$$
$$\mathrm{dom}\,(Assignment') \subseteq \mathrm{dom}\,(Programmer') \wedge$$
$$\mathrm{ran}\,(Assignment') \subseteq \mathrm{dom}\,(Project')\}$$

Just like the *Homework* problem, every operator that changes the state data will have to include $\Delta Project\_Programmer$ in its declaration list in order to maintain its responsibility towards the state invariant. Each operator will then be further characterized with additional declarations and predicates that convey just *what* it achieves. Unlike the *Homework* problem, however, certain operations we have listed appear to leave the state data unchanged, e.g. listing the programmers on a particular project. Here nothing is added, amended or deleted. In such cases the inclusion of $\Delta Project\_Programmer$ as part of the definition of the operator would seem to be inappropriate. However, even for these operations, the persistent objects exist in some after state once the operation has been performed. The only difference is that the after states are the same as the before states! This observation provides a clue to the descriptions of such operations: we again include $\Delta Project\_Programmer$ as part of the definition but qualify it with additional predicates that ensure that each persistent object remains unchanged. Such operations on *Project_Programmer* are therefore described (in part) by the tuple:

$$\{Programmer, Programmer' : Prog\_Num \nrightarrow Prog\_Name;$$
$$Project, Project' : Proj\_Code \nrightarrow Proj\_Name;$$
$$Assignment, Assignment' : Prog\_Num \leftrightarrow Proj\_Code \mid$$

$$\mathrm{dom}\,(Assignment) \subseteq \mathrm{dom}\,(Programmer) \wedge$$
$$\mathrm{ran}\,(Assignment) \subseteq \mathrm{dom}\,(Project) \wedge$$
$$\mathrm{dom}\,(Assignment') \subseteq \mathrm{dom}\,(Programmer') \wedge$$
$$\mathrm{ran}\,(Assignment') \subseteq \mathrm{dom}\,(Project') \wedge$$
$$Programmer' = Programmer \wedge$$
$$Project' = Project \wedge$$
$$Assignment' = Assignment\}$$

and if we make use of our existing shorthand notation we can express this more conveniently as:

$$\{\Delta Project\_Programmer \mid$$
$$Programmer' = Programmer \wedge$$
$$Project' = Project \wedge$$
$$Assignment' = Assignment\}$$

A number of operations need to include these declarations and predicates in their definitions and these will benefit from some additional shorthand notation such that if:

$$\Xi Project\_Programmer ==$$
$$\{\Delta Project\_Programmer \mid$$
$$\quad Programmer' = Programmer \wedge$$
$$\quad Project' = Project \wedge$$
$$\quad Assignment' = Assignment\}$$

then the appearance of $\Xi Project\_Programmer$ in the declaration part of a definition conveys the notion that no change of state occurs yet the operator is still aware its obligation to the object types and the invariant. (The symbol Ξ is a Greek letter called 'Xi'.)

We will make appropriate use of both $\Delta Project\_Programmer$ and $\Xi Project\_Programmer$ in the operations described later, but before these definitions are presented, we should address one final point which was ignored in the earlier *Homework* problem—the process of system initialization. There is presumably an operation that creates the structures required for the *Project_Programmer* system and (optionally) populates them with a first *well-formed data* that satisfies the state invariant. Operations 1–12 (may) subsequently change that data, but each is obliged to preserve the original 'well-formedness'. Initialization of the system therefore simply describes a set of acceptable starting conditions and, using values corresponding to Fig. 2.4(a) we suggest a definition of this operator such that:

$$Initialize ==$$
$$\{Programmer' : Prog\_Num \twoheadrightarrow Prog\_Name;$$
$$\quad Project' : Proj\_Code \rightarrowtail\mkern-14mu\twoheadrightarrow Proj\_Name;$$
$$\quad Assignment' : Prog\_Num \leftrightarrow Proj\_Code \mid$$

$$\quad dom\ (Assignment') \subseteq dom\ (Programmer') \wedge$$
$$\quad ran\ (Assignment') \subseteq dom\ (Project') \wedge$$

$$\quad Programmer' = \{(P1, Jack), (P2, Jill), (P3, Julie), (P4, Jenny)\} \wedge$$
$$\quad Project' \quad\ = \{(J1, Note), (J2, Biblio), (J3, Norma), (J4, RDBMS)\} \wedge$$
$$\quad Assignment' = \{(P1,J1), (P1,J2), (P1,J3), (P2,J2), (P2,J3), (P3,J1),$$
$$\quad\quad\quad\quad\quad\quad\quad (P3,J2), (P3,J4), (P4,J2), (P4,J4)\}$$

$$\}$$

Notice that this definition describes the operation in terms of after objects exclusively and this is consistent with the notion of creation where before objects do not exist. The operation also populates our structures and we can see by inspection that the process has occurred in such a way that *Assignment* is a relation, while *Programmer* and *Project* are clearly functions thereby satisfying the constraint implicit in the declaration of each. However, initialization is also an activity that must maintain the invariant on the after states and when we use actual data we are immediately confronted with a *proof obligation* that requires us to demonstrate the validity of the state we produce. This obligation can be discharged in a somewhat simplistic fashion as follows:

$$dom\ (Assignment') = \{P1,P2,P3,P4\}$$
$$dom\ (Programmer') = \{P1,P2,P3,P4\}$$

hence $dom\ (Assignment') \subseteq dom\ Programmer') = true.$

$$ran\ (Assignment') = \{J1,J2,J3,J4\}$$
$$dom\ (Project') = \{J1,J2,J3,J4\}$$

hence $\mathrm{ran}(Assignment') \subseteq \mathrm{dom}(Project') = true$. Consequently, the invariant:

$$\mathrm{dom}\,(Assignment') \subseteq \mathrm{dom}(Programmer') \wedge$$
$$\mathrm{ran}\,(Assignment') \subseteq \mathrm{dom}(Project')$$

is *true* and provides some proof of the correctness of the initial state. Obligations such as these are a common and important aspect of formal specifications and can be conducted in a rigorous fashion unlike the equivalent exercise in quasi-formalisms. Reasoning like this explores the behaviour of the specification without going to the trouble of implementation.

9.6 FORMAL DESCRIPTIONS OF THE OPERATORS

The specifications for the operators marked with * in the original list are given below. Following the convention used with sets, an input to an operator is denoted by *?* while the new notation *!* indicates an output from an operation. This choice is meant to be consistent with the observation that, in computing, the output sometimes surprises us (!). In the specifications that follow a number of the relational and function operators are used—those that provide the most simple and readable descriptions. In most cases alternative formulations are possible that involve more complex operators. Bearing in mind that the specifications may well be involved in subsequent proofs mechanisms, over-elaboration is best avoided.

1. *Add_prog* ==
   {Δ*Project_Programmer*;
   Progname? : *Prog_Name*;
   Prognum? : *Prog_Num* |
   $\mathrm{dom}\,(Programmer) \cap \{Prognum?\} = \{\,\} \wedge$
   Programmer' = *Programmer* $\oplus$ {(*Prognum?*, *Progname?*)} $\wedge$
   Project' = *Project* $\wedge$
   Assignment' = *Assignment*}

2. *Add_prog_proj* ==
   {Δ*Project_Programmer*;
   Prognum? : *Prog_Num*;
   Projcode? : *Proj_Code* |
   Prognum? $\in \mathrm{dom}\,(Programmer) \wedge$
   Projcode? $\in \mathrm{dom}\,(Project) \wedge$
   $\neg((Prognum?, Projcode?) \in Assignment) \wedge$
   Assignment' = *Assignment* $\cup$ {(*Prognum?*, *Projcode?*)} $\wedge$
   Programmer' = *Programmer* $\wedge$
   Project' = *Project*}

3. *Rem_prog_ona_proj* ==
   {Δ*Project_Programmer*;
   Prognum? : *Prog_Num*;
   Projcode? : *Proj_Code* |
   Prognum? $\in \mathrm{dom}\,(Programmer) \wedge$
   Projcode? $\in \mathrm{dom}\,(Project) \wedge$

$(Prognum?, Projcode?) \in Assignment \land$
$Assignment' = Assignment \setminus \{(Prognum?, Projcode?)\} \land$
$Programmer' = Programmer \land$
$Project' = Project\}$

4. $Amend\_prog\_name ==$
   $\{\Delta Project\_Programmer;$
   $Prognum?: Prog\_Num;$
   $Progname?: Prog\_Name \mid$
   $Prognum? \in \text{dom} (Programmer) \land$
   $Programmer' = Programmer \oplus \{(Prognum?, Progname?)\} \land$
   $Project' = Project \land$
   $Assignment' = Assignment\}$

7. $Prognames\_ona\_proj ==$
   $\{\Xi Project\_Programmer;$
   $Projcode?: Proj\_Code;$
   $Progs!: \mathbb{P} Prog\_Name \mid$
   $Projcode? \in \text{dom} (Project) \land$
   $Progs! = \text{ran} ((\text{dom} (Assignment \rhd \{Projcode?\})) \lhd Programmer)\}$

9. $Projnames\_withno\_Progs ==$
   $\{\Xi Project\_Programmer;$
   $Projs!: \mathbb{P} Proj\_name \mid$
   $Projs! = \text{ran} ((\text{dom} (Project) \setminus \text{ran} (Assignment)) \lhd Project)\}$

11. $Rem\_prog\_from\_org ==$
    $\{\Delta Project\_Programmer;$
    $Prognum?: Prog\_Num \mid$
    $Prognum? \in \text{dom} (Programmer) \land$
    $Assignment' = \{Prognum?\} \lhd Assignment \land$
    $Programmer' = \{Prognum?\} \lhd Programmer \land$
    $Project' = Project\}$

Each operator is described in terms of a tuple whose input(s), output(s) and persistent objects are related in accordance with the intended meaning of the operator. The declaration part of the tuple introduces each variable while the predicates provide details of:

- The relationships that must prevail prior to the operation if normal behaviour is to be observed (these are the 'preconditions').
- The relationships that must exist among participants after the operation if it has behaved normally (these are the 'postconditions').

(Strictly speaking, the preconditions and postconditions must also take into account the requirement(s) of the state invariant 'hidden' in the delta and xi notations. Our use of these terms is therefore simplistic but commensurate with our understanding at this point.)

The use of the shorthand notations Δ (delta) and Ξ (xi) reduce the specifications to manageable proportions, while at the same time providing details of the state invariant and distinguishing those operators that change the state data from those that do not. The economy of the notation is only really appreciated by writing out operator specifications in full (and you are encouraged to do this at least once!). Notice also that in cases where changes in state data occur not all persistent objects need be affected, e.g. in the *Add_Prog* operator the inclusion of $\Delta Project\_Programmer$ is qualified with predicates such as:

$$Project' = Project \wedge$$
$$Assignment' = Assignment$$

because only *Programmer* has been changed.

Some comments concerning each operator are appropriate. The declaration list of *Add_Prog* alerts us to the fact that it brings about a change of state ($\Delta Project\_Programmer$) and that it accepts two inputs: a programmer name and a programmer number. The statement:

$$\mathrm{dom}\,(Programmer) \cap \{Prognum?\} = \{\,\}$$

is a precondition that ensures that the incoming programmer number is not already mapped in the *Programmer* function. In other words it ensures that the operator is only defined to add a *new* programmer to the system (we make no comment at this stage as to what action should be taken if this condition is not met). The system state is consequently updated by overriding the *Programmer* function with the new pair (*Prognum?*, *Progname?*) and the use of override ensures that *Programmer'* remains a function. Finally:

$$Project' = Project \wedge Assignment' = Assignment$$

shows that *Project* and *Assignment* are unaffected by this operator. Notice also that *Programmer* could well have been updated with set union because the precondition prevents duplicate programmer numbers being added in any case! The use of override, however, represents the safer choice and the combination of precondition and override together make it abundantly clear to the implementor that the quality of *Programmer* must be maintained.

The specification of *Add_prog_proj* follows a similar pattern. The declaration list shows that it brings about a state change and that it accepts two inputs: a programmer number and a project code. The precondition, however, is more complex in that the programmer must currently exist ($Prognum? \in \mathrm{dom}\,(Programmer)$), the project must be a valid project ($Projcode? \in \mathrm{dom}\,(Project)$) and this programmer should not already be recorded as assigned to this project, i.e. $\neg((Prognum?, Projcode?) \in Assignment)$.

Because this operator updates a relation, set union can be safely used to include the new pair:

$$Assignment' = Assignment \cup \{(Prognum?, Projcode?)\}$$

while the effect of $\Delta Project\_Programmer$ is qualified by:

$$Programmer' = Programmer \wedge Project' = Project$$

showing that only the *Assignment* relation changes.

The specifications for *Amend_prog_name*, *Rem_prog_ona_proj* and *Rem_prog_from_org* follow very similar patterns, but the specification of the operator that lists the names of programmers on a particular project (*Prognames_ona_proj*) introduces some additional features. The presence of $\Xi Project\_Programmer$ in the declaration list shows that no state change occurs, while at the same time providing details of the obligation towards the invariant. The operator accepts a project code (*Projcode?*) as input and declares an output variable *Progs!* Remember that this operator provides a *list* of programmer names and so the output variable is declared as a member of the power set of programmer names (*Progs!*: $\mathbb{P}\ Prog\_Name$) thereby representing the list as any one of its possible combinations.

The precondition is quite straightforward and demands that a valid project code is input:

$$Projcode? \in \mathrm{dom}\ (Project)$$

while the effect of the operator is described by:

1. First, restricting our interest in *Assignment* to those pairs that have the required project as their second element: ($Assignment \rhd \{Projcode?\}$).
2. Extracting their programmer numbers: $\mathrm{dom}\ (Assignment \rhd \{Projcode?\})$.
3. Restricting our interest in *Programmer* to only those that have numbers in this set: ($\mathrm{dom}\ (Assignment \rhd \{Projcode?\})) \lhd Programmer$.
4. Finally, assigning the names of these programmers to the output variable:
$$Progs! = \mathrm{ran}\ ((\mathrm{dom}\ (Assignment \rhd \{Projcode?\})) \lhd Programmer)$$

This specification describes the effect of the operator quite well but has one serious flaw. In cases where different programmers share the same name, the final operator (ran) may be applied to a set containing pairs such as:

$$Progs! = \mathrm{ran}\ \{23,\ J.\ Williams),\ (45,\ J.\ Williams),\ (34,\ D.\ Sheppard),\ (53,\ M.\ Read)\}$$

Consequently:

$$Progs! = \{J.\ Williams,\ D.\ Sheppard,\ M.\ Read\}$$

and this output fails to account for the possibility of multiple occurrences of a programmer name. To some extent this is not the fault of the specification. The problem lies with the original informal description which is far too slack. The requirement for a list of names probably *implies* that each individual on the list is uniquely identifiable, but the obligation is not expressed explicitly and leads to difficulty in the specification. The specification must of course be unambiguous and so further clarification of the behaviour of this operator must be sought and different mathematical structures used to support the possibility of multiple occurrences of programmers' names (see Chapter 10).

9.7 PROVING PROPERTIES OF THE SPECIFICATION: THE IDENTITY OPERATION

The specification of the *Prognames_ona_ proj* operator is an example where the rigour of the formal approach ultimately leads to a much clearer informal description of an operator's behaviour. Furthermore, formal descriptions can be reasoned about to ensure their correctness prior to implementation, and we have seen a simple example of this process with initialization. Reasoning, however, can be extended to examine many other aspects of a specification. For example, consider the two operations *Add_ prog_ proj* and *Rem_ prog_ona_ proj*. If we add a programmer to a project and then immediately remove the same programmer from the project the state of the *Assignment* relation should remain unchanged, i.e. the two operations together define the *identity operation*. This consequence should be deducible from the specification. Assuming that *Prognum?* and *Projcode?* are the same in both operations, the specifications of the two operations show that adding the programmer to the project is to effect:

$$Assignment^+ = Assignment \cup \{(Prognum?, Projcode?)\} \qquad (9.1)$$

while subsequently removing the same programmer is described by:

$$Assignment' = Assignment^+ \setminus \{(Prognum?, Projcode?)\} \qquad (9.2)$$

where the superscripts are used to distinguish the various versions of the assignment relation. Clearly, we wish to prove:

$$Assignment' = Assignment$$

We begin by eliminating the intermediate version by substituting for $Assignment^+$ in (9.2) using (9.1):

$$Assignment' = (Assignment \cup \{(Prognum?, Projcode?)\}) \setminus \{(Prognum?, Projcode?)\}$$

and using this observation, together with the various laws governing sets (see Spivey (1992)) we try to prove this expression true as follows:

$$Assignment' = (Assignment \setminus \{(Prognum?, Projcode?)\})$$
$$\cup \{(Prognum?, Projcode?)\} \setminus \{Prognum?, Projcode?)\}$$

because the set laws show that $(a \cup b) \setminus c = (a \setminus c) \cup (b \setminus c)$. Hence:

$$Assignment' = (Assignment \setminus \{(Prognum?, Projcode?)\}) \cup \{\ \}$$

simply because of a known fact about the set difference operator. Similarly, this reduces to:

$$Assignment' = (Assignment \setminus \{(Prognum?, Projcode?)\})$$

because of the way in which union works with empty sets. The precondition for the update of *Assignment*, however, declares:

$$\neg ((Prognum?, Projcode?) \in Assignment)$$

so assuming this is true and knowing how the difference operator works we can deduce:

$$Assignment \setminus \{(Prognum?, Projcode?)\} = Assignment$$

Consequently: $Assignment' = Assignment$.

The ability to reason in this fashion allows us to examine a specification prior to its implementation to ensure that it has the desired properties. This clearly saves much effort later in the development process.

10

SEQUENCES

CHECKLIST OF OBJECTIVES

After reading this chapter you should be able to:

- Understand how sequences model order among the elements of some set of interest.
- Understand the typing system associated with sequences.
- Understand and use each of the sequence operators.
- Understand the role of lambda abstraction in the definition of these operations.

10.1 INTRODUCTION

The mathematical structures introduced so far have enabled us to model collections of items as sets and the relationships between them as relations and functions. Using these structures we have seen how data and events of interest to the software engineer can be described unambiguously and independent of implementation detail. Useful though these structures are, their properties render them inadequate to model certain other aspects of data which have an important role in the real world—that of *order* among the items that interest us.

We must take care here, however, as the perception of order among the members of some community can be based simply upon an arbitrary place value that they occupy or upon the value of some particular property that they all possess. In the former case the collection is ordered simply because it can be seen as having has a first, a second, ..., and a last element. This may be called *inherent order*. In the latter case the community still has inherent order but the place value within this order occupied by a member of the collection is now dependent upon the value of some particular property that it possesses. For example the first member could have the largest value of that property and the last the smallest value (or vice versa). We therefore distinguish between *ordered* collections and *sorted* collections. Clearly the more fundamental of these is the ordered collection; the sorted collection is then seen as an ordered collection with some additional predicate to assign members to a particular place value.

Ordered and sorted collections occur frequently in real life. People gathering outside a cinema to see a film represent an ordered collection of people. The position occupied by a person in the collection is determined by the time that person joined it. Joining the collection of people is seen as a largely random activity and so the place value a person occupies is entirely arbitrary. There is no sense of priority among members of

143

the collection such that *Sheppard* should be first or *Jones* should be last, for no account is taken of the 'value' or quality of the people that are waiting. In other circumstances, however, the members may well be 'prioritized', and it is the priority value which dictates the position they occupy in the set rather than the time they entered it. As an example of such a structure, some of the people standing outside the cinema may also be on the local authority action list waiting to be allocated to community housing. When added to the list, the position a person occupies is determined by the need for accommodation relative to other members of the community. (Does the person have children? Is the person disabled? How long has that person been waiting?) Those with the greatest need occupy corresponding positions in the list and so the collection of people is ordered accordingly. There are many similar situations.

Order is therefore an important property of real-life data and must be described by an appropriate mathematical structure. To describe a collection where order *is* important, we introduce the *sequence*.[1] Fortunately for us we already have enough notation to describe such ordered sets and so we shall build on this in the discussion that follows.

10.2 SEQUENCE DEFINITION, DECLARATION AND NOTATION

The mathematical description of a sequence is based upon set theory in that the sequence can be seen as a set of ordered pairs (p_i,i) where p_i represents the position of item i relative to other members of the set. Thus in the following example (which draws names from the set of all possible names *Names*):

$$CinemaQueue == \{(3,Mike), (1,Deri), (2,Huw)\}$$

Deri is first, *Huw* is second and *Mike* is third. The set of pairs of course can be written in any order such that:

$$CinemaQueue == \{(1,Deri), (2,Huw), (3,Mike)\}$$
$$CinemaQueue == \{(3,Mike), (2,Huw), (1,Deri)\}$$

or any other combination still implies the same order among the names. Clearly, *CinemaQueue* is a function from natural numbers to *Names* but it is more than that because the domain of *CinemaQueue* must start at 1 and continue in unbroken discrete steps up to a value equal to the number in the set. This observation motivates a more formal definition of our model of sequences of items of type X. They are functions from $\mathbb{N}$ to X whose domain is the subrange $1..n$ and where $n \in \mathbb{N}$. By modelling sequences in this fashion we continue on an already well-established learning curve, because sequences are built upon functions which are built upon relations which are built upon sets.

The formal definition for the set of all possible sequences over some set X is given by:

$$seq\ X == \{f:\mathbb{N} \nrightarrow X \mid \operatorname{dom} f = 1..\#f\}$$

[1]The use of the term 'sequence' is unfortunate and reflects the different experiences of the mathematical and software engineering communities. For example, a sequential file is understood to contain data items in sorted order, while a non-sequential file contains data in arbitrary order. To a mathematician, however, a sequence is simply something in which we can detect a first, second, ..., and last element.

which states that: 'the set of all possible sequences of elements of some set X is a finite partial function from natural numbers to X such that the domain of the function is a subrange of the set of natural numbers from 1 up to the cardinality of the function'. Here seq X acts as a shorthand notation for the complete set of such sequences, while the corresponding declaration that s is a particular sequence within this set is made by $s : \text{seq } X$.

Some of the operators met later are not defined for empty sequences and so the notation $\text{seq}_1 X$ is often used to describe a *non-empty sequence* of elements of X. Notice also that the definition models the sequence as a finite partial function because of the need to limit the domain to a subrange of natural numbers with upper limit $\#f$. Consequently all our non-empty sequences are predicated to be of finite length.

SAQ 10.1   It is perfectly possible to have an *injective sequence*, i.e. a sequence where an element appears at most once. Write a formal definition for the set of all possible injective sequences, i.e. iseq X.

These declarations lead us naturally to consider the type of a sequence. Because a sequence such as $s : \text{seq } X$ is a function, the type of each individual element is the Cartesian product $\mathbb{N} \times T$ where T is the underlying type of set X. However, the underlying type of $\mathbb{N}$ is $\mathbb{Z}$ so that the underlying type of a sequence is therefore $\mathbb{P}(\mathbb{Z} \times T)$.

Because sequences are sets, the tuple notation used for the introductory example *CinemaQueue* is perfectly adequate but rather cumbersome when used for the representation of sequences in general. We have used shorthand notation in a number of areas to reduce definitions to manageable levels and a further example is introduced here. Sequence brackets $\langle\,\rangle$ are used to enclose the elements of a sequence, and the order associated with the enumeration of the elements between these sequence brackets determines the natural number (the *index*) associated with the element in the corresponding set of ordered pairs. Some examples of this notation and its relationship with set notation make this point clearer:

$$\langle Huw, Deri, Mike \rangle = \{(1, Huw), (2, Deri), (3, Mike)\}$$
$$\langle Deri, Huw, Mike \rangle = \{(1, Deri), (2, Huw), (3, Mike)\}$$
$$\langle Deri \rangle = \{1, Deri)\}$$
$$\langle\,\rangle = \{\}$$

In each of these examples the pairs in the sets are written out in the same order as the elements of the corresponding sequence. This is purely for convenience and clarity. The point was made earlier that any combination of these pairs represents the same set and hence the same sequence. Notice also that:

$$\langle Huw, Deri, Mike \rangle \neq \langle Deri, Huw, Mike \rangle$$

so that sequences are exactly equal only when they have the same elements in the same order.

SAQ 10.2   Write out the sets corresponding to the following sequences:

(a) $\langle 7, 8, 9 \rangle$ (b) $\langle 2, 2, 2 \rangle$ (c) $\langle \{Deri\}, \{Huw\} \rangle$

Which of the following sets are sequences?

(a) $\{1 \mapsto Huw, 2 \mapsto Huw, 3 \mapsto Deri\}$
(b) $\{n : \mathbb{N} \mid 0 < n < 10 \bullet (n, 2n)\}$
(c) $\{1 \mapsto 0\}$
(d) $\{0 \mapsto Deri, 1 \mapsto Mike\}$
(e) $CinemaQueue \cup \{1 \mapsto Tom\}$
(f) $\{n : 0..9 \bullet (n, n + 1)\}$
(g) $CinemaQueue \oplus \{1 \mapsto Mike\}$

10.3 OPERATIONS ON SEQUENCES

Sequences are modelled by functions, which in turn are modelled by relations and sets. Consequently, in theory all of the operators that can be applied to functions, relations and sets can be applied to sequences. In practice, however, this observation is not of great use, for many of the operators cannot be relied upon to preserve the special property of being a sequence. The same problem was seen earlier when we examined the effect of certain set and relational operators on the function. This in turn led to special operations, e.g. function override, whose purpose was to preserve functional quality. To illustrate the corresponding case for the sequence, consider the union of the following two sets that represent sequences with just one member each:

$$\langle Huw \rangle \cup \langle Deri \rangle = \{(1, Huw)\} \cup \{(1, Deri)\} = \{(1, Huw), (1, Deri)\}$$

Clearly the result is not a sequence; indeed it is not even a function! With the sequence as with the function then, we have to take particular care if we want to ensure that the quality of the sequence is preserved after an operation upon it. We therefore tend to consider operations on sequences in two categories:

- Those of set/relation/function theory that can be safely applied to a sequence.
- Those special operations that are peculiar to sequences.

Of the former collection there are two that are immediately useful given the derivation of sequences from sets and functions. The length of a sequence can be determined by the application of the cardinality operator (#) to the set such that, for example, $\#CinemaQueue = 3$, while the application of the sequence using a natural number in its domain returns the value associated with that number in the sequence. Therefore, assuming $1 \leqslant i \leqslant \#CinemaQueue$, the general application $CinemaQueue\ i$ returns:

$$CinemaQueue\ 1 = Deri$$
$$CinemaQueue\ 2 = Huw$$
$$CinemaQueue\ 3 = Mike$$

Of the latter collection, the operations that largely characterize the sequence are *concatenation, head, tail, front, last, reversal, squash* and *restriction*. Each is discussed in detail below.

10.3.1 Concatenate

We begin our understanding of these operators by examining *concatenate*, which creates a new sequence from two others. This operator is of particular interest, for its definition not only influences the role of other but also exemplifies some of the problems associated with the formal definition of sequence operators in general.

The concatenation of two sequences s and t is written $s \char94 t$ and is formed by taking the elements of s and following them with the elements of t. The following examples illustrate its effect:

$$\langle a,b,c,d\rangle \char94 \langle x,y\rangle = \langle a,b,c,d,x,y\rangle$$
$$\langle x,y\rangle \char94 \langle a,b,c,d\rangle = \langle x,y,a,b,c,d\rangle$$
$$\langle\rangle \char94 \langle p,r,w\rangle = \langle p,r,w\rangle$$
$$\langle p,r,w\rangle \char94 \langle\rangle = \langle p,r,w\rangle$$

In general, the operator is not commutative in that, given two sequences s and t:

$$s \char94 t \neq t \char94 s$$

An exception to this rule clearly occurs when one sequence is empty. The definition of concatenation is only complicated by the need to adjust the index values of the elements of the second sequence. Assuming:

$$s = \langle a,b,c,d\rangle \quad \text{and} \quad t = \langle x,y\rangle$$

set enumeration illustrates how the concatenation $s \char94 t$ alters the values associated with the elements of t:

$$\{(1,a), (2,b), (3,c), (4,d)\} \char94 \{(1,x), (2,y)\} = \{(1,a), (2,b), (3,c), (4,d), (5,x), (6,y)\}$$

A simple strategy for the definition of the operator therefore involves an exercise in index adjustment for the second sequence followed by set union:

$$\{(1,a), (2,b), (3,c), (4,d)\} \char94 \{(1,x), (2,y)\} = \{(1,a), (2,b), (3,c), (4,d)\} \cup \{(5,x), (6,y)\}$$
$$= \{(1,a), (2,b), (3,c), (4,d), (5,x), (6,y)\}$$

The index values of the second sequence are changed simply by adding the cardinality of the first sequence ($\#s = 4$) to each one in turn. Thus:

$$\{(1,x), (2,y)\} \quad \text{becomes} \quad \{(1+4,x), (2+4,y)\} \quad \text{or more concisely} \quad \{(5,x), (6,y)\}$$

This operation converts the second sequence to a function whose domain consist of a subrange of natural numbers $1 + \#s \mathrel{..} \#s + \#t$. Because s is a sequence, its domain is $1 \mathrel{..} \#s$ by definition. The two domains are therefore disjoint but continuous and the union can be relied upon to produce a function with domain $1 \mathrel{..} \#s + \#t$ which is, of course, also a sequence. We can formally express the definition of the operator through index adjustment and union with the expression:

$$\forall s,t : \text{seq } X \bullet s \char94 t = s \cup \{n : 1 \mathrel{..} \#t \bullet (n + \#s) \mapsto tn\}$$

or with expansion of the subrange type, we can write:

$$\forall s,t : \text{seq } X \bullet s \char94 t = s \cup \{n : \mathbb{N} \mid \forall n \bullet 1 \leq n \leq \#t \bullet (n + \#s) \mapsto tn\}$$

The expression in set braces is responsible for the index adjustment. It describes the conversion of the second sequence to a function (using maplet notation in the term of the expression), creating a pair for each value of n in the range $1 .. \#t$. Each pair takes the form $(n + \#s) \mapsto tn$ where tn represents the application of t at n. In our example, because $\#t = 2$ we create a pair for $n = 1$ and $n = 2$ such that the set is defined by $(1 + 4, t1)$ and $(2 + 4, t2)$, i.e. $\{(5,x), (6,y)\}$. The complete definition of the concatenation operator may therefore be read as: 'for all s and t that are sequences of elements of some type X, the concatenation of s and t is equal to the union of s with the function produced by mapping each of the natural numbers $n + \#s$ (where $n = 1 .. \#t$) to the corresponding values obtained by the application of t at that n'.

The type of X from which the sequence is composed is not defined and therefore the operator is regarded as generic, concatenating sequences of any type.

SAQ 10.3 How does the definition of the concatenation operator deal with the following situations?

$$\langle p,r,w \rangle \wedge \langle \rangle \quad \text{and} \quad \langle \rangle \wedge \langle p,r,w \rangle$$

Adjusting index values is a common activity when specifying operations involving sequences. For example, a sequence may be used to model a sorted collection of items. Insertion of an element into the sequence causes the index values of all elements above it to be increased by 1 and it is therefore worth examining other techniques that can bring such changes about. In the specific case of concatenation, the function that described the adjustment was expressed as a set of ordered pairs using maplet notation. We have seen previously, however, that an ideal notation for the definition of functions is lambda abstraction. Indeed, in a lambda abstraction, types made up from the variable(s) of the signature are mapped into the expression represented by the term for which the predicate is true. This is an ideal mechanism to help in the adjustment of the index values and to see how it can be used to define concatenation, consider once again $s \wedge t$ where:

$$s == \{1,a), (2,b), (3,c), (4,d)\} \quad \text{and} \quad t == \{(1,x), (2,y)\}$$

For $\#s = 4$, the lambda expression:

$$(\lambda n : \mathbb{N} \mid n > \#s \bullet n - \#s)$$

produces the function $\{(5,1), (6,2), (7,3), \ldots\}$ by mapping each of the natural numbers greater than 4 to $n - \#s$. Composition (;) of this function with t then provides the necessary adjustment:

$$\{(5,1), (6,2), (7,3), \ldots\} ; \{(1,x), (2,y)\} = \{(5,x), (6,y)\}$$

such that the complete concatenation is described by:

$$\forall s,t : \text{seq } X \bullet s \wedge t = s \cup (\lambda n : \mathbb{N} > \mid n > \#s \bullet n - \#s) ; t)$$

SAQ 10.4 Satisfy yourself that this definition properly deals with concatenations of the form:

$$\langle p,r,w \rangle \wedge \langle \rangle \quad \text{and} \quad \langle \rangle \wedge \langle p,r,w \rangle$$

This definition of the concatenation is therefore equivalent to the previous one, but illustrates both a useful role for lambda abstraction and a technique that may prove valuable for the specification of other indexed structures.

10.3.2 Head, tail, front and last

The head of a non-empty sequence such as *CinemaQueue* is written *head CinemaQueue* and is the first element of the sequence. In other words:

$$head\ CinemaQueue = CinemaQueue\ 1 = \langle Deri \rangle$$

For sequences that are empty, *head* has no meaning (is not defined) and therefore it represents a potential trap for the unwary. We must be careful when using this operator in a formal description.

The tail of non-empty sequence such as *CinemaQueue* is written *tail CinemaQueue* and is the sequence consisting of all elements of *CinemaQueue* except the first, i.e., it is the decapitated sequence. We therefore have:

$$tail\ CinemaQueue = \langle Huw,\ Mike \rangle$$

If the original sequence *CinemaQueue* is empty or contains just one element then *tail CinemaQueue* is also empty.

The last of a non-empty sequence such as *CinemaQueue* is written *last CinemaQueue* and is simply the last element of the sequence. In other words:

$$last\ CinemaQueue = CinemaQueue\ (\#CinemaQueue) = \langle Mike \rangle$$

Here the cardinality operator provides the index of the last member of the sequence and is conveniently used in the application. For sequences that are empty, *last* has no meaning (is not defined) and once again care is needed using this operator.

The front of a non-empty sequence such as *CinemaQueue* is written *front CinemaQueue* and is the sequence consisting of all elements of *CinemaQueue* except the last. We therefore have:

$$front\ CinemaQueue = \langle Deri,\ Huw \rangle$$

If the original sequence *CinemaQueue* is empty or contains just one element then *front CinemaQueue* is also empty.

As the final comment notice that these operators have a relationship such that:

$$front\ \langle Huw \rangle = \langle \rangle; \quad head\ \langle Huw \rangle = Huw \quad \text{hence} \quad front\ \langle Huw \rangle \neq head\ \langle Huw \rangle$$
$$tail\ \langle Huw \rangle = \langle \rangle; \quad last\ \langle Huw \rangle = Huw \quad \text{hence} \quad tail\ \langle Huw \rangle \neq last\ \langle Huw \rangle$$

A sequence containing a single member is therefore considered to possess a *first* and *last* item but an empty *front* sequence and an empty *tail* sequence. These properties clearly follow from the definition of concatenation earlier.

Before we examine the remaining sequence operators let us pause to define *head* and *tail* formally while their characteristics are still fresh in our minds. The generic definitions are:

$$\forall s : \text{seq}_1\ X \bullet heads\ s = s1$$
$$\forall s : \text{seq}\ X \bullet tail\ s = \lambda n : 1\, ..\, \#s - 1 \bullet s\,(n + 1)$$

Because the application of *head* to an empty sequence is not defined, the definition assumes that the sequence s is non-empty and reads quite simply as: 'for all (non-empty) sequences of elements of type X, the head of the sequence is the first item in the sequence and is obtained by the application of the sequence at position 1'.

The definition for *tail* is rather more involved for, just like concatenation, we have to indulge in some index adjustment. Given our previous definition of *CinemaQueue*, we can illustrate the problem as follows:

$$CinemaQueue == \{(1, Deri), (2, Huw), (3, Mike)\}$$

then:

$$tail\ CinemaQueue == \{(1, Huw), (2, Mike)\}$$

which clearly affects the index values of *Huw* and *Mike*. The general observation to be made, however, is that each index value in the *tail* sequence is decremented by 1. The definition of the operator therefore uses a lambda expression to describe the function that maps each of the natural numbers (n) in the subrange $1 .. \#s - 1$ to the application of the original sequence at $n + 1$. The lambda expression therefore effectively generates the sequence formed by the removal of the first item. In the specific case of *CinemaQueue*, we can trace its action as:

$$\#s = 3$$
$$1 .. \#s - 1 = \{1,2\}$$
$$\lambda n : 1 .. \#s - 1 \bullet s\,(n + 1) = \{(1,s2), (2,s3)\} = \{(1, Huw), (2, Mike)\}$$

The formal definition of the *tail* operator may therefore be read as: 'for all sequences of elements of type X, the tail of each sequence is that sequence formed by mapping each of the natural numbers (n) in the subrange $1 .. \#s - 1$ to the application of the original sequence at $n + 1$'. You should satisfy yourself that this definition works for non-empty sequences.

SAQ 10.5   What are the corresponding definitions for *front* and *last*?

As a final point of interest, notice that these definitions allow us to describe the following laws concerning all sequences:

$$head\,(\langle x \rangle\ ^\wedge\ s) = x \qquad \text{and} \qquad tail\,(\langle x \rangle\ ^\wedge\ s) = s$$

while for non-empty sequences we can declare:

$$s = \langle head\ s \rangle\ ^\wedge\ tail\ s$$

in other words, a non-empty sequence is made up from its head and its tail.

10.3.3 Reversal

The reversal operator (*rev*) simply reverses the order of the elements appearing in the sequence such that the first element becomes the last, the second the last but one, etc. For our sequence *CinemaQueue*:

$$rev\ CinemaQueue = rev\ \{(1, Deri), (2, Huw), (3, Mike)\}$$
$$= \{(1, Mike), (2, Huw), (3, Deri)\}$$

and clearly we have a further exercise in index adjustment. In the following generic definition we use the lambda expression to construct a function which when composed with the original sequence reverses the index values of the elements thereby retaining the sequence quality:

$$\forall s : \text{seq } X \bullet rev \ s = (\lambda n : 1 .. \#s \bullet \#s - n + 1); \ s$$

The definition technique is very similar to that used for concatenation and it is left as an exercise for the reader to work through the mechanics and to express the definition informally in English. Readers will also find a recursive specification for *rev* in Chapter 13.

10.3.4 Squash

Squashing is a useful operation that takes any function from $\mathbb{N}$ to X and converts it to a sequence s from $\mathbb{N}$ to X with domain $1 .. \#s$. The properties of *squash* are such that:

- *Squash*ing and empty function gives an empty sequence.
- *Squash*ing a sequence leaves it unchanged.
- *Squash*ing a function where the domain consists of a set of discontinuous natural numbers closes up the gaps between them and begins the indexing at 1.

These concepts are best examined using some examples:

$$squash \ \{\} = \langle \ \rangle$$
$$squash \ \langle r,p,q,p \rangle = \langle r,p,q,p \rangle$$
$$squash \ \{(5,p), (11,q), (15,p), (3,r)\} = \{(1,r), (2,p), (3,q), (4,p)\} = \langle r,p,q,p \rangle$$

Squash therefore retains the relative ordering implied by the index values in the function. An important case not covered in these examples is that of the function f with no 'holes' in its domain (e.g. $5 .. 8$) but which is not a sequence because $min(\text{dom}(f)) \neq 1$. In such cases *squash* behaves by merely shifting its indices to the new subrange $1 .. \#f$, for example if:

$$f = \{(5,p), (6,q), (7,p), (8,r)\}$$

then:

$$squash \ f = squash \ \{(5,p), (6,q), (7,p), (8,r)\}$$
$$= \{(1,r), (2,p), (3,q), (4,p)\}$$
$$= \langle r,p,q,p \rangle$$

This behaviour is formally expressed as:

$$\text{dom} f = (lo + 1) .. hi \Rightarrow squash \ f = (\lambda n : \mathbb{N} \bullet + lo); \ f$$

Clearly *squash* is an operator with much work to perform! The formal definition of the operator is best expressed using recursion and we therefore leave its definition until Chapter 13 where it forms one of a number of examples of the use of recursive techniques.

10.3.5 Restriction

Restriction, as the name implies, 'filters out' from a sequence only those items that interest us at the time and produces a new sequence from them. To illustrate the operation of restriction, consider a sequence s which models a queue of programs waiting to be served by the operating system of some machine. The current status of the queue may be represented by s as:

$$s == \{(1, Prog9), (2, Prog5), (3, Prog25), (4, Prog18), (5, Prog101), (6, Prog1)\}$$

The restriction of this sequence can proceed in two ways:

- By filtering out pairs with index values of interest
- By filtering out pairs with program names of interest

As an example of the first kind of restriction, if we were interested in knowing the first and last entries in the queue we need to restrict the sequence to those with index values 1 and $\#s$ respectively. Because s is a function as well as a sequence, we can use the domain restriction operator to filter the items of interest, thus:

$$\{1, \#s\} \lhd s = \{(1, Prog9), (6, Prog1)\}$$

This can be converted to a sequence by the use of *squash* such that:

$$squash\ (\{1, \#s\} \lhd s) = \{(1, Prog9), (2, Prog1)\}$$

The final result is therefore interpreted as a sequence that contains the names of the first and last programs in the queue.

As an example of the second kind of restriction, we may be interested in the relative positions that particular programs are occupying in the queue, e.g. *Prog25* and *Prog101*. Range restriction on s gives:

$$s \rhd \{Prog25, Prog101\} = \{(3, Prog25), (5, Prog101)\}$$

consequently:

$$squash\ (s \rhd \{Prog25, Prog101\}) = \{(1, Prog25), (2, Prog101)\}$$

The final sequence therefore provides information on the relative placing of these programs.

These two forms of restriction are *index restriction* and *sequence restriction*, respectively. Index restriction is simply a domain restriction followed by *squash*, while sequence restriction is a range restriction followed by *squash*. Assuming $s : \text{seq } X$, $A : \mathbb{PN}$ and $B : \mathbb{P}X$, these operations are written:

- Index restriction $A \upharpoonright s$ (sometimes called *extraction*)
- Sequence restrictions $s \upharpoonright s$ (sometimes called *filtering*)

A definition of the sequence restriction is given by:

$$\forall s : \text{seq } X;\ B : \mathbb{P}X \bullet s \upharpoonright B = squash\ (s \rhd B)$$

while the definition for index restriction follows directly and is left as an exercise for the reader. Chapter 12 illustrates the use of sequences in software engineering specifications.

10.4 SUMMARY

Sequences are mathematical objects where the notion of order among the collection of items is important. The operators that characterize sequences can bring about permanent changes in the condition of these structures. Therefore like sets, relations and functions, sequences can act as persistent objects whose condition at any time reflects a history of events carried out upon them. These properties make sequences a familiar component of formal specifications in typed set theory. Readers will also be aware that the sequence is the analogue of the list. Once again a number of laws apply to the sequence operators; these are gathered together in Spivey (1992).

11

BAGS

CHECKLIST OF OBJECTIVES

After reading this chapter you should be able to:

- Understand how bags model circumstances where the duplication of elements in a set is significant.
- Understand the bag typing mechanism.
- Understand and apply the standard bag operators.

11.1 INTRODUCTION

This short chapter introduces the concept of *bags*, sometimes called *families* or *multi-sets*. A bag of things is similar to a set but, unlike a set, the number of occurrences of each element in the set *is* significant. Bags are therefore useful structures to model events where duplication may occur.

The notation used to denote a bag encloses its elements in (outlined) square brackets, [[..]]. An empty bag is denoted by the symbolism [[ ]], while a bag formed from a set of *Names* might be:

$$[[Deri, Huw, Deri, Wyn, Huw, Marilyn, Mike]]$$

In this bag *Deri* and *Huw* occur twice, while *Wyn, Marilyn* and *Mike* occur just once each. A bag is like a set in that the order of enumeration of its elements is unimportant. The bag above is therefore equally well written as:

$$[[Deri, Deri, Huw, Huw, Wyn, Marilyn, Mike]]$$

or indeed any other combination. However the bag:

$$[[Deri, Huw, Wyn, Marilyn, Mike]]$$

is a different bag because although the individual elements are the same the number of occurrences of each differs. The following examples illustrate how sets, bags and sequences (of natural numbers, for example) are related:

- *Sets* $\{1,2,2,2\} = \{1,2,2\} = \{2,1,2\} = \{1,2\} = \{2,1\}$
- *Bags* $[[1,2,2,2,]] \neq [[1,2,2]] = [[2,1,2]] \neq [[2,1]] = [[1,2]]$
- *Sequences* $\langle 1,2,2,2 \rangle \neq \langle 1,2,2 \rangle \neq \langle 2,1,2 \rangle \neq \langle 1,2 \rangle \neq \langle 2,1 \rangle$

In set theory we can regard a bag as a mapping from the set containing elements of the bag (*e.g. Names* or numbers) to members of the set of strictly positive natural numbers ($\mathbb{N}_1$)—there is clearly no need for zero occurrences!—representing the number of occurrences of each element in the bag. Therefore, in the case of:

[[*Deri, Huw, Deri, Wyn, Huw, Marilyn, Mike*]]

we may write:

$$\{Deri \mapsto 2, Huw \mapsto 2, Wyn \mapsto 1, Marilyn \mapsto 1, Mike \mapsto 1\} \qquad \text{(maplet)}$$

or:

$$\{(Deri, 2), (Huw, 2), (Wyn, 1), (Marilyn, 1), (Mike, 1)\} \qquad \text{(tuple)}$$

All of this suggests that the bag can be modelled as a partial function from the type of the elements of the bag to $\mathbb{N}_1$. Therefore, in general, given some set X:

$$\text{bag } X == X \nrightarrow \mathbb{N}_1$$

11.2 OPERATORS THAT MANIPULATE BAGS

As with all the other mathematical structures that have been introduced, there are a number of useful operators that can be used with bags and in particular we have: *count, in, bag union* and *items.*

The function *count* tells us exactly how many times a particular item occurs in a bag. We can illustrate its action with the bag *Person*:

$$Person == [[Deri, Huw, Deri, Wyn, Huw, Marilyn, Mike]]$$

such that:

$$count\ Person\ Deri = 2$$
$$count\ Person\ Huw = 2$$
$$count\ Person\ Wyn = 1$$
$$count\ Person\ Marilyn = 1$$
$$count\ Person\ Mike = 1$$
$$count\ Person\ Dave = 0$$

where the final example shows that if x is not a member of the bag then *count bag* $x = 0$. The relation *in* is analogous to set membership ($\in$) and returns *true* if the element is a member of the bag and *false* otherwise. Thus:

$$Wyn\ in\ Person = true$$
$$\neg\ (Dave\ in\ Person) = true \qquad and$$
$$Dave\ in\ Person = false$$

Bag union represents the corresponding analogue of set union. (Some authors argue that this operation should really be called *bag_sum*. The reason for this becomes obvious by examining the definition of the operator.) It is symbolized as $\uplus$ and some examples of its effect are:

$\{(Deri, 2), (Huw, 2), (Wyn, 1), (Marilyn, 1), (Mike, 1)\} \uplus \{(Wyn, 2)\}$
$= \{(Deri, 2), (Huw, 2), (Wyn, 3), (Marilyn, 1), (Mike, 1)\}$
$= [\![Deri, Deri, Huw, Huw, Wyn, Wyn, Wyn, Marilyn, Mike]\!]$
$\{(Deri, 2), (Huw, 2), (Wyn, 1), (Marilyn, 1), (Mike, 1)\} \uplus \{(Deri, 3), (John, 2)\}$
$= \{(Deri, 5), (Huw, 2), (Wyn, 1), (Marilyn, 1), (Mike, 1), (John, 2)\}$
$= [\![Deri, Deri, Deri, Deri, Deri, Huw, Huw, Wyn, Marilyn, Mike, John, John]\!]$

The final function, *items*, returns the bag of elements of the sequence, for example:

$$items \langle Huw, Wyn, Marilyn, Wyn \rangle = \{(Huw, 1), (Wyn, 2), (Marilyn, 1)\}$$
$$= [\![Huw, Wyn, Wyn, Marilyn]\!]$$

Bags are interesting structures but they are used only infrequently in most specifications. Even so, each operator can be defined using typed set theory and for the sake of completion some definitions are included here. Thus:

$$x : X;\ b : \text{bag } X \mid \forall x : X;\ b : \text{bag } X \bullet x \text{ in } b \Leftrightarrow x \in \text{dom } b$$
$$b : \text{bag } X \mid \forall b : \text{bag } X \bullet count\ b = (\lambda x : X \bullet 0) \oplus b$$
$$\forall \omega : \text{seq } X;\ x : X \bullet count\ (items\ \omega)\ x = \#\{i : \text{dom } \omega \mid \omega i = x\}$$
$$\forall a,b : \text{bag } X;\ x : X \bullet count\ (\uplus (a,b))\ x = count\ ax + count\ bx$$

in is regarded as a relation over X and bag X (i.e., $in : X \leftrightarrow \text{bag } X$) and whether or not an element x is *in* a bag b is simply reflected by the appearance (or otherwise) of the pair (x,b) in the relation (i.e. x in b or $(x,b) \in in$).

count is regarded as a total bijection from the set of bags of some type X to the set of total functions from X to $\mathbb{N}$ (i.e. $count : \text{bag } X \rightarrowtail\!\!\!\rightarrow (X \rightarrow \mathbb{N})$). In other words, the application of *count* to a particular bag (e.g. *count Person*) returns a function.[1] It is the subsequent application of the function (e.g. *count Person Wyn*) that provides the multiplicity for the argument. However, the nature of the function returned by *count* needs some explanation. Using the earlier discussion, we know that the function represented by *count Person* should return zero when applied to an argument that is not a member of the bag (*count Person Dave* = 0). The definition shows that this function has values formed by overriding $\lambda x : X \bullet 0$ (i.e., $\{(x_1,0), (x_2,0)..(x_i,0)\}$) by the pairs that constitute the bag. This mechanism clearly leads to *count Person* returning a function such as:

$$\{(Dave, 0), (Phil, 0), \ldots, (Deri, 2), (Huw, 2), \ldots, (Mike, 1)\}$$

where those elements mapped to zero are members of X but not of the bag. Applications of this function with x therefore return the corresponding multiplicities.

The definition of *items* shows that it is a total function (i.e. *items* : seq $X \rightarrow$ bag X) that maps a sequence to a bag. The function is total because every sequence has a corresponding bag. The definition simply says that if ω is a sequence of X, then *items* ω must be the bag in which each element x appears exactly as often as x appears in ω.

$\uplus$ is regarded as a total function of the form $\{((a,b), c)..((p,q), r)\}$ mapping a pair of bags from the Cartesian product to a new bag. Each element in the new bag clearly has the sum of the multiplicities of the element in the old bags. It is therefore

---

[1]We use the term 'higher function' to describe functions where the type of the domain or the range is itself a function.

not difficult to see why some authors prefer the term *bag_sum* for this operator. The type of the operator is:

$$\uplus : (\text{bag } X \times \text{bag } X) \rightarrow \text{bag } X$$

11.3 SUMMARY

Bags are objects where the notion of duplication among the collection of items is important. The operators that characterize bags can bring about permanent changes in the condition of these structures. Therefore like sets, relations, functions and sequences, bags can act as persistent objects whose condition at any time reflects a history of events carried out on them. These properties make bags a useful component of formal specifications in typed set theory. They are, however, less familiar than some of the other objects we have studied. The operators described here represent the standard bag operators. Further operators are available, such as bag subtraction, bag negation, bag multiplication and multiplication of a bag by a constant. Definition of these and other operators are available in Hayes (1989). Some of these also appear in Spivey (1992) together with the laws concerning bags.

12

CASE STUDY: A SPECIFICATION USING SEQUENCES AND BAGS

12.1 INTRODUCTION

One of the most common exercises undertaken by computer systems is that of placing a group of elements in either ascending or descending order with respect to one another. Indeed, because of the frequent use of ordering (in commercial systems especially) intensive research over the years has led to a large number of sorting algorithms, each with their particular advantages and disadvantages. Designers therefore have a very wide choice when considering the most efficient method for a given environment.

From the perspective of the specification of such events, however, the individual characteristics of these algorithms are irrelevant. We simply view sorting as an operation that accepts a sequence of data items of some type as input (seq X) and provides a sequence of the same items as output. The output sequence, however, must have the assured quality of order and we can enforce this by describing the effect of the sorting process (in tuple notation) as:

$$Sort\_Ascending == \{in?, out! : \text{seq } X \mid \forall i, j : \text{dom } out! \bullet i < j \Rightarrow out!\, i \leq out!\, j\} \quad \text{or}$$
$$Sort\_Descending == \{in?, out! : \text{seq } X \mid \forall i, j : \text{dom } out! \bullet i < j \Rightarrow out!\, i \geq out!\, j\}$$

These predicates capture the essential nature of sorting, but in terms of a general definition of the process they have two serious weaknesses:

1. The predicates do not describe the relationship between the input and output sequences. Sorting is subject to conservation in that elements can be neither lost nor gained during the process, i.e. *out!* must contain the same items in the same frequency as *in?*
2. We have used relations such as $\leq$ and $\geq$, accepting that these exist when X is a set of numbers. We sometimes forget that sorting would be impossible without such relations, but if we are trying to provide a general specification of the sorting process, one that applies to a wide range of types, we cannot guarantee that a given type has numeric qualities. A notion of order among the elements of X must exist, otherwise the process of sorting is meaningless. Consequently, we have to show that we can define corresponding relations such as $\leq_X$ and $\geq_X$ on the elements of X.

12.2 CONSERVATION AND ORDER

The first of these problems can be specified quite easily by using appropriate bag notation, while to satisfy the second we need to examine more carefully the relationships that must exist among the elements of a set that permit ordering. Only when the requirements of (1) and (2) are added to the predicates do we have a truly general description of what the sorting process must achieve.

Let us deal first with the problem of conservation. The combined consideration of population and frequency equivalence can be specified by converting the sequences to bags (using *items*) and then comparing the two. The bags of course will only be equal if the original sequences have population/frequency equivalence so that the additional predicate to enforce this becomes:

$$items(in?) = items(out!)$$

The sort specifications (if X is a set of numbers) now read as:

$$Sort\_Ascending == \{in?, out!: \text{seq } X \,|\, \forall i, j: \text{dom } out! \bullet i < j \Rightarrow out!\,i \leq out!\,j \wedge$$
$$items(in?) = items(out!)\}$$

or:

$$Sort\_Descending == \{in?, out!: \text{seq } X \,|\, \forall i, j: \text{dom } out! \bullet i < j \Rightarrow out!\,i \geq out!\,j \wedge$$
$$items(in!) = items(out!)\}$$

The second problem of order must be dealt with by closely examining the relationships that could exist among the elements of the set. You will recall from earlier parts of the book that for a relation R on some set X (i.e. where $R: X \leftrightarrow X$) a number of useful and interesting properties were identified, namely that relations may be variously described as:

- Reflexive (r) if $\forall x \in X \bullet xRx$
- Symmetric (s) if $\forall x, y \in X \bullet xRy \Rightarrow yRx$
- Transitive (t) if $\forall x, y, z \in X \bullet xRy \wedge yRz \Rightarrow xRz$
- Antisymmetric (anti) if $\forall x, y \in X \bullet xRy \wedge yRx \Rightarrow x = y$

and any homogeneous relation over the elements of some arbitrary set X is capable of being classified in terms of one or more of these properties. Exactly how this observation is of use to us can be made more tangible by considering a small set of three integers, $X == \{1,3,2\}$, which we know can be sorted. The set of all possible relations that can exist between elements of this set is given by $\mathbb{P}(X \times X)$ and some familiar relations that are members of this set are shown together with their classification as (r), (s), (t) or (anti) (these relations and their characteristics appear in Chapter 8):

- *Equality*
$$=:X \leftrightarrow X == \{(1,1), (2,2), (3,3)\} \text{ (t,r,s)}$$
- *Greater_than*
$$>:X \leftrightarrow X == \{(2,1), (3,1), (3,2)\} \text{ (t)}$$
- *Less_than*
$$<:X \leftrightarrow X == \{(1,2), (1,3), (2,3)\} \text{ (t)}$$
- *Greater_than_or_equal_to*
$$\geq:X \leftrightarrow X == \{(1,1), (2,1), (2,2), (3,1), (3,2), (3,3)\}$$
$$\text{(t,r,anti)}$$

- *Less_than_or_equal_to*

$$\leq : X \leftrightarrow X == \{(1,1), (1,2), (1,3), (2,2), (2,3), (3,3)\}$$
$$(\texttt{t,r,anti})$$

- *Not_equal_to*

$$\neq : X \leftrightarrow X == \{(1,2), (1,3), (2,1), (2,3), (3,1), (3,2)\} \text{ (s)}$$

From the perspective of being able to sort these elements, the relations of interest are of course $\leq$ and $\geq$. The inference we are tempted to draw is that for some arbitrary type X, if we can define relations over the elements that are reflexive, transitive and antisymmetric then we have the equivalent properties of $\leq_X$ or $\geq_X$ and consequently an 'ordering' of the elements is feasible. A relation that is reflexive, transitive and antisymmetric is a *partial order*. The term 'partial' is critical and suggests (as it has throughout the book) that certain elements of X may not be related. Although this is not the case with our example of the relations $\leq$ and $\geq$ on the integers (i.e. $\forall x,y : X$ either $x \leq y$ or $y \leq x$), this is not necessarily true generally. An example where this can occur is the 'is a subset of' relation $\subseteq$ over a family of sets such as $P == \{\{ \}, \{a\}, \{b\}, \{a,b\}\}$. The *graph* of the relation $\subseteq : P \leftrightarrow P$ is as follows:

```
⊆        {}   {a}   {b}   {a,b}
{}        •    •     •      •
{a}            •            •
{b}                  •      •
{a,b}                       •
```

A graph is simply a more convenient form of the mapping diagrams we have used throughout the book and related elements are indicated by the presence of '•' at the row–column intersection. Thus: $\{\} \subseteq \{\}$, $\{\} \subseteq \{a\}, \ldots, \{\} \subseteq \{a,b\}$, $\{a\} \subseteq \{a\}$, $\{a\} \subseteq \{a,b\} \ldots$ all stand in the relation. We can see from the graph that the relation is reflexive (every position on the diagonal is occupied), antisymmetric (no two positions are occupied that are reflections of one another across the diagonal) and transitive by inspection of each case. Relation $\subseteq : P \leftrightarrow P$ is therefore a partial order and the fact that not every element is related to every other is evidenced by $\neg(\{a\} \subseteq \{b\})$ and $\neg(\{b\} \subseteq \{a\})$ with a corresponding 'hole' in the graph. Contrast this with the graph of the $\leq$ relation over the integers:

```
≤    1   2   3
1    •   •   •
2        •   •
3            •
```

Here every element of the set is related to every other in one direction or another. The identification of a set of partial orders over the elements of X therefore does not itself guarantee the ability to sort, for we cannot sort completely if some of the elements are not related to one another! In addition to those predicates that determine a set of partial orders, we require the additional constraint that every pair of elements of X are related. Therefore, assuming $R : X \leftrightarrow X$ we phrase this quite simply as:

$$\forall x, y : X \bullet xRy \lor yRx$$

This additional predicate converts a set of partial orders on X to a set of *total orders* and the formal definitions of these follow naturally from the discussion.

- The set of *partial_orders* on X

$$partial\_order\ X == \{R : X \leftrightarrow X \mid \forall x, y, z : X \bullet xRx \land$$
$$xRy \land yRz \Rightarrow x = y \land$$
$$xRy \land yRz \Rightarrow xRz\}$$

- The set of *total_orders* on X

$$total\_order\ X == \{R : partial\_order\ X \mid \forall x, y : X \bullet xRy \lor yRx\}$$

By including the requirement that a total order exists on the elements of X the specification of sorting may finally be expressed:

$$Sort\_Ascending == \{in?, out! : seq\ X \mid \forall i, j : \text{dom}\ out! \bullet i < j \Rightarrow out!\ i \leq_X out!\ j \land$$
$$items(in?) = items(out!)\}$$

or:

$$Sort\_Descending == \{in?, out! : seq\ X \mid \forall i, j : \text{dom}\ out! \bullet i < j \Rightarrow out!\ i \geq_X out!\ j \land$$
$$items(in?) = items(out!)\}$$

where $\leq_X \in total\_order\ X$ and $\geq_X \in total\_order\ X$.

13

RECURSIVE SPECIFICATION

CHECKLIST OF OBJECTIVES

After reading this chapter you should be able to:

- Understand the basic form of a recursive specification.
- Read and understand recursive specifications expressed in typed set theory.
- Appreciate the role of recursive specifications in a formal specification.

13.1 INTRODUCTION

This chapter assumes that the reader is somewhat familiar with the technique of recursion through its support by certain programming languages such as Pascal. Recursive programming techniques involve the notion of a procedure 'calling itself' and the appropriate use of recursion can lead to particularly pleasing and concise programming solutions. These advantages, however, are obtained at a price. First, a program written in recursive style may not be easy to understand and maintain. Often, the effect of a particular routine can be appreciated only by following the calls using simple examples, thereby 'unwinding' the recursion. Secondly, when a procedure calls itself, all its local variables must be saved so that their values can be reinstated on return. This clearly requires memory at execution time and this may be considerable if the procedure is large. Finally, it is important that the programmer provides a sound mechanism to terminate the recursive calls, otherwise the program will proceed to consume all available memory in the system, reducing the efficiency of other programs and ultimately causing runtime errors. Because of these difficulties, most programming language implementations limit the number of recursive calls that can be made by a program and there may be a practical limit on the use of the technique in certain cases. In spite of these difficulties, however, recursion is widely used and indeed represents the most natural solution to many programming problems.

The use of recursion in programming stems from its previous (and well known) use in mathematics. Although translation to the computer leads to certain difficulties, the use of recursion in a specification is an exercise in abstraction and is not necessarily bound by practical considerations. We are therefore biased towards the power and elegance of the technique rather than its failings. Even so, recursive specifications like programs still remain quite difficult to read and understand (especially when the technique is used inappropriately) and it is these features above all that should be conveyed most urgently by a specification. The tendency of recursion to commit some of the 'deadly sins' of specification, however, is often overlooked when we consider a further attribute it possesses—the ability to *reason* about its descriptions in a formal fashion. This, together with the compact nature of its descriptions, means that recursion is widely used in most specification languages.

This chapter introduces the technique with a simple classical[1] example. In the remainder of the book efforts are made to limit recursion to appropriate areas, but readers must always be aware that the use of recursion in specification does not mean the automatic use of recursion in the corresponding program implementation.

13.2 A CLASSICAL EXAMPLE OF RECURSION

Suppose we wished to describe a function whose purpose was to accept a natural number and determine the sum of its series, i.e. given n we wish to find $nat\_sum(n)$ where:

$$nat\_sum(n) = 1 + 2 + 3 + \ldots + n$$

This description of the function corresponds to an explicit definition, i.e. it provides a rule for the calculation of the result from the argument. An alternative approach to the description could be to enumerate the function as a set of pairs:

$$nat\_sum(n) == \{(1,1), (2,3), (3,6), (4,10), \ldots\}$$

Both of these descriptions represent entirely acceptable ways of describing the function, but are they widely applicable? Enumeration, of course, becomes totally unmanageable for functions with large domains and it fails to make clear the relationship between the elements in each pair. Similarly, for more complex functions, the 'rule' can become quite algorithmic and unwieldy. If we make the further observation that a function expressed in a cumbersome way leads to correspondingly tortuous logic when reasoning about its behaviour, then neither approach presents us with a platform that migrates easily to more complex structures. There is, however, another approach to the definition of a function and the evaluation of $nat\_sum(n)$ with some simple examples reveals an interesting pattern upon which our definition can be based:

$$nat\_sum(1) = 1$$
$$nat\_sum(2) = 1 + 2 = 3$$
$$nat\_sum(3) = 1 + 2 + 3 = 6$$
$$nat\_sum(4) = 1 + 2 + 3 + 4 = 10$$

Clearly each sum appears to be expressed in the form:

$$nat\_sum(n) = nat\_sum(n - 1) + n \tag{13.1}$$

[1]What I really mean by 'classical' is that every other author uses the same example to introduce the technique! I hope this can be sympathetically viewed as preserving a tradition rather than as laziness, as writing a book is difficult enough without being dogmatic in one's approach to originality.

such that:

$$nat\_sum(2) = nat\_sum(1) + 2$$
$$nat\_sum(3) = nat\_sum(2) + 3 \text{ and}$$
$$nat\_sum(4) = nat\_sum(3) + 4$$

Equation (13.1) therefore seems to act as an eminently suitable definition for the function and defines the outcome of an application of *nat_sum* in terms of itself! Unfortunately, there is one small problem with the definition that needs some attention. Application of the function to $n = 1$ is defined as:

$$nat\_sum(1) = 1$$

but strict evaluation of the definition provides:

$$nat\_sum(1) = nat\_sum(0) + 1$$

In an attempt to determine *nat_sum*(0) we might apply the function again:

$$nat\_sum(0) = nat\_sum(-1) + 0$$

Clearly this repeated application will continue ad infinitum and is leading nowhere for *nat_sum*(−1) is a nonsense. What we need is a *terminating condition* that can be used to prevent further applications by providing a value for *nat_sum*(0), and in order to correspond to:

$$nat\_sum(1) = nat\_sum(0) + 1 = 1$$

we must assume:

$$nat\_sum(0) = 0$$

We can summarize our arguments for this simple function formally as:

$$\forall n : \mathbb{N} \bullet nat\_sum(n) = nat\_sum(n - 1) + n \wedge nat\_sum(0) = 0$$

which represents a recursive specification i.e. it describes the outcome of the application of the function in terms of applications of itself. We also notice that the specification is particularly compact.

SAQ 13.1 An explicit definition for the factorial function *fact* can be written as:

$$fact(n) = n * (n - 1) * (n - 2) * (n - 3) * \ldots * 3 * 2 * 1$$

while evaluations of the function proceed:

$$fact(1) = 1$$
$$fact(2) = 2 * 1 = 2$$
$$fact(3) = 3 * 2 * 1 = 6$$
$$fact(4) = 4 * 3 * 2 * 1 = 24$$

From the patterns apparent in these evaluations write a recursive specification for *fact*.

13.3 GENERALIZING THE ROUTE TO RECURSION

The formal specifications for *nat_sum* and *fact* were deduced by spotting patterns in the sequence of results obtained by repeated applications of the function. In general this is a tedious route to follow to a recursive definition for a mathematical object of interest. However, we can distil the essence of the approach as one that asks two very simple questions of us:

1. How can the specification of this object be expressed in terms of the application of the object with a slightly smaller argument?
2. How can repeated applications to successively smaller arguments be terminated?

In order to demonstrate this more general route we tackle the specification of a function we have already defined, that of set *cardinality* (#) (see Chapter 8). The first question essentially requires us to express the relationship between the cardinality of a set and the cardinality of the same set from which an element has been removed. Clearly, the cardinality of the former is one greater than the latter (regardless of which element has been removed). Therefore, assuming we have some set S whose elements are of arbitrary type T we may write:

$$\forall S: \mathbb{F}T; \forall s \in S \bullet \#S = \#(S \backslash \{s\}) + 1$$

(Note: the type of a set is the power set of the type of its elements. However, for cardinality to have any meaning the set must be finite, hence the declaration $S: \mathbb{F}T$ in the specification.)

The second question requires a termination condition for the continual regression that can occur because of the previous definition. Repeated removal of an element will, of course, ultimately leave an empty set and so this question requires us to provide a meaning for the application: $\#\{\}$. The natural choice is to define the cardinality of an empty set as zero, hence the full recursive specification becomes

$$\forall S: \mathbb{F}T; \forall s \in S \bullet \#S = \#(S \backslash \{s\}) + 1 \wedge \#\{\} = 0$$

The interested reader may like to return to Chapter 8, where the cardinality operator was defined in terms of a total function, to compare the two approaches.

13.4 SOME RECURSIVE SPECIFICATIONS FROM TYPED SET THEORY

This section compares the use of recursion in the specification of two interesting operators from sequence theory—*rev* and *squash*.

The definitions based on typed set theory are as follows:

$$\forall s : \operatorname{seq} X \bullet rev\, s = \langle last\, s \rangle \,^\wedge rev\, front\, s \wedge rev\langle \rangle = \langle \rangle$$

$$squash\, \{\} = \langle \rangle \wedge \forall f: \mathbb{N} \nrightarrow X \bullet squash\, f$$
$$= \langle f\, min\, (\operatorname{dom} f) \rangle \,^\wedge squash\, (\{min(\operatorname{dom} f)\} \lhd f)$$

In the first definition, the reverse of a sequence is generated by concatenating the sequence formed from the last element with the reverse of the remaining sequence; repeated applications of *rev* being terminated by $rev \langle \rangle = \langle \rangle$. We can follow the evaluation of this function quite easily:

$$rev \langle 1, 2, 3 \rangle = \langle 3 \rangle {}^\wedge rev \langle 1, 2 \rangle \qquad (13.2)$$
$$rev \langle 1, 2 \rangle = \langle 2 \rangle {}^\wedge rev \langle 1 \rangle \qquad (13.3)$$
$$rev \langle 1 \rangle = \langle 1 \rangle {}^\wedge rev \langle \rangle = \langle 1 \rangle \qquad (13.4)$$

Termination occurs at (13.4) and substituting from (13.4) into (13.3) gives:

$$rev \langle 1, 2 \rangle = \langle 2 \rangle {}^\wedge \langle 1 \rangle = \langle 2, 1 \rangle$$

while further substitution of this result into (13.2) yields:

$$rev \langle 1, 2, 3 \rangle = \langle 3 \rangle {}^\wedge rev \langle 1, 2 \rangle = \langle 3 \rangle {}^\wedge \langle 2, 1 \rangle = \langle 3, 2, 1 \rangle$$

The definition for *squash* is rather more complex but reads: '*squash*ing an empty function produces an empty sequence, while for all finite partial functions *f* from natural numbers to some arbitrary type *X squash*ing *f* is achieved by concatenating the sequence formed by the application of *f* with the minimum value in the domain of *f* with the sequence obtained by *squash*ing *f* after the pair containing the minimum value has been excluded'.

SAQ 13.2   Clearly the definition is recursive because of the repeated use of *squash*. How is the process terminated?

The answer to SAQ 13.2, together with a small example, makes the definition clear. Consider applying *squash* to the function *f* which is a finite partial function from $\mathbb{N}$ to char. We enumerate *f* as:

$$f == \{(26,z), (3,c), (16,p)\}$$

Using the definition we may write:

$$squash \, f = \langle f \, min \, (dom \, f) \rangle {}^\wedge squash \, (\{min \, (dom \, f)\} \lhd f)$$

and evaluating *min* (dom *f*) as 3 gives:

$$squash \, f = \langle f \, 3 \rangle {}^\wedge squash \, \{(26, z), (16, p)\} = \langle c \rangle {}^\wedge squash \, \{(26, z), (16, p)\}$$

The remaining applications are presented without comment:

$$squash \, \{(26, z), (16, p)\} = \langle p \rangle {}^\wedge squash \, \{(26, z)\}$$
$$squash \, \{(26, z)\} = \langle z \rangle {}^\wedge squash \, \{ \}$$
$$squash \, \{ \} = \langle \rangle$$

Substitution in much the same manner as with *rev* therefore produces:

$$squash \, f = squash \, \{(26, z), (3, c), (16, p)\} = \langle c, p, z \rangle \quad or \quad \{(1, c), (2, p),(3, z)\}$$

SAQ 13.3   Use the notation of typed set theory to assign types to both *rev* and *squash*.

13.5 SUMMARY

Recursion is a very powerful technique that expresses functionality in a highly compact form. Recursion is not always easy to understand but it is used widely in formal specification because the economy of its expression is coupled with an ability to reason about its descriptions. Recursive specifications do not necessarily imply recursive implementations.

14

STRENGTHENING OUR SPECIFICATIONS

CHECKLIST OF OBJECTIVES

After reading this chapter you should be able to:

- Understand what is meant by the terms 'partial' and 'total' operation.
- Deduce the error conditions to which an operation is sensitive.
- Construct total operations from partial ones and appreciate the role of the invariant.

14.1 INTRODUCTION

This part of the book has used a number of case studies to illustrate the role of discrete mathematics in software engineering. Each study, however, has dealt with 'normal' operations only, i.e. they described the behaviour of their operations in circumstances where all their prerequisites have been satisfied. In real applications exceptions can occur, and some consideration of these must be made in the specification. Such consideration requires us to address not only what exceptional events can occur but also what should be done when they arise. In this respect the addition of some mechanism of *error reporting* is regarded as strengthening the specification by making it more realistic.

Exceptions occur when preconditions are offended. Preconditions describe the circumstance(s) under which an operator can be legally applied. It is possible (but unusual) to discover that an operation may never be applicable because its precondition always offends the state invariant. In such cases redesign is necessary. Tabulation of a precondition presents an obligation to prove the applicability of the operation, while simultaneously identifying the range of error conditions to which it is sensitive. The *Homework* and *Project–Programmer* case studies isolated certain preconditions.

Because preconditions describe the circumstances under which operations can be legally applied, *negation* of the preconditions reveals the range of cases which have to be treated as exceptions. Each of these has to be handled appropriately. Our case studies ignored the treatment of exceptional circumstances, and in this respect the operations we described were *partial operations* only. It is possible, however, to improve our earlier treatment by considering what must occur when an exception is raised. Such considerations convert partial operations into *total operations* and clearly improve the quality of a specification. This short chapter examines some of the ways in which typed set theory can be pushed a little further to strengthen its specifications.

14.2 A CASE STUDY REVISITED

Consider the case study involving the *Project–Programmer* scenario in Chapter 9, where the partial operations required by the system are listed. One of the simplest of these is the *Add_prog* operation which adds a new programmer to the organization. The specification is as follows:

> *Add_prog* ==
> {Δ*Project_Programmer*;
> *Progname?* : *Prog_Name*;
> *Prognum?* : *Prog_Num* |
> dom(*Programmer*) $\cap$ {*Prognum?*} = { } $\wedge$
> *Programmer'* = *Programmer* $\oplus$ {(*Prognum?*, *Progname?*)} $\wedge$
> *Project'* = *Project* $\wedge$
> *Assignment'* = *Assignment*}

The precondition for this operation is:

$$\text{dom}\,(Programmer) \cap \{Prognum?\} = \{\,\}$$

which expresses the requirement that the programmer should be a new programmer and therefore not already known to the system. The corresponding error condition is obtained by negation:

$$\neg\,(\text{dom}\,(Programmer) \cap \{Prognum?\} = \{\,\})$$

which if true indicates that the programmer is not a new programmer and is already known to the system. In order to describe the operation fully then, the specification must be able to cope with the possibility of normal *OR* exceptional behaviour occurring. Of course, if an operation behaves normally it cannot behave exceptionally and vice versa, while the specification of the operation should ideally report which event it has encountered. One way to achieve all this is shown in the following specification for the total operation *Total_Add_prog*:

> *Total_Add_prog* ==
> {Δ*Project_Programmer*;
> *Progname?* : *Prog_Name*;
> *Prognum?* : *Prog_Num*;
> *Report!* : *Message* |
> ((dom(*Programmer*) $\cap$ {*Prognum?*} = { } $\wedge$
> *Programmer'* = *Programmer* $\oplus$ {(*Prognum?*, *Progname?*)}$\wedge$
> *Project'* = *Project* $\wedge$
> *Assignment'* = *Assignment* $\wedge$
> *Report!* = *OK*) $\vee$
> ($\neg$ (dom(*Programmer*) $\cap$ {*Prognum?*} = { }) $\wedge$
> *Programmer'* = *Programmer* $\wedge$
> *Project'* = *Project* $\wedge$
> *Assignment'* = *Assignment* $\wedge$
> *Report!* = *Known Programmer*))}

Here we assume that a new set is available—a set of error messages such that:

$Message == \{OK, Known\ Programmer, Unknown\ Project, Already\ assigned, \ldots\}$

The additional declaration: *Report!* : *Message* introduces a variable whose condition is permitted to range over any of the *Message* values and is used by the specification to report which event has occurred. In this respect we take the view that if we are to report exceptions we should, for the sake of consistency, report success as well (*OK*).

In addition to the extra declaration we have also extended the predicate. The new predicate is written as a disjunction of two clauses of general form:

$((P1 \wedge Report! = OK) \vee (P2 \wedge Report! = Known\ Programmer))$

where *P1* and *P2* represent the predicates for normal and exceptional behaviour respectively. The two clauses are mutually exclusive for if:

$\text{dom}(Programmer) \cap \{Prognum?\} = \{\}$ *in P1 is true*

then:

$\neg (\text{dom}(Programmer) \cap \{Prognum?\} = \{\})$ in *P2* is *false*

Only one of the clauses can be *true* at any time, therefore the operation either adds a new programmer and reports *OK*, or it detects an attempt to add an existing programmer, preserves the status quo and reports a *Known Programmer*.

14.3 THE ROLE OF THE INVARIANT

So here we have a technique that we can use to specify total operations in typed set theory. Soon we shall extend the argument to provide more manageable descriptions of such operations and to deal with situations which have a number of pre-conditions. However, let us pause for some thought; surely, hidden away in the delta notation is another predicate—the system invariant—and this must be applied whichever way the operation executes. We can show that this is so if we expand the delta notation:

$\Delta Project\_Programmer == \{$
$Programmer, Programmer' : Prog\_Num \nrightarrow Prog\_Name;$
$Project, Project' : Proj\_Code \nrightarrow Proj\_Name;$
$Assignment, Assignment' : Prog\_Num \leftrightarrow Proj\_Code \mid$
$\text{dom}(Assignment) \subseteq \text{dom}(Programmer) \wedge$
$\text{ran}(Assignment) \subseteq \text{dom}(Project)\} \wedge$
$\text{dom}(Assignment') \subseteq \text{dom}(Programmer') \wedge$
$\text{ran}(Assignment') \subseteq \text{dom}(Project')\}$

and make the simplification:

$inv = \text{dom}(Assignment) \subseteq \text{dom}(Programmer) \wedge \text{ran}(Assignment) \subseteq \text{dom}(Project) \wedge$
$\text{dom}(Assignment') \subseteq \text{dom}(Programmer') \wedge \text{ran}(Assignment') \subseteq \text{dom}(Project')$

then the definition of *Total_add_ prog* could be written:

Total_add_prog == {
Programmer, Programmer' : *Prog_Num* ↠ *Prog_Name*;
Project, Project' : *Proj_Code* ↣ *Proj_Name*;
Assignment, Assignment' : *Prog_Num* ↔ *Proj_Code*
Progname? : *Prog_Name*;
Prognum? : *Prog_Num*;
Report! : *Message* |
inv ∧ ((*P1* ∧ *Report!* = *OK*) ∨ (*P2* ∧ *Report!* = *Known Programmer*))}

where the predicate *inv* is conjoined with the existing predicate because that is what happens when we include the shorthand notation Δ*Project_Programmer* within a tuple definition. We can see that the predicate for the total operation is written in the form:

$$a \wedge (b \vee c)$$

We know from earlier work on propositional calculus that:

$$a \wedge (b \vee c) = (a \wedge b) \vee (a \wedge c) \qquad (Dist \wedge \vee)$$

Consequently, we can write:

$$(inv \wedge (P1 \wedge Report! = OK)) \vee (inv \wedge (P2 \wedge Report! = Known\ Programmer))$$

showing that whichever way the operation performs, the invariant is properly applied.

14.4 SIMPLIFYING THE DESCRIPTION OF A TOTAL OPERATION

Looking at the final predicate we are surely struck by the fact that it is composed of two self-contained parts:

$$(inv \wedge (P1 \wedge Report! = OK))$$

describes normal behaviour while:

$$(inv \wedge (P2 \wedge Report! = Known\ Programmer))$$

describes exceptional behaviour. These could act as predicates for two quite separate and independent operations such as *Add_prog_OK* and *Add_prog_error*. The specifications for these follow quite naturally if we assume that in the case of *Add_prog_error* the state of the system is protected, in that no change of state is allowed to occur:

Add_prog_OK ==
{Δ*Project_Programmer*;
Progname? : *Prog_Name*;
Prognum? : *Prog_Num*;
Report! : *Message* |
dom(*Programmer*) ∩ {*Prognum?*} = { } ∧
Programmer' = *Programmer* ⊕ {(*Prognum?*, *Progname?*)} ∧
Project' = *Project* ∧
Assignment' = *Assignment* ∧
Report! = *OK*}

and

$$
\begin{aligned}
&Add\_prog\_error == \\
&\{\Delta Project\_Programmer; \\
&Progname? : Prog\_Name; \\
&Prognum? : Prog\_Num ; \\
&Report! : Message \mid \\
&\neg (\mathrm{dom}(Programmer) \cap \{Prognum?\} = \{\}) \wedge \\
&Programmer' = Programmer \wedge \\
&Project' = Project \wedge \\
&Assignment' = Assignment \wedge \\
&Report! = Known\ Programmer\}
\end{aligned}
$$

SAQ 14.1   Could you write the *Add_ prog_error* operation in a more convenient style?

How can this observation be used to describe the total operation? Notice that both *Add_ prog_OK* and *Add_ prog_error* have precisely the same tuple type so that a total operation could be constructed by combining the results of the two through set union.

$$Total\_Add\_prog == Add\_prog\_OK \cup Add\_prog\_error$$

Although the tuples have the same type, the predicates of the tuple definitions are, of course, mutually exclusive because of the precondition parts. Only one of them could be true at any time; the other must describe the empty set { }. The total operation is therefore seen in terms of a union between an empty set and a tuple representing normal *OR* exceptional behaviour.

This method of describing a total operation is exactly equivalent to our previous approach but it is less complex because it deals with normal and exceptional behaviour separately. This is very much a 'divide and conquer' approach which leads to more manageable and readable descriptions and is particularly useful when there is more than one precondition—a case we deal with next. A further point to bear in mind is that the invariant is now clearly distributed between the normal and exceptional descriptions, making it rather more obvious that it applies in both circumstances.

14.5 THE CASE FOR MULTIPLE PRECONDITIONS

In the case of the following *Add_ prog_proj* operation:

$$
\begin{aligned}
&Add\_prog\_proj == \\
&\{\Delta Project\_Programmer; \\
&Prognum? : Prog\_Num; \\
&Projcode? : Proj\_Code \mid \\
&Prognum? \in \mathrm{dom}(Programmer) \wedge \\
&Projcode? \in \mathrm{dom}(Project) \wedge \\
&\neg ((Prognum?, Projcode?) \in Assignment) \wedge \\
&Assignment' = Assignment \cup \{(Prognum?, Projcode?)\} \wedge \\
&Programmer' = Programmer \wedge \\
&Project' = Project\}
\end{aligned}
$$

the precondition consists of three clauses which, when negated, give rise to three possible error conditions:

- Error 1 ¬(*Prognum?* ∈ dom(*Programmer*))   An unknown programmer
- Error 2 ¬(*Projcode?* ∈ dom(*Project*))   An unknown project
- Error 3   ((*Prognum?*, *Projcode?*) ∈ *Assignment*)   Programmer is already assigned

with corresponding operations: *Add_prog_proj_err1*, *Add_prog_proj_err2* and *Add_prog_proj_err3*.

SAQ 14.2 Write the definition of each the operations *Add_prog_proj_err1*, *Add_prog_proj_err2* and *Add_prog_proj_err3*. Assume each preserves the state of the system but reports a suitable error message taken from *Message*

The total operation can therefore be defined as:

$$Total\_Add\_prog\_proj == Add\_prog\_proj\_OK \cup Add\_prog\_proj\_err1 \cup$$
$$Add\_prog\_proj\_err2 \cup Add\_prog\_proj\_err3$$

The justification for this argument follows logically from the description of *Total_Add_prog* for if any (or all) of the error conditions occur then the *OK* operation will return { }, while if the *OK* operation is satisfied the error operations are not, for the latter have preconditions formed by negation of those of the former.

Notice also that in this description it is possible to get any one, any two or all three error messages. In typed set theory the term 'non deterministic' is used when more than one tuple is possible as the result of an operation. As a final point, note that in each case, while the specification reports an error it offers no bias as to how an implementation should handle it. This is an important point when other specification techniques are discussed later in the book.

14.6 SUMMARY

This short chapter has shown that it is possible to strengthen specifications in typed set theory by including error reports which make them more realistic. Typed set theory permits normal and exceptional behaviour to be separated and treated individually, thereby simplifying the description. There are, however, certain disadvantages to the approach which the chapter ignores, largely associated with the description of total operations in terms of the union of tuples. Although this technique permits the definition of complex operations through the combination of simpler ones, the union operator demands a strict type compatibility across the various tuples. Sometimes this is not convenient and later chapters show how certain specification languages get around this point and present a more flexible approach than simple typed set theory.

PART FOUR

The Specification Language Z

He that will not apply new remedies must expect new evils;
for time is the greatest innovator.

Francis Bacon (1561–1626), English philosopher

INTRODUCTION

The collection of mathematical concepts and notational conventions known as Z were first proposed around 1981 as a result of work carried out by the Programming Research Group (PRG) at Oxford University. The PRG was formed with the twin objectives of establishing a mathematical basis for programming concepts and subsequently verifying the work by undertaking collaborative projects with industry. Among early Z users therefore, some were drawn from academia with interests in the mathematical basis of software, while others came from industry and were concerned with the production of high-quality, reliable software systems. Z brought these two groups together through pilot projects and case studies. In this respect the work of the PRG establishes itself as both relevant to contemporary software engineering environments and flexible enough to find practical solutions to a wide variety of real problems.

A specification written in Z is a mixture of formal mathematical statements and informal explanatory text. Both aspects are important. The formal component provides a precise description of the intended behaviour of the system and is based on set theory—a subject taught for many years in our schools and familiar to almost everyone with some scientific training. Formal components are, of course, part of many specification languages, but a distinguishing feature of Z is that it adds the notion that objects in its universe can be separated into distinct groups with no overlap among the groups. In this respect a Z specification is expressed through a typed set theory and we shall soon see that certain benefits accrue by its use. The second important distinguishing feature of the formal component of Z is the use of a device known as a *schema*. This acts as a basic organising mechanism for the specification allowing us to group together objects into named units which can be referenced throughout the document.

The informal component makes a Z document more approachable and understandable. It is, of course, unreasonable to expect formal specifications to be read by customers; the informal text therefore provides the comprehension they require while the construction of this text is always made much easier by the existence of the (precise) specification. The text is often equally useful to those well versed in specification techniques. Reading a specification for the first time does not always result in our understanding it. We may well parse what we read but find it difficult to deduce its meaning. The accompanying text therefore supports our understanding of the semantics. It is for this reason that most of the formal phrases in this book have been accompanied by explanatory text. We shall see later, however, that the explanatory text is the main structural component of the Z document.

There have been three major events marking what could be called the consolidation of Z. First, in 1985 the Z User Workshop series began. Secondly, in 1987 a collection of Z case studies covering software engineering, distributed computing and transaction processing appeared edited by Ian Hayes (1987). The third event occurred in 1989 with the publication of the Z reference manual by Mike Spivey (1989, 1992). These books established a precise description of the notation together with tutorials and examples of its use, while the workshops brought together those using Z in research, development and education.

The use of Z in both academia and industry now has quite a long history and this raises an important issue for those thinking of adopting a formal notation in their software development—the issue of standardization. The appearance of Spivey's book has accelerated developments to the stage where standards are now being put in place. Consequently, we can expect the continuing development of software support tools that create, verify and manipulate Z specifications, indeed catalogues of such products are already available. This part of the book introduces the basic elements, notation and structure of a Z specification, ultimately demonstrating their use through a series of illustrative case studies. These can be usefully compared later to the alternative approach of VDM.

15

ESSENTIAL Z

CHECKLIST OF OBJECTIVES

After reading this chapter you should be able to:

- Understand the structure of a typical Z document.
- Identify the various paragraphs that constitute the document.
- Appreciate the role of the Z typing system and the various type constructors.
- Understand the need for the Z basic system library.
- Understand the terminology used for each of the Z definitions.

15.1 INTRODUCTION

Probably one of the most common reactions that students display when confronted with their first formal specification in Z is that of sheer disbelief. How can anyone make sense of *that*! This was certainly so for me and for many of my colleagues, and a sharp intake of breath or shuffling of feet can often be heard in my lectures as I try to convince students that after a few weeks of patient work, the complex description on the screen before them will make sense! In this respect there are three aspects of a formal specification that need explanation before readers feel comfortable. The first of these is the mathematics, the second is the notation and syntax of the method under study, and the third is the structure of the formal specification document itself.

Part 3 of this book introduced, justified and developed the mathematics in (I hope) a fashion suited to the software engineer, with an emphasis on descriptive aspects rather than formal proofs. The point has already been made that some investment in this area is essential for anyone wishing to have an understanding of formal methods. This chapter examines the fundamental notational conventions of a particular method, namely Z, but we begin by understanding not the detail of the method, but its overall philosophy, conveyed to us by the structure of the specification document itself. The justification for this rests largely on the benefits that a typical top-down approach offers over that of bottom-up. The notational conventions exist at the 'dirty' end of Z. Overemphasis on these can lead to a lack of appreciation of their *raison d'être*, whereas, by understanding what Z is trying to say to us first, the need for and the form of many of its conventions become clearer. In this respect the specification structure is seen as a 'glue' that binds the various components of the document together, while the structure also acts as a factor common to a wide range of specifications of quite different types.

This approach inverts that taken by other authors where the document is treated largely as a postscript. We must remember, however, that the specification document drives the whole subsequent software engineering process, and an understanding at least of its structure permits meaningful questions to be asked by those who may not be expected to understand the full detail of its paragraphs. A further point to bear in mind is that the specification document is the first thing the customer sees in the engineering process. By presenting you with the document structure prior to its detail you are placed in a similar position to the customer.

15.2 THE STRUCTURE OF A Z DOCUMENT

The structure of a Z document has yet to be formally standardized[1] but it has already been suggested in the introduction to Part 4 that it should consist of a mixture of two components: formal Z phrases and informal (explanatory) text. The relationship between these is such that Z takes a subordinate role embedded within the natural language rather than the other way around—a point often overlooked by beginners who tend to concentrate on the Z rather than on its explanation. In this fashion the document presents a more friendly face than might otherwise be the case.

In the absence of a standard there have been suggestions—principally from IBM, Hursley Park (Wordsworth 1987) and the PRG at Oxford—which seem to present a reasonably stable structure for the foreseeable future at least. The format offered here follows directly from the suggestions of these workers and to some extent was used to develop the ideas in some of the case studies used in Part 3 (although the expression of Z concepts was limited in these examples).

There are, of course, considerable advantages to be gained from the adoption of consistency of style among the Z user community which parallels the advantages obtained by the use of a standard methodology in contemporary software engineering; both specifier and customer develop certain expectations about the structure of the document which in turn aids comprehension and communication. The proposed structure of a Z document contains the following sections taken in strict order:

1. Introduction—a comprehensive informal statement of the purpose and intention(s) of the system being specified.
2. An introduction to the sorts of data that interest us and the global variables used throughout the specification.
3. Present any general theories that might be applicable and assumed throughout the specification.
4. Introduce and describe the abstract state(s) of the system.

---

[1]Spivey (1992) is currently taken as the standard formal definition of Z. However, it does not address the problem of the structure of the specification document. At the time of writing, work is proceeding on a Z base standard which is (eventually) expected to provide such detail.

5. Describe suitable initializations for the system.
6. Define the behaviour of the operations of the system under 'normal' conditions.
7. Derive the preconditions for each of the operations that has been described.
8. Using (7), detail the error conditions that can occur for each of the operations identified in Point 6.
9. Provide a summary and index for the specification.

There is, of course, no requirement on the Z user community to develop the constituent parts of the specification in this order. Development may well be dictated by the nature of some tool that the specifiers are using while certain aspects may proceed in parallel or in background.

Throughout the document, explanatory text is used to augment the formal phrases: setting scenes, explaining objectives and summarizing what has been achieved so far. A further useful restriction on the structure is that within each section objects are declared before they are used or referenced. This clearly follows a pattern that software engineers are used to in programming environments, but it also permits the extraction of the purely formal content of the document in such a fashion that preserves the requirement of the formal notation. We are now in a position to expand somewhat on the content of each section assuming of course that Section 1 is fully understood. It would also seem sensible to relate the requirements of each section to work we have already done in specifying certain case studies using typed set theory, such as the *Programmer-Project* example (Chapter 14). The formal Z notation required for each section is developed in subsequent chapters.

2. An introduction to the sorts of data that interest us and the global variables used throughout the specification.

The given sets represent the sorts of data that characterize the software engineering problem that we are specifying. An important property of these sets is that at the level of abstraction represented by the specification, we need know nothing of their internal structure. Such detail represents an unnecessary complication and is best addressed later. However, the accompanying text will provide us with a general understanding of their qualities. In the case studies we examined in Part 3 given sets were introduced as 'the sorts of data that interest us'. Examples are:

- *STUDENT*   The set of all possible students
- *PROG_NUM*   The set of all possible programmer numbers
- *PROJ_CODE*   The set of all possible codes for projects.

Given sets are introduced early in a Z document because they are used throughout the specification both in their simple form and in the construction of more complex types such as functions and relations.

Like given sets, the global variables and constants permeate the whole specification and represent generally available useful definitions or constraints that may be required throughout the document. None of the case studies in Part 3 employed such constraints but examples might be *Classmax* or *Maxproj*, representing the maximum class size for the *Homework* problem and the maximum number of projects permitted for a programmer in the *Project-Programmer* example.

3. Present any general theories that might be applicable and assumed throughout the specification

In the case study used in Chapter 11 the behaviour of a *Sort* operation was described. A fundamental requirement of the operation was that a total order was capable of being defined over the elements to be sorted and the properties of this requirement were explained prior to presenting the specification of the operator itself. In Z, it often happens that some body of theory needs to be explained before the specification can be properly understood. The early part of the document is a natural place to present such considerations, while the separation of generalities from the detail of specific operations makes the document more readable.

4. Introduce and describe the abstract state(s) of the system

The abstract state is composed of mathematical objects used to model the natural relationships that occur between the data in the real-world application we are specifying. Relations, sequences, partial injections, etc. were used to represent the various associations between the given sets in the case studies in Part 3. The choice of an object is made with respect to the perceived properties of the real-world relationship. This part of a Z document should expand and justify why that choice has been made and introduce the state invariant which represents the relationship between state objects that all operations must maintain.

5. Describe suitable initializations for the system

Initial states for the system have to conform to the requirements of the state invariant(s), while an initial state has to be defined before operations upon the state can proceed. This part of a Z document clearly generates proof obligations in much the same manner that we had in the *Programmer-Project* case study. The obligations must be satisfactorily discharged by formal and/or informal reasoning.

6. Define the behaviour of the operations of the system under 'normal' conditions

The case studies of Part 3 dealt only with 'normal' operations, i.e. they described the outcome of operations in circumstances where all their prerequisites had been satisfied. In real applications, exceptions can occur. The philosophy of a Z document is such that the description of normal behaviour is separated from—and appears before—the description of exceptional behaviour.

7. Derive the preconditions for each of the operations that has been described

Exceptions occur when preconditions are offended. This part of the document determines and tabulates the precondition(s) for each of the operations in (6). Preconditions describe the circumstances under which the operator can be legally applied. It is possible (but unusual) to discover that an operation may never be applicable because its precondition always offends the state invariant. In such cases redesign is necessary. Tabulation of a precondition presents an obligation to prove the applicability of the operation while simultaneously identifying the range of error conditions to which it is sensitive. The case studies in Part 3 isolated certain pre-conditions.

8. Using 7, detail the error conditions that can occur for each of the operations identified in part 6

Because preconditions describe the circumstance under which operations can be legally applied, negation of the preconditions reveals the range of cases which have to be treated as exceptions. Each of these has to be handled appropriately. In our case studies we ignored the possibility of exceptional circumstances and in this respect the operations so described are partial operations only. In this part of a Z specification, the approach is strengthened by considering what must occur when an exception is raised. Such considerations convert partial operations into total operations.

9. Provide a summary and index for the specification

Whenever a real-world application reaches the non-trivial stage, it is almost certain that the specification becomes correspondingly large. It is important that readers find their way around the document comfortably. Summaries and an index should therefore accompany the document in much the same way as they do in normal textbooks.

15.3 WHY TYPES ARE USED IN Z

The mathematics introduced in Part 3 was based on a theory in which items (e.g. cars, students) were grouped into collections or sets of the same type and where sets of different types had no common members. Although it is possible for an element to be a member of many different sets, it belongs to just one type. Types are therefore special kinds of sets. They are often referred to as 'maximal sets' since they correspond to the largest possible set to which an element can belong.

A Z specification is a mathematical model of an information system based on such a typed set theory and every expression which appears in Z is given a type which in turn identifies a maximal set known to contain the value of the expression. Expressions in Z therefore yield values belonging to specific sets and, because sets of different types cannot have common members, a discipline is imposed when writing Z specifications that demands phrases to involve corresponding types. Therefore, the expression:

$$\{a,b,c\} = \{(0,1), (0,2), (0,3)\}$$

is meaningless in Z because the left-hand side is a set of characters while the right-hand side is a set of pairs, i.e. a relation.

This type correspondence extends throughout a Z document without exception. For those creating Z specifications their phrases must always be written in terms of this discipline—a failure to do so (typographic errors excepted) often indicates a lack of understanding. There is, of course, no guarantee that a specification free from type errors can be implemented or indeed represents what the customer wants, but the discipline that the typing system confers generally leads to a more robust specification than would otherwise be the case.

There is, however, a more theoretical reason for introducing a type system, which stems from a curious, yet famous, logical argument concerning sets—the very objects that form the backbone of Z. *Russell's paradox* arises from a consideration of the set S (say) which is the set of all sets which are not members of themselves (notice that we place no type restriction on the sets that are members of this set). This set can be expressed through comprehension as:

$$S == \{x \mid \neg (x \in x)\}$$

The question that arises concerning this expression is as follows: 'is S a member of S?' Our logic proceeds as follows:

1. Assume first that S *is* a member of S, i.e. $S \in S$.
2. The definition for S, however, shows that for any x, if $x \in S$ then $\neg (x \in x)$.
3. But we have just assumed that S belongs to S and so we deduce $\neg (S \in S)$.

The result of this argument is that if we assume S is a member of S we can show that S is not a member of S! This is clearly a nonsense but it cannot be dismissed as a pure trickery of logic (as was Russell's after-dinner proof that he was the Pope (see Sec. 4.4)), neither can we get out of it by repeating the argument, assuming our original assumption was wrong, i.e. $\neg (S \in S)$. If such logic were permitted then almost anything becomes provable.

In a strongly typed system such as Z, we avoid problems like this because a set such as S cannot be defined. $\{x \mid \neg (x \in x)\}$ is not a valid Z expression; x has not been given an explicit type. If we try to provide a type, say T, we generate further difficulties. In Z, the symbol $\in$ can be used only between an *element* of T on the left and a *set of elements* of T on the right. The expression clearly refers to $x \in x$ which has the same type (that of x) on both sides so that a type-checker for Z would immediately reject the statement. Discipline, detection of a certain degree of misunderstanding and the avoidance of paradoxes are the principal reasons for Z's adopting its typed system.

15.4 BUILDING A Z DOCUMENT—Z PARAGRAPHS

A Z document consists of sections of formal text separated by informal explanatory prose. The formal mathematical text consists of a sequence of *paragraphs* (sometimes called *phrases*) and a complete Z specification is built up by successively introducing new paragraphs, some of which rely upon others that have gone before. This incremental evolution of the specification therefore involves a notion of *definition before use* and the formal vocabulary of the specification can be regarded as consisting of paragraphs that introduce *definitions* or *theorems*.

Definitions in Z are used to introduce types together with variables and constraints on their use. The nature of each definition dictates the global or local *scope* of any variables involved, while the definitions themselves can be categorized as: *basic type* (*given sets*), *simple data type*, *axiomatic*, *abbreviation* and *schema*. The first two introduce the fundamental types needed throughout the specification, while the remainder act as the building blocks that ultimately describe the functionality of the information system we are modelling.

Theorems, on the other hand, are introduced into Z specifications specifically to show that initial states are legal, that preconditions exist or to show that the specification enjoys certain properties. In most cases the statement of a theorem takes the form:

$$premise1 \mid premise2 \mid premise3 \mid \ldots \; premise \; n \; \vdash \; conclusion$$

where the turnstile symbol ($\vdash$) separates a series of premises from some conclusion. The premises are assumed to be true and used to establish the truth (or otherwise) of the conclusion, which usually represents some property of the specification. Some theorems have no premises.

This chapter discusses the ways in which definitions can be used to introduce various types into a Z document; the ways in which new types can be constructed from the basic types; the variable declaration mechanism that assigns types to variables, and the role of the remaining definitions in building a Z specification. Theorems are introduced in the case studies after Chapter 16.

15.4.1 Basic types in Z

We have already noted that every Z specification introduces a number of basic types or given sets which are known throughout the document. In Z, objects such as sets can be named[2] and these names are *identifiers*. The given sets are introduced using a paragraph with a special notation that encloses their names in square brackets [ ]. In general, the paragraph takes the following form:

$$[Ident1, \ldots, IdentN]$$

and the following specific example:

$$[STUDENT, PERSON, BOOK]$$

makes the types *STUDENT*, *PERSON* and *BOOK* globally available. Such paragraphs consequently appear early in the formal text. The given sets are usually those that characterize the software engineering problem we are specifying and are often elicited by discussion with the customer. These sets may have a quite complex internal structure but at this stage we are not really interested in such detail. All that concerns the specifier is that when such types are introduced they can be relied upon to bear the restriction that different types have no common members and that individual members are unique.

15.4.2 Simple data types

A further definition available to the Z specifier is that of the simple data type which is used to construct and define types, which, unlike the given types, contain well-known and relatively few named elements. Typically, such types are used to define sets of error messages that might have to be reported by the systems operations, for example:

Message ::= OK | Unknown Programmer | Unknown Project | Already Assigned

[2]A Z identifier consists of a base name preceded by an optional prefix and followed by an optional decoration. Later sections will introduce prefixes and decorations.

This paragraph uses the symbol ::= to define a type *Message* which is a set containing the members *OK*, *Unknown Programmer*, *Unknown Project* and *Already Assigned*. Members of the set are separated by the 'branch separator' (|) which should not be confused with the 'such that' bar (|) of set comprehension. The notation also conveys the idea that members are mutually distinct and that they are the only elements in the type.

The definition becomes a given set and hence a basic type for the specification document. All the set operators apply to *Message* and, because *Message* is a type, the power set and Cartesian product constructors can be used to create more complex types. Having now examined two definitions that introduce types, we examine constructor mechanisms next.

15.5 COMPOUND TYPES AND COMPOUND TYPE CONSTRUCTORS

The given sets are to some extent symptomatic of the particular problem being specified, but these objects alone are often too simple to capture fully the properties of the system we are modelling. Most specifications will use their given sets to generate more complex objects such as relations, functions, sequences or bags and for each type we construct there will be a corresponding collection of operators that characterize the object. For example, the given sets of one of our earlier specifications were *PROG_NUM* and *PROG_NAME*, and with these elementary objects we were able to define the set of partial functions; a compound structure representing the many-to-one relationship between programmer numbers and programmer names. Compound objects can of course be built in various ways and the *type constructors* of Z are used to form new types from old ones.

There are three kinds of compound type in Z: set types, tuple types and schema types. Schema types will not form a large part of the discussion in this book, but some reference to them will be made later when the notion of a schema is introduced (Chapter 16) Set types are constructed using the type constructor power set ($\mathbb{P}$), while tuples are built using the type constructor Cartesian product ($\times$). By repeatedly applying either the individual constructors or combinations of the constructors to the basic types in the specification, other types can be created.

15.5.1 Power sets

The most common use for the power set constructor is to provide a type for a variable whose value is intended to be a set. This has already been illustrated in the case studies where the variable *Class* in the *Homework* problem or *Projs!* in the *Project-Programmer* example were sets of *STUDENT* and *PROJ_NAME* respectively. Therefore in Z terminology, assuming given sets, [*STUDENT, PROJ_NAME*], $\mathbb{P}$*STUDENT* and $\mathbb{P}$*PROJ_NAME* introduce new types from old ones. Notice, however, that although power set can be applied to any set to produce another set, *only when it is applied to a type will another type result* and this follows largely from our earlier definition of a type as a maximal set.

Using the basic types of the specification a new range of types becomes available by judicious use of the power set operator. Thus if *S* and *R* are basic types: $\mathbb{P}S$ and $\mathbb{P}R$ are types; $\mathbb{PP}S$ and $\mathbb{PP}R$ are types; $\mathbb{PPP}S$ and $\mathbb{PPP}R$ are types; with of course increasingly complex structure and size for individual elements. As an example of this progression, consider what happens with repeated applications of $\mathbb{P}$ to the set S where:

$$S == \{a\}$$
$$\mathbb{P}S == \{\emptyset, \{a\}\}$$
$$\mathbb{PP}S == \{\emptyset, \{\emptyset\}, \{\{a\}\}\}$$
$$\mathbb{PPP}S == \{\emptyset, \{\emptyset\}, \{\{\emptyset\}\}, \{\{\{a\}\}\}, \{\{\emptyset,\{a\}\}\}, \{\emptyset,\{\emptyset\}\}, \ldots\}$$

Notice also here the different meanings carried by the symbol $\emptyset$ in each set. In all cases $\emptyset$ is different from $\{\emptyset\}$; the former refers to an empty set while the latter corresponds to a set containing an empty set, while in $\{\emptyset, \{\emptyset\}, \{\{a\}\}, \{\emptyset, \{a\}\}\}$ the first occurrence of $\emptyset$ refers to the empty set of type $\mathbb{PP}S$ while the second refers to an empty set of type $\mathbb{P}S$. Thus, as the repeated application of the power set operator creates different types it also generates empty sets of different types. This must be so for there cannot be a single empty set that belongs to all types. That offends the basic type mechanism of Z which does not permit an element—any element—to belong to sets of different types.

This interesting argument is just one of the many important consequences of the Z typing system. Another, of course, is that with the power set operator we can decide whether or not Z expressions involving sets make sense. With this new role for the power set, readers may like to read again Chapter 6 where the sections on the type of a set and the null set may now be a little more meaningful.

15.5.2 Cartesian product

The Cartesian product and extended Cartesian product were introduced in Part 3 primarily as a mechanism to construct tuples which represent combinations of elements of different sets. However in Z, when we take products of sets that are types we produce new types—tuple or product types. Once again the type mechanism of Z allows us to determine whether or not the expression involving products is sensible, while a combination of power set and product permits new complex types to be created from the basic types of the specification. Relations, functions and sequences are all complex types built up from the power set and product constructors. Given two sets A and B we have seen in Part 3 that:

- Relations over these sets have type $\mathbb{P}(A \times B)$.
- Functions over these sets have type $\mathbb{P}(A \times B)$.
- Sequences can be defined with types $\mathbb{P}(\mathbb{N} \times A)$ and $\mathbb{P}(\mathbb{N} \times B)$ respectively.

However, many more types are possible such as:

$$\mathbb{P}(A \times A), \mathbb{P}(B \times B), \mathbb{P}(A) \times B, A \times \mathbb{P}(B), \mathbb{P}(A \times A \times A)$$

Once more the Z type-checking mechanism permits the detection of nonsense statements such as:

$$\{a,b,c\} = \{(0,1), (0,2), (0,3)\}$$

which was introduced earlier. Assuming we have a given set $[CHAR]$, the type of the left-hand side is $\mathbb{P}CHAR$ while the type of the right-hand side is $\mathbb{P}(\mathbb{Z} \times \mathbb{Z})$ showing formally that the statement is still a nonsense!

15.5.3 Schema types

Schema types are discussed in Chapter 16 where the notion of a schema is given in detail.

15.6 THE BASIC Z LIBRARY

It is never possible to predict what sorts of given sets a specification will introduce, but sets are sets no matter what their contents and relations are relations irrespective of the sets over which they are formed. The same will be true for functions, sequences and bags, of course. The implication here is that for the type constructors to make effective use of the given sets to build more complex objects, a Z document must be supported by a collection of generic definitions that define the characteristics of these objects independent of the sets used in their construction. This ensures that once a type is introduced, all its operators are available without further reference.

Such a collection of generic definitions constitutes the basic library of a Z system or in Spivey's terms a *mathematical toolkit* (Spivey 1992). The basic library is therefore a Z document itself and contains these definitions.

Each entry in the library follows the same format. First, the name of the object is introduced, followed by the generic definition of its operators, then an informal (English) description of their effect and finally any mathematical laws involving the operators to be used in proofs. The objects defined in the library are the common ones: sets, relations and function (as sets of pairs), numbers and finiteness, sequences and bags. The formal Z notation used is described in Chapter 16.

The content of the basic library is frequently customized with additional object definitions to reflect the requirements of the various organizations using Z. The basic library for those specifying problems closely related to hardware design, such as floating-point processors, will be quite different from those specifying problems related to business activities. Any group of people writing Z specifications must therefore agree upon what constitutes their basic library.

15.7 DECLARING VARIABLES IN Z SPECIFICATIONS

Wherever variables are introduced into a specification the rule of *definition before use* demands that they be assigned a type before they are used. However, the declaration of a variable as being of a particular type does not mean that it becomes available throughout the specification, so that a notion of scope applies to the mechanism with a distinction being made between local and global variable declarations. *Global variables* are known throughout the document, *local variables* are known only within the paragraph that introduced them. The declarations themselves can occur only once a type has been established.

The general form of a declaration in Z is consistent with that used in Part 3:

identifier list : set expression

where *identifier list* is a list of variable names separated by commas, while *set expression* is an expression that defines a set. The value that each variable can take is thus declared to be in the set determined by *set expression*, while the type taken by the variable is the underlying type of the elements of the set. Some examples are:

$$p, q : \{1,2,3,4,5,6\}$$
$$p, q : 1..6$$
$$p, q : set1to6$$
$$x : \{a,b : \mathbb{N} \mid 0 \leq a \leq 100 \wedge 0 \leq b \leq 100 \wedge \exists k : \mathbb{N}_1 \bullet a + k = b \bullet (a,b)\}$$

A *declaration list* consists of two or more declarations. These can be written on separate lines or on the same line separated by semicolons. Thus we might have:

$$std\,1, std\,2, std\,3 : STUDENT ; y : \mathbb{N}$$

where *std1*, *std2* and *std3* are variables allowed take any one of the values in the set *STUDENT*, while *x* takes values corresponding to any one of the natural numbers. This list is entirely equivalent to:

$$std\,1, st\,2, std\,3 : STUDENT$$
$$y : \mathbb{N}$$

and in every context where a series of single declarations is permitted an equivalent declaration list may also appear. Declarations occur in many areas of a Z document as part of the structure of certain definition paragraphs and the extent to which variables are global or local depends very much on the type of paragraph used.

15.8 ABBREVIATION DEFINITIONS AND DECLARATION ABBREVIATIONS

Suppose we wish to introduce a set representing the *is_less_than* relation over numbers in the subrange $0..100$ such that some variable *x* is permitted to range over the pairs in the set. The Z declaration might take the form:

$$x : \{a,b : \mathbb{N} \mid 0 \leq a \leq 100 \wedge 0 \leq b \leq 100 \wedge \exists k : \mathbb{N}_1 \bullet a + k = b \bullet (a,b)\}$$

If this set is required frequently within the specification there will naturally be many references to its use. If each new declaration takes the same form the specification will rapidly become unwieldy, especially if many such set expressions are involved. In these circumstances it is best to regard the set as a *global constant* and declarations can be made more manageable if we employ a paragraph whose purpose is to define an abbreviation for a commonly used global constant. The abbreviation definition symbol (==) has already been introduced in Part 3 where we took it to read 'is defined as' and this is consistent with its use in Z. The Z paragraph that provides an abbreviation for the set expression therefore takes the form:

$$is\_less\_than == \{a,b : \mathbb{N} \mid 0 \leq a \leq 100 \wedge 0 \leq b \leq 100 \wedge \exists k : \mathbb{N}_1 \bullet a + k = b \bullet (a,b)\}$$

and subsequent declaration(s) can now happily proceed with variables, for example:

$$x : is\_less\_than$$

An argument very similar to this extends of course to our use of $\mathbb{N}$, $\mathbb{N}_1$, $\mathbb{F}$, in declarations such as:

- $p : \mathbb{N}$ p is a natural number
- $q : \mathbb{N}_1$ q is a strictly positive natural number, or
- $r : \mathbb{FZ}$ r is a finite subset of integers

Like *is_less_than*, none of these are in fact types but rather subsets of types defined in terms of the abbreviation definitions introduced in Part 3:

- $\mathbb{N} \;\; == \{a : \mathbb{Z} \mid 0 \leq a\}$ so that $\mathbb{N} \subset \mathbb{Z}$
- $\mathbb{N}_1 == \{a : \mathbb{Z} \mid 1 \leq a\}$ so that $\mathbb{N}_1 \subset \mathbb{Z}$
- $\mathbb{FZ} == \{S : \mathbb{PZ} \mid \exists n : \mathbb{N}; f : 1 .. n \rightarrowtail\!\!\!\rightarrow S \bullet \; true\}$ so that $\mathbb{FZ} \subset \mathbb{PZ}$

With definitions such as these in the 'numbers and finiteness' section of the basic library, the Z type-checker can easily deduce that the types of p and q are really $\mathbb{Z}$, while r has type $\mathbb{PZ}$. The use of a subset in the declaration of a variable is therefore permissible in Z as long as the subset has been previously defined by an abbreviation definition in the document or forms part of the library. Using these definitions the type-checker is able to deduce the type of *is_less_than* and its elements. Here, the type of each of the elements introduced by the set expression is $(\mathbb{Z} \times \mathbb{Z})$ from which we infer that the type of the set itself is $\mathbb{P}(\mathbb{Z} \times \mathbb{Z})$.

Abbreviation definitions can even be applied to the shorthand notation employed in a specification. In the *Programmer-Project* case study (Chapter 9), we made widespread use of the shorthand for the set of partial functions $PROG\_NUM \nrightarrow PROG\_NAME$ with declarations such as:

$$Programmer, Programmer' : PROG\_NUM \nrightarrow PROG\_NAME$$

Using the abbreviation definition symbol we can provide an even more convenient notation for this type:

$$PROG == PROGNUM \nrightarrow PROG\_NAME$$

which benefits subsequent declarations in that we write:

$$Programmer, Programmer' : PROG$$

Notice that the constant *PROG* is not given a type explicitly but its type is ultimately deducible from the expression on the right-hand side in the abbreviation definition. An abbreviation definition paragraph is therefore used to make the specification shorter and more readable and allows us to make use of sets and notation already introduced. Such paragraphs therefore appear at the head of the specification document along with given sets and simple data types.

15.9 AXIOMATIC DEFINITIONS

Abbreviation definitions are often used to introduce global constants that are going to be used as types. However, there is frequently a need for other global constants to be introduced which represent (say) finite functions (as sets of pairs) which provide some useful fixed mapping from argument(s) to result, or for global variables known throughout the specification and (optionally) endowed with particular properties. For example, the specification might require the function *fact*, which accepts a number and returns its factorial value. Additionally, we might need two variables, *a* and *b*, both of which are natural numbers. In such cases the basic declaration mechanism $(x : T)$ must be qualified with some device to convey the fact that the constants or variables being introduced have global scope and that they enjoy particular properties. This is achieved in Z using a further paragraph notation known as an *axiomatic definition* or *axiomatic description*.

Global variables can be introduced in their simplest form with the paragraph | *Declaration*(*s*). Examples might be | *a,b* : $\mathbb{N}$ and | *Mintemp* : $\mathbb{Z}$.

Here we introduce the variables *a* and *b*, which are natural numbers, together with a variable *Mintemp* whose value is meant to represent a minimum (Celsius) temperature. If the variables need to be constrained beyond that which is implicit in their type, further predicates can be added using the general form:

| *Declaration*(*s*)
| --- |
| *Predicate*(*s*)

We might therefore qualify the properties of *a*, *b* and *Mintemp* as follows:

| *a,b* : $\mathbb{N}$
| --- |
| $a > b$

| *Mintemp* : $\mathbb{Z}$
| --- |
| $Mintemp = -50$

constraining the value of *a* to be always greater than that of *b* throughout the specification, while the minimum permissible temperature is $-50\,°C$.

The factorial function *fact* (a constant of the form $\{(0,1), (1,1), (2,2), (3,6), \ldots\}$) can be similarly introduced as a total function using the definition provided in Chapter 13:

| $fact : \mathbb{N} \to \mathbb{N}$
| --- |
| $fact\,(0) = 1 \wedge \forall n : \mathbb{N} \mid n > 0 \bullet fact\,(n) = n * fact\,(n-1)$

and where a number of such variables are introduced a single axiomatic definition may be written. Thus:

| $a,b : \mathbb{N}$
 $Mintemp : \mathbb{Z}$
 $fact : \mathbb{N} \to \mathbb{N}$
| --- |
| $a > b$
 $Mintemp = -50$
 $fact\,(0) = 1 \wedge \forall n : \mathbb{N} \mid n > 0 \bullet fact\,(n) = n * fact\,(n-1)$

Global variables/constants and their definitions are known throughout the specification document. The box-like device is characteristic of Z and distinctively separates the formal aspect of a specification from surrounding text. Further variations on this theme will be introduced later.

SAQ 15.1 A temperature-measuring device needs to display the temperature (measured in Celsius) in Fahrenheit . The formula for the conversion of °C to °F is given by:

$$T_f = T_c \times (9/5) + 32$$

where T_f and T_c represent the temperatures in Fahrenheit and Celsius, respectively. Write an axiomatic definition for the function *FartoC* that can be used throughout the Z specification whenever the conversion is required.

Finally, it should be mentioned that Z has a further variation on the axiomatic description known as a *constraint*, which is simply a predicate such as *user_limit* $\leq$ 80. Constraints can appear as independent paragraphs within the document. They specify limitations on the values of previously declared global variables. The effect is as if the constraint had been included as part of the original axiomatic definition that introduced the variables.

15.9.1 Schema definitions

We devote the whole of the next chapter to schemas and schema definitions.

15.10 SUMMARY

The Z specification language is based on a typed set theory. Such a theory has advantages to offer us with regard to the specification of systems:

- Certain mathematical paradoxes which could cripple our reasoning are avoided.
- Variables are permitted certain values only; this allows a degree of consistency-checking that can be used to detect genuine mistakes or confused thinking.

The main features of the Z typing system are:

- Z types are simply maximal sets. All elements in a set are of the same type.
- There is no notion of a subtype. Subsets are not subtypes; they are always of the same type as the set from which they were derived.
- Types are introduced into a document as given sets, simple data types or schema types.
- Compound types can be constructed from simple types using the type constructors
- and ×.
- Each variable in the document must be declared to be a member of a set and hence has a singular type.
- All Z expressions must be well typed, i.e. they must be constructed from types that are compatible.
- Some expressions may use abbreviations for types. These make Z specifications more manageable and readable.

The major features of a Z document are:

- Documents consist of interleaved passages of formal mathematical text and informal prose explanation.
- The formal mathematical text consists of paragraphs that introduce definitions or theorems.
- Definitions often introduce variables and the nature of the definition determines the type and scope of the variable. Variables can be global and known throughout the document or local and known only within the Z paragraph that introduces them.
- A different paragraph notation is used for each sort of definition; definitions may be categorized as basic type definitions, data type definitions, abbreviation definitions, axiomatic definitions or schema definitions.
- Theorems are used to prove important properties of Z specifications such that: specifications are self-consistent; suitable initial states exist; and preconditions exist for each operation that satisfy the state invariant(s) and from which a legal final state can be guaranteed.

16

Z SCHEMA AND THE SCHEMA CALCULUS

CHECKLIST OF OBJECTIVES

After reading this chapter you should be able to:

- Understand how the Z schema is used to describe abstract states, initial states and operations.
- Combine schemas using the various operators of the schema calculus.
- Simplify complex schema and reason about their properties.
- Use generic schema definitions.

16.1 INTRODUCTION

Large specifications are best developed using an approach which separates our considerations into a number of smaller—but more manageable—units or components. The advantage that this 'divide and conquer' tactic offers us is that it avoids our having to deal with too much complexity at any one time. Complexity and difficulty of course go hand in hand; by reducing the former we would hope to bring about an improvement in our understanding of a problem and hence a reduction in the latter.

The informal specifications in Part 3 illustrated a number of areas where the various considerations to be made were separated. For example, the abstract state and its requirements were dealt with before the individual operations; this left us free to concentrate on their characteristic features at a later stage. Similarly, partial operations were described before total operations because by understanding normal behaviour first we more easily recognize the conditions which give rise to errors.

Of course this separation is all well and good, but there must come a time when individual aspects have to be combined to create the overall specification. In the case of the abstract state of a system, we composed the before and after descriptions quite separately but then combined them with the use of an operator ($\wedge$) which we invented simply as a convenience. Because the combined description had to appear in all the operations, we devised some additional notation (Δ and Ξ) which acted as a convenient shorthand and the inclusion of either of these within a tuple definition was taken as a mechanism for combining particular state properties with those of an individual operation. Finally, in the case of a total operation, the union operator ($\cup$) was used to combine separate descriptions of normal and exceptional behaviour into one single description.

Plenty of evidence then, pointing not only to the success of separation but also to the need for a mechanism that can be used to combine descriptions. So what is wrong with what we have already done? First, union is too restrictive; the operator is naturally limited to tuples of the same type and therefore to those with the same declaration order. There may well be times, however, when we do not want the type system to impose so vigorously; we may want to be able to combine descriptions with different declarations or maintain that the declaration order need not be significant. Secondly, our use of the operator $\wedge$ and the shorthand notations Δ and Ξ were really only wishful thinking, they were conveniences used by the case studies to make our life easier because there are no operators available in typed set theory that can combine tuple descriptions in the way we wanted to in the case studies. This final point suggests that if we persist with the tuple as the major structural unit in our specifications, we will be limiting the ways in which our specifications can be created by the combination of simpler units while without the shorthand notations our descriptions are likely to be very long-winded indeed. In Z therefore, we decide to invent a whole new structural device; one that retains aspects of the tuple definition format we have become used to but is in fact different. This device is a *schema* and along with given sets, simple data types, abbreviation definitions and axiomatic descriptions its definition provides another paragraph around which the formal aspect of a Z document is organized.

Because schemas are not tuples they are not restricted by the considerations of typed set theory. In particular we are free to devise a whole new *schema calculus* that operates upon schemas, combining them in various ways and permitting us to have at our fingertips those features (and more) that we found useful in the case studies. Schema definitions often use the types, global constants and variables previously introduced in Z. Together with other schemas, type constructors and local variables, the schema definition is used to provide the functionality of the specification in much the same way as the tuple definition did for typed set theory. This chapter discusses the notational device(s) that distinguish schemas and the associated Z schema calculus.

16.2 THE SCHEMA NOTATION

Schemas are not tuples, but Z evolved from typed set theory where the tuple formed a central role in our descriptions. The general form of the tuple definition as we have used it is:

$$Name\ of\ tuple(s) == \{declaration(s) \mid predicate\}$$

It would be sensible therefore to persist with a device which retains the familiar form of a tuple definition yet is sufficiently different to permit it to be immediately recognizable as such. The general format for a schema definition paragraph is:

```
_____ Schema name _____
|
|  Declaration(s)
|_____
|
|  Predicate
|_____
```

The schema is therefore a two-dimensional box-like device with a structure similar to the tuple but where the style is now vertical rather than horizontal and where the distinctive curly brackets of the tuple are replaced by horizontal lines. This vertical style should really come as no surprise. In the case studies it has been almost impossible to present all the detail of a tuple on a single line and the format:

$$
\begin{aligned}
&\{declaration\,(1);\\
&\quad declaration\,(2);\;\ldots\\
&\quad declaration\,(n)\mid\\
&\quad predicate\,(1)\wedge\\
&\quad predicate\,(2)\wedge\ldots\\
&\quad predicate\,(n)\wedge\\
&\}
\end{aligned}
$$

was commonly adopted for clarity. The schema takes advantage of this practical difficulty and incorporates a vertical expression mechanism directly in its design.

The middle line of a schema corresponds to the 'such that' bar ($\mid$) in the tuple declaration and serves as a physical separation between the declaration list and the predicate. The top line of the schema bears the schema name embedded in it. The schema name serves to identify a schema uniquely throughout the Z document for which the schema is written i.e. the name has *global scope*. No Z specification can have two schemas with the same name exactly, while any identifier used as a schema name cannot be used for any other purpose.

As first examples of schemas we return to the *Homework* and *Project-Programmer* case studies. The schema and tuple descriptions of the state data for these are as follows:

$$
\begin{aligned}
&Homework ==\\
&\{Class,\ Handed\_in,\ Not\_handed\_in : \mathbb{P}Student\mid\\
&\quad Handed\_in \cup Not\_handed\_in = Class \wedge\\
&\quad Handed\_in \cap Not\_handed\_in = \{\,\}\}
\end{aligned}
$$

Homework

$Class,\ Handed\_in,\ Not\_handed\_in : \mathbb{P}Student$

$Handed\_in \cup Not\_handed\_in = Class$
$Handed\_in \cap Not\_handed\_in = \{\,\}$

$$
\begin{aligned}
&Project\_Programmer ==\\
&\{Programmer : Prog\_Num \rightarrowtail Prog\_Name;\\
&\quad Project : Proj\_Code \rightarrowtail Proj\_Name;\\
&\quad Assignment : Prog\_Num \leftrightarrow Proj\_Code\mid\\
&\quad \mathrm{dom}(Assignment) \subseteq \mathrm{dom}(Programmer) \wedge\\
&\quad \mathrm{ran}(Assignment) \subseteq \mathrm{dom}(Project)\}
\end{aligned}
$$

```
┌─── Project_Programmer ─────────────────────────────────────────
│ Programmer : Prog_Num ↠ Prog_Name
│ Project : Proj_Code ↣↠ Proj_Name
│ Assignment : Prog_Num ↔ Proj_Code
├────────────────────────────────────────────────────────────────
│ dom(Assignment) ⊆ dom(Programmer)
│ ran(Assignment) ⊆ dom(Project)
└────────────────────────────────────────────────────────────────
```

By now we should be quite familiar with these tuple definitions and the corresponding schemas follow quite closely. There are, however, some subtle points that should be brought to your attention:

1. Each set of declarations in the tuple definitions are separated by the semi-colon (;). In the schema, if declarations appear on separate lines then the semi-colon character can be omitted.
2. In the tuple definitions the predicates are written in the general form $P1 \land P2 \land \ldots Pn$. In the corresponding schema, if the predicates are written each on a separate line the $\land$ symbol can be omitted.
3. Schema are often written which have a declaration part and no predicate, e.g. we might like to define the abstract state of the *Project-Programmer* problem by the schema:

```
┌─── Proj_Prog_Data ─────────────────────────────────────────────
│ Programmer : Prog_Num ↠ Prog_Name
│ Assignment : Prog_Num ↔ Proj_Code
│ Project : Proj_Code ↣↠ Proj_Name
└────────────────────────────────────────────────────────────────
```

Such schema are used to factor out common collections of objects, defined once but used throughout a specification. When the predicate is omitted it is equivalent to using the single predicate *true* which says that there are no further constraints on the declared data other than those imposed by their type (see, however, normalized schema in 5).

4. In a tuple, the form of the *signature* dictates the tuple type. In the case of the *Project_Programmer* tuple, for example, the type is:

$$\mathbb{P}(Prog\_Num \times Prog\_Name) \times \mathbb{P}(Proj\_Code \times Proj\_Name)$$
$$\times \mathbb{P}(Prog\_Num \times Proj\_Code)$$

and not, say:

$$\mathbb{P}(Prog\_Num \times Prog\_Name) \times \mathbb{P}(Prog\_Num \times Proj\_Code)$$
$$\times \mathbb{P}(Proj\_Code \times Proj\_Name)$$

because in a tuple the order in which the declarations are made is significant. The declaration list of a schema similarly defines its signature but, unlike the tuple, the signature of a schema is simply the *unordered* collection of names introduced in the declaration part together with their corresponding types. The declaration part of the *Project-Programmer* schema could therefore be equally written as:

```
┌─── Project_Programmer ──────────────────────────────────────────
│ Programmer : Prog_Num ⇸ Prog_Name
│ Assignment : Prog_Num ↔ Proj_Code
│ Project : Proj_Code ⤔ Proj_Name
│
```

or:

```
┌─── Project_Programmer ──────────────────────────────────────────
│ Project : Proj_Code ⤔ Proj_Name
│ Assignment : Prog_Num ↔ Proj_Code
│ Programmer : Prog_Num ⇸ Prog_Name
│
```

or any other combination for each of these schema that has the same signature. The variables in the signature of a schema are called its *components*. They are essentially definitions of local variables known only within the predicate part of the schema. (See, however, Sec. 16.6.2.)

5. In addition to its signature a schema is also regarded as having a *property* which is conveyed by the nature of the constraints applied to the collection of variables introduced by the schema. We normally think of these as being associated with the predicate part exclusively but constraints can be introduced by the declaration part as well and this is illustrated in the *Project_Programmer* schema where the declaration list involves some common abbreviations. If we expand the schema the shorthand definitions have to be written out in full and some additional predicates that appear as relations are converted to partial functions and partial functions to partial injections. By adapting the general definitions for these objects given in Chapter 8 the full schema becomes:

```
┌─── Project_Programmer ──────────────────────────────────────────
│ Programmer : ℙ(Prog_Num × Prog_Name)
│ Project : ℙ(Proj_Code × Proj_Name)
│ Assignment : (Prog_Num × Proj_Code)
├──────────────────────────────────────────────────────────────────
│ ∀a : Prog_Num; ∀p,q : Prog_Name • ((a,p) ∈ Programmer ∧ (a,q) ∈ Programmer ⇒ p = q)
│ ∀b : Proj_Code; ∀r,s : Proj_Name • ((b,r) ∈ Project ∧ (b,s) ∈ Project ⇒ r = s)
│ ∀c₁,c₂ : dom(Project) • Project(c₁) = Project(c₂) ⇒ c₁ = c₂
│ dom(Assignment) ⊆ dom(Programmer)
│ ran(Assignment) ⊆ dom(Project)
│
```

When a schema is written out in its full form, any predicates that appear as a consequence of the expansion of its declaration abbreviations are appended to the existing predicates and the schema is *normalized*. If the original schema was written without a predicate then normalization may well add one as it does for the example used in 3. Normalization can obviously transform a relatively simple schema into a quite complex structure and for this reason we tend to stick to the shorthand notations, but there are occasions in Z where schema expansion must occur and these are dealt with later in the book. It is a useful exercise however, even this early in our schema experience, to be aware of the 'iceberg effect' of declaration abbreviations in Z and the additional properties of a schema that their use implies.

16.3 SCHEMA COMBINATION

The evolution of the schema from the tuple naturally leads to the notion of a schema signature. The notion of a schema signature being a loose collection of variables and their types, however, is not quite what we might have expected and it represents a clear relaxation of the stranglehold grip of the tuple type system. In fact, with schemas we go even further. Because we would wish to combine schemas in a variety of different ways to provide descriptions of complete systems, the only restriction we wish to place upon the signatures is that they are type compatible, in the sense that if a variable appears in both it is of the same *underlying* type so that unlike tuples, schemas with totally different signatures can be combined as long as this simple rule is obeyed. It may at first seem strange to combine schemas with different signatures but the operators of schema calculus are deliberately defined this way so that composite schemas can be built from others that deal with distinct issues or distinct parts of the abstract state. Ways of combining schemas will be introduced soon but for now suffice to say that the combination of the following schemas (predicates *true*) is quite legal:

___ *schema A* _____

$p, q : \mathbb{Z}$
$c_1 : \text{char}$

___ *schema B* _____

$q, r : \mathbb{Z}$
$c_2 : \text{char}$
---

because in both cases q is of the same type. However, the combination of the following schemas:

___ *schema X* _____

$a, b : \mathbb{Z}$
$c : \text{char}$

___ *schema Y* _____

$a : \mathbb{Z}$
$c, b : \text{char}$
---

is illegal because the types of the two references to b are different. When schemas are legally combined their declaration lists are simply merged and duplicate references eliminated. The effect of the combination of *schema A* and *schema B* on the resulting declaration is therefore:

```
 ___ schema AB _____
| p, q, r : Z
| c_1, c_2 : char
|_____
```

However, the situation is not always as clear-cut as this, especially when dealing with declaration abbreviations, e.g. consider the following combination of *schema 1* and *schema 2*:

```
 ___ schema 1 _____
| p, q : Z
| c_1 : char
|_____
```

```
 ___ schema 2 _____
| q : N
| c_2 : char
|_____
```

The combination is legal because as the normalized form of *schema 2* (below) shows, q is of the same underlying type (Z) in both schemas, but in *schema 2* it carries with it a property about q—$q \geq 0$—because of the use of the declaration abbreviation $q : N$.

```
 ___ schema 2 normalized _____
| q : Z
| c_2 : char
|_____
| q \geq 0
|_____
```

The combination of schemas in these circumstances therefore has to take into account the iceberg effect and rules have to be developed in the calculus to show how we can safely combine their property parts. Because schema combination is a corner-stone of Z specifications, problems like this can arise all the time. It is prudent therefore to introduce the normalized form of the schema before tackling the detail of schema calculus which defines the activity of schema combination.

16.4 THE HORIZONTAL SCHEMA FORM

The main reasons for adopting the schema box notation are that schemas are differentiated from tuples and stand out from surrounding informal text. However, when the schema definitions are small—as in the previous discussion—the notation becomes a little unwieldy and an alternative horizontal form can be used. This notation takes the general form:

$$schema\_name \triangleq [declaration(s) \mid predicate]$$

and encloses the schema body in delimiting square brackets, [ ]. The name of the schema cannot now be embedded as it is in the box version and so the special schema definition symbol $\triangleq$ is used to associate an identifier with the schema definition. The horizontal versions of the schema definitions used in the previous discussion are as follows:

$$\text{\textit{schema } } A \triangleq [p,q : \mathbb{Z}; c_1 : \texttt{char}] \qquad \text{\textit{schema } } B \triangleq [q,r : \mathbb{Z}; c_2 : \texttt{char}]$$
$$\text{\textit{schema } } X \triangleq [a,b : \mathbb{Z}; c : \texttt{char}] \qquad \text{\textit{schema } } Y \triangleq [a : \mathbb{Z}; c,b : \texttt{char}]$$
$$\text{\textit{schema } } 1 \triangleq [p,q : \mathbb{Z}; c_1 : \texttt{char}] \qquad \text{\textit{schema } } 2 \triangleq [q : \mathbb{N}; c_2 : \texttt{char}]$$

and

$$\text{\textit{schema 2 normalized}} \triangleq [q : \mathbb{Z}; c_2 : \texttt{char} \mid q \geq 0]$$

Where there is more than one predicate in the schema, they can be separated by semi-colons just as for multiple declarations in the declaration list. The general horizontal form is therefore:

$$S \triangleq [D_1; D_2; \ldots; D_n \mid P_1; P_2; \ldots; P_n]$$

Be aware that there is absolutely no difference in meaning between the box and horizontal definition formats; it is simply a matter of convenience.

16.5 SCHEMA AS TYPES

The signature of a schema is a loose collection of variables and their types. The predicate of the schema introduces a property that constrains the values that the variables can take in combination. The schema therefore defines a collection of possible values often called *bindings*; composite structures rather like records in programming terms. For example, in the schema definition:

$$S \triangleq [a,b : \mathbb{N} \mid a < b < 3]$$

there are just three combinations or bindings that are possible:

$$a \rightarrow 0; b \rightarrow 1$$
$$a \rightarrow 0; b \rightarrow 2$$
$$a \rightarrow 1; b \rightarrow 2$$

The notation we use here avoids writing the bindings as a collection of pairs $(0,1)$, $(0,2)$, $(1,2)$, because this makes the bindings look like tuples. The order in which the components of a binding are written is arbitrary because of the way in which we define the schema signature, but this is certainly not the case with a tuple. In short, bindings are not tuples.

In Z, a collection of values is a type, and the type of a schema simply describes a collection of bindings that satisfy its property. In the example, the type of the schema S is $a : \mathbb{Z}$; $b : \mathbb{Z}$ (or indeed $b : \mathbb{Z}$; $a : \mathbb{Z}$) because the *underlying* types of a and b are both $\mathbb{Z}$. (Notice our avoidance of the use of $\mathbb{Z} \times \mathbb{Z}$ which of course again suggests a tuple.)

Since a schema can represent a type, it must follow that we can declare a variable whose value is a schema binding. The variable will therefore have components, each of a type given in the schema signature and with current component values compliant with the schema property. However, no order is applied to the components in a binding unlike the fields in a record or indeed the elements in a tuple. Referring again to the schema S, the declaration $s : S$ defines s to be a variable representing a binding of the schema S with components called a and b, such that at all times $a < b < 3$. Because the schema S has global scope then s is known everywhere that S is.

The only operation that can be applied to a schema variable is *projection* or *selection*. The selection operator (.) applied to a schema variable produces a component value. Thus $s.a$ and $s.b$ refer to the current values of the a and b components of the schema variable s.

Sometimes in Z, we may wish to refer to the current binding value of a schema without using a specific variable to represent the binding. We can do this using the notation θS (referred to as *binding formation*) which represents the binding of S that has component values equal to the current values of the variables in S.

Schema types and bindings are not often used in Z specifications but when they are they can make the specifications more elegant than they might otherwise be. An example that will make the concept of schema bindings and binding formation a little clearer will be presented in Sec. 16.6.2.

16.6 SCHEMA CALCULUS

The term *schema calculus* refers to the collection of notational conventions that permit the manipulation of schemas and their combination into composite structures. The schema notation allows us to divide a specification into logically related parts. Several schemas may well be defined representing various aspects of a system. Using the operators of schema calculus these can be combined to form the complete specification. The schema notation therefore allows the specifier to concentrate on one aspect of the system at a time. When the final specification is formed by combination, the individual detail of the component schemas can be suppressed. The calculus is therefore a tool that assists the separation of concerns that makes a specification more manageable. We should be aware, however, that the separation of concerns in a specification need not be reflected in the same way in the implementation. Practical factors such as efficiency may well dictate the aggregation of concerns that form separate considerations at the abstract level.

All schemas consist of two components: a signature expressed as an unordered collection of typed variables and a property expressed as a predicate (even if the predicate is simply *true*). Operations upon schemas can therefore affect both parts. We have already seen that in order to combine schemas we require only type compatibility between their signatures. Properties, however, are expressed as predicates and we know from earlier work that these can be combined in interesting ways using the connectives of logical calculus. Thus, schema calculus includes operations such as schema *conjunction*, *disjunction*, *negation*, *implication* and *equivalence* that each reflect these origins. The major features of Z schema calculus are listed below. Some of these considerations are more important to us than others. The list aggregates features into (loosely) related groups.

- schema decoration ($!$, $?$, $'$)
  schema inclusion
  the delta (Δ) and Xi (Ξ) notation
- schema conjunction ($\wedge$)
  schema disjunction ($\vee$)
  schema negation ($\neg$)
  schema implication ($\Rightarrow$)
  schema equivalence ($\Leftrightarrow$)
- schema renaming
  schema hiding
  schema precondition ($\mathtt{pre}\,OP$ or $PreOP$)
- schema composition ($;$)
  schema overriding ($\oplus$)
  schema piping ($\gg$)

Using schema definitions and schema calculus, schema expressions can be written that are combinations of schema names and schema operators, e.g. if A, B and C are schemas the following are all possible schema expressions:

$$X \triangleq A \wedge B \wedge C$$
$$\neg B$$
$$A \Rightarrow B \vee C$$

Exactly what each of these expressions means depends of course on the content of A, B and C and the semantics of the individual operators, but notice how schema calculus forms expressions using connectives that we previously assumed were defined only for use with propositions. The calculus of course overloads the operators in exactly the same way we did with $\wedge$ in the case studies of Part 3. The symbolism is chosen because it reflects the influence the operators have on the predicate parts of the schemas. When these connectives are used in schema expressions their arguments are schemas and so the context of their use makes clear which way they are defined.

Before looking at how the calculus can be used to build a complete specification from component parts we need to understand the effect of the individual operators. The following discussion concentrates on the most important ones and illustrates their usefulness by revisiting the earlier case studies and reworking them through Z terminology rather than typed set theory.

16.6.1 Schema decoration

One of the simplest features of schema calculus is schema decoration (an example of a more general technique called 'renaming': see Sec. 16.6.5). In Part 3 we developed a notation that decorated variables with characters such as $?$, $!$ and $'$. These choices were made to be consistent with their use in Z where the characters are used to decorate to much the same effect. In Z each of these can be used to decorate a schema, the effect being that the decoration is applied to all the variables in the schema in both the declaration and predicate parts. To illustrate schema decoration we return to the classroom homework case study of Part 3. The schema that describes the abstract state *before* any operation is performed is as follows:

```
┌─── Homework ─────────────────────────────────────
│ Class, Handed_in, Not_handed_in : ℙStudent
├───────────────────────────────────────────────────
│ Handed_in ∪ Not_handed_in = Class
│ Handed_in ∩ Not_handed_in = { }
└───────────────────────────────────────────────────
```

The decorated schema *Homework'* is a *new* schema and corresponds to:

```
┌─── Homework' ────────────────────────────────────
│ Class', Handed_in', Not_handed_in' : ℙStudent
├───────────────────────────────────────────────────
│ Handed_in' ∪ Not_handed_in' = Class'
│ Handed_in' ∩ Not_handed_in' = { }
└───────────────────────────────────────────────────
```

which describes the abstract state *after* any operation has been performed.

The *?* and *!* decorations are often applied to create schemas that describe collections of input or output variables. Again, referring to the same case study we could define a schema that simply introduces a variable:

$$Std\_var \triangleq [std : Student]$$

where the horizontal form is used for simplicity. *Std_var?* and *Std_var!* are therefore new schemas with signatures corresponding to input and output variables respectively:

$$Std\_var? \triangleq [std? : Student] \quad \text{and} \quad Std\_var! \triangleq [std! : Student]$$

and where of course *std?* and *std!* are different variables. A proviso that applies to schema decoration is that global variables involved in the schema and bound variables in quantified expressions are never decorated. We will return to these points later when we examine some Z case studies.

16.6.2 Schema inclusion

Ideally, schema definitions should correspond to conceptually independent aspects of a specification. When such schemas need to be combined one of the simplest ways is to include the name of one schema within the definition of another. The schema name is included in the definition as part of the signature and inclusion has the effect of merging their declaration lists and conjoining (*AND*ing) their predicates. The schemas must of course be type compatible, while the local variables of the included schema now become local to the new definition.

Continuing with the examples in Sec. 16.6.1 we could use schema decoration and schema inclusion to produce a schema definition that describes the *Submit* operation. Thus:

```
___ Submit _____
Homework
Homework'
Std_var?
_____
Std? ∈ Not_handed_in
Not_handed_in' = Not_handed_in \ {Std?}
Handed_in' = Handed_in ∪ {Std?}
Class' = Class
_____
```

The expansion of this schema shows clearly the effect of the inclusions and the decorations:

```
___ Submit _____
Class, Handed_in, Not_handed_in : ℙ Student
Class', Handed_in', Not_handed_in' : ℙ Student
Stud? : Student
_____
Handed_in ∪ Not_handed_in = Class
Handed_in ∩ Not_handed_in = { }
Handed_in' ∪ Not_handed_in' = Class'
Handed_in' = Not_handed_in' = { }
Stud? ∈ Not_handed_in
Not_handed_in' = Not_handed_in \ {Stud?}
Handed_in' = Handed_in ∪ {Stud?}
Class' = Class
_____
```

The inclusion of the *Std_var* schema is probably a little overelaborate—the declaration *Stud? : Student* would have been much simpler—but it does illustrate a useful technique. Inclusion of all sorts are used heavily in Z and even in a simple example like the classroom homework problem we can see that it permits the specification to be built from smaller parts, each one identifying a particular concept. A further advantage of schema inclusion is that it suppresses unnecessary detail. For example, no explicit reference is made to the state when defining the role of the *Submit* operation because the variables and predicates introduced by the inclusion are displayed only if the schema is expanded. We are therefore free to concentrate on the predicate that characterizes *Submit*. Notice, however, that the variables from included schema can be used when defining this predicate because the declaration lists are implicit.

It is also possible to include schemas in the predicate part rather than the declaration part of another schema. This technique is used when we wish to emphasize that it is the *property* of the included schema we are interested in rather than its signature. There are some restrictions on this kind of inclusion, namely the predicate of the included schema can refer only to variables declared in the signature of the schema in which it is included and/or global variables. The signature of the included schema is therefore restricted. This inclusion technique is far less common but some discussion can be found in McMorran and Nicholls (1989).

Finally, using schema inclusion we can illustrate a role for schema bindings and binding formation. Consider specifying part of a small order processing system which accepts orders for a particular product. Two types of order exist: a normal order which is limited only in that the number of items required must be less than or equal to the number of items in stock, and a small order which is characterized by the additional requirement that the order value does not exceed a particular order value limit. If an order is classified as a small order then the order may be dispatched without reference to a customer's credit limit—although this aspect is not reflected in the discussion here. We assume the given sets:

$$[MONEY, ORDERNOS]$$

with obvious meanings, while the global variables *Maxitems* and *Small_limit* provide information on current stock levels and order value limits. We define these as:

$Maxitems : \mathbb{N}$	$Small\_limit : MONEY$
$Maxitems \leq 500$	$Small\_limit = 1000.00$

We may also define a global function *Value* that calculates the value of a particular order:

$$Value :\ Order \to MONEY$$
$$\forall ord : Order \bullet Value = ord . qty * ord . item\_price$$

Value is a total function because every order will have some total value based on the quantity ordered and the price per item. The function accepts an object of (*Schema*) type *Order* and returns the monetary value of the order. The variable *ord* is therefore a schema variable, hence the definition of the function in terms of the selection operator (.) which isolates particular components from the current binding. Normal orders are described by the schema:

```
__ Order _____
Orderno : ORDERNOS
qty : N
item_price : MONEY
_____
qty ≤ Maxitems
```

Small orders can be subsequently described by schema inclusion:

```
__ Small_Order _____
Order
_____
qty * item_price ≤ Small_limit
```

However, the calculation performed here can be achieved using the function *Value* and so a more elegant and more appealing definition for this schema would be:

```
┌─── Small_Order ────────────────────────────────────
│ Order
├────────────────────────────────────────────────────
│ Value (θ Order) ≤ Small_limit
└────────────────────────────────────────────────────
```

Here the use of binding formation (θ Order) presents *Value* with an argument that is the current binding of the schema *Order*. The result of the application of *Value* is therefore the monetary value of a particular order. This example hopefully goes some way to justifying the notions of schema types and binding formation.

You will by now be aware that the schema inclusion feature of schema calculus is what was referred to as *inclusion* in the case studies of Part 3, except of course that there we dealt with tuples and not schemas. By including the definition of one tuple within another we found that tuple construction became much more manageable but we were really cheating when we did this because typed set theory does not permit definitions to be built in such a way—however convenient it may be! The operators that apply to schemas, however, can be defined as we wish and since the case studies established inclusion as a very useful technique we naturally find it accepted formally as a part of the Z schema calculus.

16.6.3 The delta (Δ) and xi (Ξ) notation

The case studies took even more liberties with typed set theory and introduced two other conventions that we found convenient: the Δ and Ξ notations. These again are Z conventions and really alien to typed set theory but, tongue in cheek, they were used to make our specifications shorter and more readable and in doing so of course established that they were indispensable in any non-trivial specification.

Recall that the Δ notation was used to combine the definitions of two tuples, one describing the abstract state before an operation and the other describing the state after the operation. In Z we can achieve such combinations quite legally by the following schema definitions which use the *Homework* and *Project_Programmer* definitions introduced earlier in this chapter:

```
┌─── ΔHomework ──────────────────────────────────────
│ Homework
│ Homework′
│
└────────────────────────────────────────────────────
```

and

```
┌─── ΔProject_Programmer ────────────────────────────
│ Project_Programmer
│ Project_Programmer′
│
└────────────────────────────────────────────────────
```

In Z , the delta notation is taken by convention to be defined as:

```
┌─── ΔS ─────────────────────────────────────────────
│ S
│ S′
│
└────────────────────────────────────────────────────
```

where S and S' are schemas describing the before and after system states respectively. Notice that we use the term 'by convention' which means that specifiers are really free to define ΔS in any way they want—even though the convention is recognized by Spivey's Reference Manual! However, it has become generally accepted that it always refers to a change of state, and to redefine it drastically would be mischievous—although no one would object to some additional predicate over and above those of the before and after states as long as it is properly defined. Because ΔS is a schema, it can be included in other schema definitions, which is what we (naively) tried to parallel in the case studies of Part 3. Its inclusion is also taken as an indication that the schema describes a state change.

The explanation of the Z convention for the use of Δ leads naturally to a consideration of the convention for Ξ. In the case studies, the inclusion of ΞS within a tuple definition indicated that *no state change occurred* and this was achieved by a simple qualification to the Δ notation that declared after objects to equal before objects. For the case studies then, we could imagine the equivalent Z schema definitions being:

```
┌─── ΞHomework ────────────────────────────────────
│ ΔHomework
├──────────────────────────────────────────────────
│ Handed_in' = Handed_in
│ Not_handed_in' = Not_handed_in
│ Class' = Class
└──────────────────────────────────────────────────
```

```
┌─── ΞProject_Programmer ──────────────────────────
│ ΔProject_Programmer
├──────────────────────────────────────────────────
│ Programmer' = Programmer
│ Project' = Project
│ Assignment' = Assignment
└──────────────────────────────────────────────────
```

To generalize these observations, the Z convention for ΞS is simply:

```
┌─── ΞS ───────────────────────────────────────────
│ ΔS
├──────────────────────────────────────────────────
│ No change
└──────────────────────────────────────────────────
```

where, depending upon the definition of the schema S, we would have to supply the appropriate predicate in place of *No change* such that the corresponding decorated (primed) and undecorated variables introduced by the inclusion of ΔS are equal.

A more elegant description of this convention is given by the use of binding formation in that the *No change* predicate can be written $\theta S = \theta S'$; here we suggest that, for any schema S, the schema bindings before and after are always equal. Readers wishing to pursue this point are referred to McMorran and Nicholls (1989) which presents a discussion of the role of θS.

Once again ΞS is a schema and can be included in the definition of others. If the schema describes an operation, its inclusion is taken (conventionally) to indicate that no change of state occurs.

16.6.4 The logical schema connectives ($\wedge$, $\vee$, $\neg$, $\Rightarrow$ and $\Leftrightarrow$)

The logical schema connectives owe their existence to the observation that schemas consist of two parts—declarations and predicates. New schemas can therefore be produced from old ones by operators that merge declarations but combine the predicates according to the connectives of logical calculus. Of these operators, schema conjunction and disjunction are the most important while conjunction is used to define the meaning of other features of schema calculus—particularly inclusion and the Δ notation. Like inclusion and Δ they are heavily used in most Z specifications. In the discussion that follows first the 'bare bones' of each operator are presented, followed (where appropriate) by an example of its use.

Schema conjunction ($\wedge$)

The conjunction of two schemas is written:

$$R \triangleq A \wedge B$$

and it produces a schema R with the signatures of A and B merged and with their properties conjoined, i.e. *AND*ed. In this respect schema inclusion is no different from schema conjunction so that the following schema:

___ S _____

declaration part of S
T

_____

Predicate part of S

_____

---

is in fact defined by $S \wedge T$. Similarly we could provide another explanation for the Δ notation in terms of schema conjunction:

$$\Delta S \triangleq S' \wedge S$$

Because both these forms of inclusion are defined in terms of conjunction the question may well be asked as to why we need inclusion at all. The difference between the use of conjunction or inclusion is really only one of emphasis. Schema inclusion is generally used in situations where we wish to define a schema without too much reference to its underlying detail. Conjunction is really a decomposition technique often used to express the definition of an operation in terms of how other schemas combine to express its effect. The examples that follow shortly make the role of conjunction little clearer.

Schema disjunction ($\vee$)

The disjunction of two schemas is written:

$$R \triangleq A \vee B$$

and it produces a schema R with the signatures of A and B merged and with their properties disjoined, i.e. *OR*ed. Schema disjunction is frequently used in the definition of operators that may have a behavioural pattern dependent on certain conditions, i.e. the operator will do ... if ... *OR* ... if ... *OR* ... etc. Schemas are defined for each of the individual conditions and the effect of the operation as a whole is described by the disjunction of all the schemas which naturally enough expresses a range of alternatives.

Error reports using schema calculus

A common use of schema conjunction and disjunction in Z is in the construction of total operations. The discussion presented here can be usefully compared to Chapter 14 on exceptions in Part 3, especially with regard to the flexibility of the calculus compared to the set operators of type set theory. Imagine we define a schema called *Success* whose purpose is simply to report the message *OK*. With the simple data type *Message* introduced in Chapter 14 that is:

$$Message ::= OK \mid Unknown\ Programmer \mid Unknown\ Project \mid Already\ Assigned \dots$$

we might define *Success* as:

$$Success \triangleq [Report! : Message \mid Report! = OK]$$

The schema describing the *Add_prog* operation of the *Project_Programmer* case study is defined as follows:

```
┌─── Add_prog ─────────────────────────────────
│ ΔProject_Programmer
│ Progname? : Prog_Name
│ Prognum? : Prog_Num
├──────────────────────────────────────────────
│ dom(Programmer) ∩ {Prognum?} = { }
│ Programmer' = Programmer ⊕ {(Prognum?, Progname?)}
│ Project' = Project
│ Assignment' = Assignment
└──────────────────────────────────────────────
```

so that the *Add_prog_OK* operation that describes normal behaviour can be expressed as:

$$Add\_prog\_OK \triangleq Add\_prog \wedge Success$$

Here the conjunction is used to emphasize the fact that the *Add_prog_OK* operation is defined in terms of two other schemas whose individual behaviour is known to us. In this sense the behaviour of *Add_prog_OK* is conveyed by a schema expression which *decomposes* its specification through conjunction—a primary role for this operator in Z. Notice also that the conjunction operator of the schema calculus has combined schemas with different signatures and is therefore much less restrictive than the union operator of set theory. A further point to appreciate is that because we now understand the behaviour of *Add_prog_OK* we probably will not need to expand the schema in the specification. However, for the sake of completeness the expansion is as follows:

```
 ___ Add_ prog_OK _____
  ΔProject_Programmer
  Progname? : Prog_Name
  Prognum? : Prog_Num
  Report! : Message
 ├──────────────────────────────────────────────────────────────────────
  dom(Programmer) ∩ {Prognum?} = { }
  Programmer' = Programmer ⊕ {(Prognum?, Progname?)}
  Project' = Project
  Assignment' = Assignment
  Report! = OK
 └──────────────────────────────────────────────────────────────────────
```

The negation of the precondition (see Sec. 16.6.7) for this operation:

$$\neg \,(\mathrm{dom}(Programmer) \cap \{Prognum?\} = \{ \})$$

represents a condition where the programmer is already known to the system. Using the negation as a precondition we can write a schema *Add_ prog_error* which describes what should happen when the error is detected. Assuming that this operation does not change the state of the system we can define the schema thus:

```
 ___ Add_ prog_error _____
  ΞProject_Programmer
  Prognum? : Prog_Num
  Report! : Message
 ├──────────────────────────────────────────────────────────────────────
  ¬(dom(Programmer) ∩ {Prognum?} = { })
  Report! = Already known
 └──────────────────────────────────────────────────────────────────────
```

so that the total operation *Total_Add_ prog* can be defined through expressions such as:

$$Total\_Add\_prog \triangleq Add\_prog\_OK \lor Add\_prog\_error$$

or

$$Total\_Add\_prog \triangleq (Add\_prog \land Success) \lor Add\_prog\_error$$

Here we use schema disjunction to decompose the specification of the total operation but this time to reveal a series of alternative actions based on the mutual exclusivity of the preconditions of the operations involved. Once again the behaviour of *Total_Add_ prog* can be understood without recourse to expansion of its schema.

SAQ 16.1 Write the expanded schema for the operation *Total_Add_ prog* to confirm the effect of the conjunction.

As a final illustration of the use of these operators we could examine the specification of an operation that has multiple preconditions and therefore a range of alternative actions to be considered when the preconditions are offended. In Part 3 we looked at the *Add_ prog_ proj* operation of the *Project-Programmer* case study which had precisely these qualities, and a rework of the definition of that operation through Z notation provides an interesting comparative exercise. The corresponding schema for *Add_ prog_ proj* is as follows:

```
┌─── Add_ prog_ proj ──────────────────────────────────────────────
│ ΔProject_Programmer
│ Prognum? : Prog_Num
│ Projcode? : Proj_Code
├───────────────────────────────────────────────────────────────────
│ Prognum? ∈ dom(Programmer)
│ Projcode? ∈ dom(Project)
│ ¬((Prognum?, Projcode?) ∈ Assignment)
│ Assignment' = Assignment ∪ {(Prognum?, Projcode?)}
│ Programmer' = Programmer
│ Project' = Project
└───────────────────────────────────────────────────────────────────
```

As shown in Chapter 14 the precondition consists of three clauses which, when negated, give rise to three possible error conditions:

- *Error 1* ¬(*Prognum?* ∈ dom(*Programmer*))...   An unknown programmer
- *Error 2* ¬(*Projcode?* ∈ dom(*Project*))...   An unknown project
- *Error 3* ((*Prognum?*, *Projcode?*) ∈ *Assignment*)...   Programmer already assigned

Therefore, assuming these negations are used to form the basis of the schema definitions:

Add_ prog_ proj_error1, Add_ prog_ proj_error2 and *Add_ prog_ proj_error3*

each of which suppresses a state change, the total operation *Total_add_ prog_ proj* can be defined as:

Total_add_ prog_ proj ≜ (*Add_ prog_ proj* ∧ *Success*) ∨ *Add_ prog_ proj_error1*
$$\lor\ Add\_prog\_proj\_error2$$
$$\lor\ Add\_prog\_proj\_error3$$

which by now is self-explanatory. The definition is again what was referred to in Part 3 as non-deterministic, in that it is possible to get more than one result.

SAQ 16.2 Write the schemas for each of the operations *Add_ prog_ proj_error1, Add_ prog_ proj _error2* and *Add_ prog_ proj _error3*

The case studies that follow this chapter provide further examples of the use of ∧ and ∨ in Z specifications.

Schema negation, implication and equivalence (¬, ⇒ and ⇔)

In addition to the ∧ and ∨ operators, schema calculus offers other connectives which are defined much as expected. The primary operator of this group is negation because, as we know from earlier parts of the book, implication and equivalence are defined in terms of ¬, ∧ and ∨. Thus:

$$(P1 \Rightarrow P2) \Leftrightarrow \neg P1 \lor P2$$

while

$$(P1 \Leftrightarrow P2) \Leftrightarrow (P1 \Rightarrow P2) \wedge (P2 \Rightarrow P1) \text{ or } (\neg P1 \vee P2) \wedge (\neg P2 \vee P1)$$

Given any schema S, we may obtain the schema $\neg S$ by retaining the declaration and negating the predicate. Unfortunately this mechanism is not as simple as it might seem because a schema declaration list may well contribute to the predicate when the shorthand notation is removed on normalization. As a simple example we might consider the following schema which employs an abbreviation definition introduced in Chapter 15:

$$Numbers \triangleq [x : \mathbb{N}_1 \mid x < 100]$$

When we negate *Numbers* we would expect to generate a definition in which x is restricted to values greater than or equal to 100:

$$not\_Numbers \triangleq [x : \mathbb{N}_1 \mid x \geq 100]$$

However, because of the use of the abbreviation definition for the strictly positive natural numbers, we have an additional predicate implied by the declaration and this is revealed when we normalize the schema:

$$Normalized\_Numbers \triangleq [x : \mathbb{Z} \mid 1 \leq x \wedge x < 100]$$

which when negated gives:

$$\neg Normalized\_Numbers \triangleq [x : \mathbb{Z} \mid \neg(1 \leq x \wedge x < 100)]$$

and by De Morgan:

$$\neg Normalized\_Numbers \triangleq [x : \mathbb{Z} \mid 1 > x \vee x \geq 100)]$$

which is clearly not what we wanted because the predicate $1 > x$ permits negative values of x!

Even worse problems can arise when more complex abbreviations are involved. For example, if we were to negate some of the schemas used in the *Project–Programmer* scenario we would have to deal with schemas containing declarations such as:

Project_Programmer

$Programmer : Prog\_Num \nrightarrow Prog\_Name$

$\vdots$

$\vdots$

We showed earlier that the normalization of this schema exposes the predicate implicit in the use of the shorthand such that the definition becomes:

Project_Programmer

$Programmer : \mathbb{P}(Prog\_Num \times Prog\_Name)$

$\vdots$

$\forall a : Prog\_Num; \; \forall p,q : Prog\_Name \bullet ((a,p) \in Programmer \wedge (a,q) \in Programmer \Rightarrow p = q)$

$\vdots$

Negation of a schema involving this predicate is therefore going to lose the quality that *Programmer* remains a function and that is probably not what was intended at all!

Schema negation is therefore of limited use and certainly does not offer us the structuring qualities of conjunction and disjunction. In most circumstances negation does not result in the meaning that was intended, that is, the same schema with just the *explicit* predicate negated. Because implication and equivalence can be defined in terms of negation, the same argument applies. However, readers interested in the application of these operators may like to read Potter *et al.* (1991) and McMorran and Nicholls (1989) where some contrived examples are presented. For the sake of completion some consideration of implication and equivalence is now presented.

The schema expression $A \Rightarrow B$ is a schema which has the signatures of A and B merged and a property that is true if the property of A implies the property of B. Similarly, the schema expression $A \Leftrightarrow B$ is a schema which has the signatures of A and B merged and a property that is true if the property of A is equivalent to the property of B. With schemas:

```
__ A _____          and      __ B _____
  declaration of A                  declaration of A
  _____               _____
  predicate of A                    predicate of A
```

the schemas formed by the expressions $A \Rightarrow B$ and $A \Leftrightarrow B$ are, respectively:

```
__ A_imp_B _____
  declaration of A
  declaration of B
  _____
  predicate of A ⇒ predicate of B
```

and:

```
__ A_equiv_B _____
  declaration of A
  declaration of B
  _____
  predicate of A ⇔ predicate of B
```

16.6.5 Schema renaming

Renaming is really a convenience operator that permits an existing schema to be used again by changing the name of selected variables in both the declaration and predicate parts. The general form of the renaming expression is written:

$$S[new_1/old_1, new_2/old_2, \ldots]$$

where *new* and *old* represent the new and old variable names respectively. The most common use of renaming is in the definition of schema decoration. Thus, the expressions:

Homework [*Class′/Class*, *Handed_in′/Handed_in*, *Not_handed_in′/Not_handed_in*] and

$$Project\_Programmer \ [Programmer'/Programmer, \ Project'/Project,$$
$$Assignment'/Assignment]$$

define the schemas *Homework'* and *Project_Programmer'* used widely throughout this chapter, while the schemas *Std_var?* and *Std_var!* are similarly defined by renaming as:

$$Std\_var? \triangleq Std\_var \ [std?/std] \qquad \text{and} \qquad Std\_var! \triangleq Std\_var \ [std!/std]$$

Renaming of course is a general operation and is not restricted to schema decoration. When used for decoration, however, be careful with global and bound variables.

16.6.6 Schema hiding (\ )

In the *Add_prog* operation for the *Project-Programmer* case study, the operation was specified to accept a programmer number along with the programmer's name. The schema for this operation is:

```
┌─ Add_ prog ──────────────────────────────────────────────
│ ΔProject_Programmer
│ Progname? : Prog_Name
│ Prognum? : Prog_Num
├──────────────────────────────────────────────────────────
│ dom(Programmer) ∩ {Prognum?} = { }
│ Programmer' = Programmer ⊕ {(Prognum?, Progname?)}
│ Project' = Project
│ Assignment ' = Assignment
└──────────────────────────────────────────────────────────
```

An alternative specification might decide to allow the *system* to assign the (unused) number to the programmer name thereby reducing some of the input effort. This approach is reflected in the following *New_Add_prog* schema:

```
┌─ New_Add_ prog ──────────────────────────────────────────
│ ΔProject_Programmer
│ Progname? : Prog_Name
├──────────────────────────────────────────────────────────
│ ∃Prognum? : Prog_Num • (dom(Programmer) ∩ {Prognum?} = { }
│                ∧ Programmer' = Programmer ⊕ {(Prognum?, Progname?)})
│ Project' = Project
│ Assignment' = Assignment
└──────────────────────────────────────────────────────────
```

where the brackets are used to enclose the predicate(s) containing the existentially quantified variables. Here the quantification demands that *there exists* an *unused* programmer number that can be assigned to *Prognum?* In this way we manage to associate the incoming name with a unique identifier without having to input a value explicitly. Notice also that the variable is still decorated as an input but the input to the abstract state now comes from the system and is therefore implicit.

The definition of *New_Add_prog* is related to *Add_prog* by a simple relationship: the former is deduced from the latter by removing the variable *Prognum?* from the declaration list and using it to quantify existentially (all of) the predicate. Strictly speaking, this rule means that the *New_Add_prog* operation should be described by the following schema:

___ *New_Add_prog* _____

Δ*Project_Programmer*
Progname? : *Prog_Name*
_____

$\exists$*Prognum?* : *Prog_Num* $\bullet$ (dom(*Programmer*) $\cap$ {*Prognum?*} = { }
$\qquad\qquad \wedge$ *Programmer'* = *Programmer* $\oplus$ {(*Prognum?*, *Progname?*)}
$\qquad\qquad \wedge$ *Project'* = *Project*
$\qquad\qquad \wedge$ *Assignment'* = *Assignment*)
---

where of course the $\wedge$ operators have to be reintroduced within the quantification for it now becomes a single predicate within the schema. Expressions such as these, however, can often be simplified by making use of the various laws of predicate calculus. One law of use to us here is that in an existentially quantified expression, predicates that do not contain existentially quantified variables can be taken out of the scope of the quantifier. This is true because we showed in Chapter 5 that:

$$\exists x : X \bullet P \wedge Q \dashv\vdash P \wedge \exists x : X \bullet Q$$

where P represents some predicate not involving x. Consequently, by removing predicates not containing *Prognum?* from the quantification the *New_Add_prog* schema becomes:

___ *New_Add_prog* _____

Δ*Project_Programmer*
Progname? : *Prog_Name*
_____

$\exists$*Prognum?* : *Prog_Num* $\bullet$ (dom(*Programmer*) $\cap$ {*Prognum?*} = { }
$\qquad\qquad \wedge$ *Programmer'* = *Programmer* $\oplus$ {(*Prognum?*, *Progname?*)})
Project' = *Project*
Assignment' = *Assignment*
---

which is of course as we originally introduced it. Removing variables in this way is termed *hiding* and Z has a special operator ($\backslash$) which accepts a schema and a set of variable names as arguments and brings about this effect. (Notice that Z overloads the difference symbol to indicate hiding, the implication being that variables are 'taken away'.) Thus, for our simple example:

$$New\_Add\_prog \triangleq Add\_prog \backslash \{Prognum?\}$$

This technique is useful when we wish to allow the system to make choices as to the values of certain variables. However, the hiding operator is also used in the definition of others in schema calculus, notably schema precondition which we examine next.

16.6.7 Schema precondition (pre*OP* or *PreOP*)

Z supports a special operator called pre which is really only a version of schema hiding but is useful if we wish to determine the precise conditions under which an operation is applicable, i.e. its precondition(s). We have already seen that it is important to deduce the precondition(s) for an operation so that partial operations can be converted into total operations by the appropriate consideration of their exceptions. This operator is quite naturally termed *schema precondition* and it can be properly applied only to schemas that represent operations upon the abstract state. Given such a schema *OP* (say), pre*OP* is a schema with all the after and output components hidden, i.e. a schema with these components removed from the declaration list and the schema property existentially quantified using them. In essence, this schema describes all those abstract states upon which the operation *OP* can be successfully carried out. By determining pre*OP* we therefore prove the implementability of the operation, i.e. the fact that the operation can be realized in practice. If preconditions cannot be found the operation cannot be achieved and some redesign will be necessary. In Z it is also conventional that for any schema (*OP*) describing an operation, the schema resulting from the application pre*OP* can be written *PreOP*.

To illustrate schema precondition we return to the *Homework* problem and the specific example of a student submitting homework. The schema for the *Submit* operation is as follows, where the delta notation has been expanded to reveal the inclusion of *Homework'*:

_____ *Submit* _____

Homework
Homework'
Std_var?

─────────────────────────────────────

$Std? \in Not\_handed\_in$
$Not\_handed\_in' = Not\_handed\_in \setminus \{Std?\}$
$Handed\_in' = Handed\_in \cup \{Std?\}$
$Class' = Class$

If we describe the precondition schema in terms of schema hiding we have:

$$PreSubmit = \text{pre}\, Submit \triangleq Submit \setminus \{Homework'\}$$

and *PreSubmit* is as follows where the predicates not involving quantified variables have already been removed from the scope of the quantifier:

_____ *PreSubmit* _____

Homework
Std_var?

─────────────────────────────────────

$Std? \in Not\_handed\_in$
$\exists Homework' \bullet (Not\_handed\_in' = Not\_handed\_in \setminus \{Std?\}$
$\qquad\qquad \wedge\ Handed\_in' = Handed\_in \cup \{Std?\}$
$\qquad\qquad \wedge\ Class' = Class)$

Notice here that the 'variable' quantified is a schema (*Homework'*) and this is perfectly acceptable because a schema is simply a declaration and a predicate. ∃*Homework'* therefore corresponds to the restricted quantifier:

$$\exists Class', Handed\_in', Not\_handed\_in' : \mathbb{P}Student \mid$$
$$(Class' = Handed\_in' \cup Not\_handed\_in' \land Handed\_in' \cap Not\_handed\_in' = \{\})$$

Unlike *Submit*, *PreSubmit* is not a schema that describes a state change. What it does describe is the relationship between the various component objects of the *Homework* state and the input *Std?* in order that the *Submit* operation be applicable. The problem we face now is to discover the nature of this relationship in its simplest form, ideally eliminating where possible the quantifier and the dashed variables. We begin by expanding the quantified *Homework'* schema to reveal all the dashed variables and combine its predicates with those of *PreSubmit*:

```
┌─── PreSubmit ─────────────────────────────────────────────
│ Homework
│ Std_var?
├────────────────────────────────────────────────────────────
│ Std? ∈ Not_handed_in
│ ∃Class', Handed_in', Not_handed_in' : ℙStudent •
│                 (Class' = Handed_in' ∪ Not_handed_in'
│               ∧ Handed_in' ∩ Not_handed_in' = { }
│               ∧ Not_handed_in' = Not_handed_in \ {Std?}
│               ∧ Handed_in' = Handed_in ∪ {Std?}
│               ∧ Class' = Class)
└────────────────────────────────────────────────────────────
```

We can achieve a degree of simplification here by making use of another law of the predicate calculus:

$$P_y \dashv\vdash \exists x : X \bullet x = y \land P_x$$

which states that for some quantified variable x, if $x = y$ and a predicate P_x exists involving x, then the conjunction of the two predicates can be replaced by P_y. Thus in our case, by assuming the truth of the postconditions(s) (there is little point in finding preconditions if we do not assume the operation behaves as intended!), we can split the quantification[1] and apply this sequent to individual expressions such as:

$$\exists Class' : \mathbb{P}Student \bullet Class' = Class \land Class' = Handed\_in' \cup Not\_handed\_in'$$

Here *Class'* corresponds to x, *Class* corresponds to y, and P_x corresponds to *Class' = Handed_in' ∪ Not_handed_in'*. The quantified predicate can be written:

$$Class = Handed\_in' \cup Not\_handed\_in'$$

This is of course just a substitution mechanism and, by repeating the application of the sequent to replace all occurrences of *Handed_in'* and *Not_handed_in'* with their equivalent plain expressions, the existentially quantified expression reduces to:

[1] $\exists a,b,c,\ldots : X \bullet P_a \land P_b \land P_c \land \ldots$ can be written $\exists a : X \bullet P_a \land \exists b : X \bullet P_b \land \exists c : X \bullet P_c \ldots$.

$\exists Class', Handed\_in', Not\_handed\_in' : \mathbb{P}Student \bullet$
$$(Class = (Handed\_in' \cup \{Std?\}) \cup (Not\_handed\_in \backslash \{Std?\})$$
$$\wedge (Handed\_in \cup \{Std?\}) \cap (Not\_handed\_in \backslash \{Std?\}) = \{\})$$

Because predicates not involving quantified variables can be removed from the scope of the quantifier we can eliminate the quantifier completely for it is vacuous. The expression is therefore simply:

$$Class = (Handed\_in \cup \{Std?\}) \cup ((Not\_handed\_in \backslash \{Std?\}) \wedge (Handed\_in \cup \{Std?\})$$
$$\cap (Not\_handed\_in \backslash \{Std?\}) = \{\}$$

The two predicates in this expression can be simplified further. First, consider:

$$Class = (Handed\_in \cup \{Std?\}) \cup (Not\_handed\_in \backslash \{Std?\}).$$

Using the law $a \cup (b \backslash c) = (a \cup b) \backslash (c \backslash a)$ (see Spivey (1992)) where:

$$a = Handed\_in \cup \{Std?\}, \qquad b = Not\_handed\_in \qquad \text{and} \qquad c = \{Std?\}$$

we proceed:

$$Class = ((Handed\_in \cup \{Std?\}) \cup Not\_handed\_in) \backslash (\{Std?\} \backslash (Handed\_in \cup \{Std?\})$$
$$Class = ((Handed\_in \cup \{Std?\}) \cup Not\_handed\_in) \backslash \{\}$$
$$Class = Handed\_in \cup \{Std?\} \cup Not\_handed\_in$$

Since we assume the postcondition to be true, the only way $Class' = Class$ can hold is if $Std?$ is already a member of either Not_handed_in or $Handed\_in$ so that this predicate finally becomes:

$$Class = Handed\_in \cup Not\_handed\_in$$

For the second predicate we first use the law $a \cap (b \backslash c) = (a \cap b) \backslash c$, where:

$$a = (Handed\_in \cup \{Std?\}), \qquad b = Not\_handed\_in \qquad \text{and} \qquad c = \{Std?\}.$$

The expression becomes:

$$((Handed\_in \cup \{Std?\}) \cap Not\_handed\_in) \backslash \{Std?\} = \{\}$$

then using the law $(a \cup b) \cap c = (a \cap c) \cup (b \cap c)$ where now:

$$a = Handed\_in, \qquad b = \{Std?\} \qquad \text{and} \qquad c = Not\_handed\_in$$

we can write:

$$((Handed\_in \cap Not\_handed\_in) \cup (\{Std?\} \cap Not\_handed\_in)) \backslash \{Std?\} = \{\}$$

Now if $Std? \in Not\_handed\_in$ then $(\{Std?\} \cap Not\_handed\_in)) = \{Std?\}$, while if it is not the result is $\{\}$. Either way, $(\{Std?\} \cap Not\_handed\_in)) \backslash \{Std?\}$ evaluates to $\{\}$ so that the predicate becomes:

$$(Handed\_in \cap Not\_handed\_in) \cup \{\} = \{\}$$

which of course finally reduces to:

$$Handed\_in \cap Not\_handed\_in = \{\}$$

```
┌─── PreSubmit ─────────────────────────────────────────
│ Homework
│ Std_var?
├───────────────────────────────────────────────────────
│ Std? ∈ Not_handed_in
│ Class = Handed_in ∪ Not_handed_in
│ Handed_in ∩ Not_handed_in = { }
└───────────────────────────────────────────────────────
```

The predicate:

$$Class = Handed\_in \cap Not\_handed\_in \wedge$$
$$Handed\_in \cap Not\_handed\_in = \{ \}$$

is effectively a demonstration that the operation preserves the invariant on the before state. However, it is already implied as part of the *Homework* schema and therefore technically redundant. The simplest form of *PreSubmit* is therefore:

```
┌─── PreSubmit ─────────────────────────────────────────
│ Homework
│ Std_var?
├───────────────────────────────────────────────────────
│ Std? ∈ Not_handed_in
└───────────────────────────────────────────────────────
```

which suggests that *Submit* can be applied to any abstract state that satisfies the invariant and has *Std?* ∈ *Not_handed_in* so that *Std?* ∈ *Not_handed_in* is the precondition for the operation.

Now, many readers will have realized that this simplification could have been achieved almost by inspection of the original *PreSubmit* schema, but the calculation of preconditions in Z—and the role of the various laws—is an important exercise and so it is as well to illustrate the mechanism with a manageable example.

There are other reasons for undertaking the exercise however. First, if we expand *PreSubmit* we get:

```
┌─── PreSubmit ─────────────────────────────────────────
│ Class, Handed_in, Not_handed_in : ℙ Student
│ Std_var?
├───────────────────────────────────────────────────────
│ Class = Handed_in ∪ Not_handed_in
│ Handed_in ∩ Not_handed_in = { }
│ Std? ∈ Not_handed_in
└───────────────────────────────────────────────────────
```

which shows that the precondition is really more complex than we suggest. But the first two lines of the property represent the system invariant and this applies to *all* operations. Only the last line is characteristic of *Submit* and it is predicates such as this that are generally referred to by the term 'precondition' in this book. Strictly speaking, the invariant will always form part of the precondition for an operation but it is normally taken as understood.

There are often times, however, when the requirements of the operation and the invariant combine to introduce a precondition which is not immediately obvious. In such cases a precondition calculation is crucial to reveal the constraint(s). For example, consider modifying the *Homework* problem somewhat so that a class is restricted to a maximum of 30 students. We could introduce a global constant *MaxClass* by means of the following axiomatic description:

$$MaxClass : \mathbb{N}$$
$$MaxClass = 30$$

and modify the state invariant in the definition of the abstract state so that all operations are aware of the maximum class size:

___ *Homework* _____

$Class, Handed\_in, Not\_handed\_in : \mathbb{P}Student$

$Class = Handed\_in \cup Not\_handed\_in$
$Handed\_in \cap Not\_handed\_in = \{\,\}$
$\#Class \leq MaxClass$

The operation *Enrol*, which simply adds a student to the class, can then be specified as:

___ *Enrol* _____

Homework
Homework'
Std?

$\neg (Std? \in Class)$
$Not\_handed\_in' = Not\_handed\_in \cup Std?$
$Class' = Class \cup Std?$
$Handed\_in' = Handed\_in$

which by now is self-explanatory. The precondition schema is therefore:

___ *PreEnrol* _____

Homework
Std?

$\neg (Std? \in Class)$
$\exists Homework' \bullet (Not\_handed\_in' = Not\_handed\_in \cup Std?$
$\qquad\qquad \wedge\ Class' = Class \cup Std?$
$\qquad\qquad Handed\_in' = Handed\_in)$

Expanding the *Homework'* schema in the quantified predicate we get:

$\exists Class', Handed\_in', Not\_handed\_in' : \mathbb{P}Student \bullet$
$\qquad\qquad (Class' = Handed\_in' \cup Not\_handed\_in'$
$\qquad\qquad \wedge\ Handed\_in' \cap Not\_handed\_in' = \{\,\}$
$\qquad\qquad \wedge\ \#Class' \leq MaxClass$
$\qquad\qquad \wedge\ Not\_handed\_in' = Not\_handed\_in \cup Std?$
$\qquad\qquad \wedge\ Class' = Class \cup Std?$
$\qquad\qquad \wedge\ Handed\_in' = Handed\_in)$

which once again reveals a series of postconditions which we assume to be true. Using the last three lines, substitutions can be made for *Class'*, *Handed_in'* and *Not_handed_in'* by splitting the quantification and using the sequent that we introduced earlier:

$$P_y \dashv\vdash \exists x : X \bullet x = y \wedge P_x$$

This process removes all dashed variables and hence the quantification can be eliminated. The expression therefore becomes:

$$Class \cup Std? = Handed\_in \cup (Not\_handed\_in \cup Std?) \wedge$$
$$Handed\_in \cap (Not\_handed\_in \cup Std?) = \{\,\} \wedge$$
$$\#(Class \cup Std?) \leq MaxClass$$

Once again we are interested in this expression in its simplest form and so we use the laws of set theory to reduce it further. Thus:

$$Class \cup Std? = Handed\_in \cup (Not\_handed\_in \cup Std?)$$

can be written as:

$$Class \cup Std? = (Handed\_in \cup Not\_handed\_in) \cup Std?$$

because union is associative. If we eliminate *Std?* from the expression we get:

$$Class = Handed\_in \cup Not\_handed\_in$$

Similarly, because intersection is also associative, the expression

$$Handed\_in \cap (Not\_handed\_in \cup Std?) = \{\,\}$$

can be written:

$$(Not\_handed\_in \cup Std?) \cap Handed\_in = \{\,\}$$

If we make use of the law, $(a \cup b) \cap c = (a \cap c) \cup (b \cap c)$ the expression becomes:

$$(Not\_handed\_in \cap Handed\_in) \cup (Std? \cap Handed\_in) = \{\,\}$$

Now, from the original postcondition we can safely infer that $\neg(Std? \in Class)$, consequently:

$\neg(Std? \in Handed\_in)$ so that $(Std? \cap Handed\_in) = \{\,\}$ and the expression becomes:

$$(Not\_handed\_in \cap Handed\_in) \cup \{\,\} = \{\,\}$$

that is:

$$Not\_handed\_in \cap Handed\_in = \{\,\}$$

The predicate for *PreEnrol* therefore reduces to:

$$\neg(Std? \in Class)$$
$$\wedge\ Class = Handed\_in \cap Not\_handed\_in$$
$$\wedge\ Not\_handed\_in \cap Handed\_in = \{\,\}$$
$$\wedge\ \#(Class \cup Std?) \leq MaxClass$$

The second and third lines are repetitions of predicates embodied in *Homework* and, although their appearance establishes that the operation preserves the invariant on the before state, they are technically redundant and so can be eliminated. The predicate is therefore:

$$\neg\,(Std? \in Class)$$
$$\wedge\ \#(Class \cup Std?) \leq MaxClass$$

However, the addition of the new student to *Class* increases its population by one. Therefore we can write:

$$\neg\,(Std? \in Class) \wedge (\#Class +1) \leq MaxClass$$

or much more simply:

$$\neg\,(Std? \in Class) \wedge \#Class < MaxClass$$

The final precondition schema is therefore:

```
___ PreEnrol _____
  Homework
  Std?
_____
  ¬(Std? ∈ Class)
  #Class < MaxClass
_____
```

which says that the operation can be legally applied only if the incoming student is not already a member of the class *and* the population of the class is *less than* the maximum. The first of these conditions was obvious from the *Enrol* schema; the second makes clear an obligation that was only implied through the invariant. This raises an interesting question concerning schema design: because the invariant often implies a series of preconditions, should these be included as explicit predicates even though they are deducible from a properly conducted precondition calculation? In other words, should $\#Class < MaxClass$ have appeared in the original specification? The answer to this is 'yes'—especially when the preconditions are fairly obvious. Justification for this view comes from the observation that all we are doing is repeating a predicate that the precondition calculation will reveal, and in this sense it is redundant but its inclusion enhances the semantics of the schema and aids our understanding. This approach was adopted throughout the *Project–Programmer* case study earlier in the book.

Finally, be aware that although precondition calculations can be rather long-winded, failure to carry them out can weaken specifications—some preconditions are not immediately obvious.

SAQ 16.3 Earlier we assumed the preconditions for the *Add_ prog_ proj* operation by inspection. Perform the precondition calculation on *Add_ prog_ proj* to deduce the preconditions formally.

16.6.8 Schema composition (;), overriding (⊕) and piping (≫)

It is well known in computing that the effect of one operation may be regarded as equivalent to the application of two other operations. Probably the most quoted example is the *Amend* operation of a database which makes changes to an existing record. The effect of *Amend* can be achieved by first deleting the record and then adding a new record with the changes made, i.e. *Amend* ≡ (*Delete* then immediately *Add*). In Z, operations are described by schemas and schema calculus provides operators that can be used to create a schema for a new operation by combining the schemas of two existing operations. Like *PreOP* then, these operators can be meaningfully applied only to schemas that describe operations.

Schema composition and schema override are the analogues of relational composition and override and this is reflected in the overloading of the symbols ; and ⊕. Piping is similar to composition but has no direct counterpart in typed set theory. Of the three, composition is probably the most heavily used in Z specifications. The basic idea behind schema composition is that the schema expression:

$$P \,\hat{=}\, Q \;;\; R$$

defines a new schema *P* such that if *Q* can bring about a state change from S_1 to S_2 and *R* can bring about a state change from S_2 to S_3 then the schema *P* can bring about a change from state S_1 to state S_3. Schema composition *Q* ; *R* is therefore a process where:

1. The before state variables of *Q* become the before state variables of *P*.
2. The after state variables of *Q* become the before state variables of *R*.
3. The after state variables of *R* become the after state variables of *P*.
4. The property of the new schema *P* is equivalent to the properties of *Q and R*.

In this process the input (*?*) and output (*!*) variables of the composed schemas are unaffected and remain as part of the new schema but the after state of *Q* and the before state of *R* are intermediates and are eliminated from the final description. Clearly composition is a process that is defined only for schemas that operate on the same sorts of abstract state and if step (2) is to be successful, the set of dashed variables in *Q* must correspond exactly in type and base name to the set of plain variables in *R*. (A variable's base name is that which remains when its decoration is removed.)

In order to illustrate the composition mechanism consider the two operations *Add_ prog_ proj* and *Rem_ prog_ona_ proj* from the *Project–Programmer* case study. The corresponding schemas are as follows with the delta notation expanded and, for obvious reasons, the variable names *OldProjcode* and *NewProjcode* are used in place of *Projcode*:

— Add_ prog_ proj —————————————————————

Project_Programmer
Project_Programmer'
Prognum? : *Prog_Num*
NewProjcode? : *Proj_Code*

Prognum? ∈ dom(*Programmer*)
NewProjcode? ∈ dom(*Project*)
¬((*Prognum?*, *NewProjcode?*) ∈ *Assignment*)
Assignment' = *Assignment* ∪ {(*Prognum?*, *NewProjcode?*)}
Programmer' = *Programmer*
Project' = *Project*

```
┌─ Rem_ prog_ona_ proj ──────────────────────────────────────────
│ Project_Programmer
│ Project_Programmer'
│ Prognum? : Prog_Num
│ OldProjcode? : Proj_Code
├─────────────────────────────────────────────────────────────────
│ Prognum? ∈ dom(Programmer)
│ OldProjcode? ∈ dom(Project)
│ (Prognum?, OldProjcode?) ∈ Assignment
│ Assignment' = Assignment \ {(Prognum?, OldProjcode?)}
│ Programmer' = Programmer
│ Project' = Project
└─────────────────────────────────────────────────────────────────
```

The first schema simply adds a programmer to a project, while the second removes a programmer from a project. The effect of moving a programmer from one project to another can therefore be defined in terms of composition:

$$Move\_ prog \triangleq Rem\_ prog\_ona\_ proj \; ; \; Add\_ prog\_ proj$$

which really amounts to amending part of the programmer's details. In order to effect the composition we perform the following steps which are generally applicable to the composition of any compatible schemas:

1. Rename all the after state variables in *Rem_ prog_ona_ proj* to something completely new, e.g., variable v' becomes v^+. Using the *Rename* operator of schema calculus we can write:

   (a) Rem_ prog_ona_ proj $\triangleq$
   Rem_ prog_ona_ proj [*Project_Programmer$^+$/Project_Programmer'*]

   $\qquad\qquad\qquad$ [*Assignment$^+$/Assignment'*]
   $\qquad\qquad\qquad$ [*Programmer$^+$/Programmer'*]
   $\qquad\qquad\qquad$ [*Project$^+$/Project'*]

2. Rename all the before state variables in *Add_ prog_ proj* the same way. Again using the *Rename* operator we have:

   (b) Add_ prog_ proj $\triangleq$
   Add_ prog_ proj [*Project_Programmer$^+$/Project_Programmer*]

   $\qquad\qquad\qquad$ [*Assignment$^+$/Assignment*]
   $\qquad\qquad\qquad$ [*Programmer$^+$/Programmer*]
   $\qquad\qquad\qquad$ [*Project$^+$/Project*]

3. Form the conjunction of the two renamed schemas so that the new schema derives its property from *Rem_ prog_ona_ proj AND Add_ prog_ proj.* Thus we form the following schema expression:

(c) *Move_ prog* $\triangleq$
Rem_ prog_ona_ proj $[Project\_Programmer^+/Project\_Programmer']$
$[Assignment^+/Assignment']$
$[Programmer^+/Programmer']$
$[Project^+/Project'] \wedge$

Add_ prog_ proj $[Project\_Programmer^+/Project\_Programmer]$
$[Assignment^+/Assignment]$
$[Programmer^+/Programmer]$
$[Project^+/Project]$

4. Finally, the variables v^+ in the schema formed in step (3) are hidden ($/$) and the resulting schema simplified.

The schemas resulting from each of the steps 1–3 are as follows:

(a) *Rem_ prog_ona_ proj* ─────────────────────────────────

Project_Programmer
Project_Programmer$^+$
Prognum? : *Prog_Num*
OldProjcode? : *Proj_Code*

Prognum? $\in$ dom(*Programmer*)
OldProjcode? $\in$ dom(*Project*)
(*Prognum?*, *OldProjcode?*) $\in$ *Assignment*
Assignment$^+$ = *Assignment* \ {(*Prognum?*, *OldProjcode?*)}
Programmer$^+$ = *Programmer*
Project$^+$ = *Project*

(b) *Add_ prog_ proj* ─────────────────────────────────

Project_Programmer$^+$
Project_Programmer$'$
Prognum? : *Prog_Num*
NewProjcode? : *Proj_Code*

Prognum? $\in$ dom(*Programmer*$^+$)
NewProjcode? $\in$ dom(*Project*$^+$)
$\neg$((*Prognum?*, *NewProjcode?*) $\in$ *Assignment*$^+$)
Assignment$'$ = *Assignment*$^+$ $\cup$ {(*Prognum?*, *NewProjcode?*)}
Programmer$'$ = *Programmer*$^+$
Project$'$ = *Project*$^+$

```
┌─── (c)Move_ prog ──────────────────────────────────────────────
│ Project_Programmer
│ Project_Programmer⁺
│ Project_Programmer'
│ Prognum? : Prog_Num
│ OldProjcode?, NewProjcode? : Proj_Code
├────────────────────────────────────────────────────────────────
│ Prognum? ∈ dom(Programmer)
│ Prognum? ∈ dom(Programmer⁺)
│ OldProjcode? ∈ dom(Project)
│ NewProjcode? ∈ dom(Project⁺)
│ (Prognum?, OldProjcode?) ∈ Assignment
│ ¬((Prognum?, NewProjcode?) ∈ Assignment⁺)
│ Assignment⁺ = Assignment \ {(Prognum?, OldProjcode?)}
│ Assignment' = Assignment⁺ ∪ {(Prognum?, NewProjcode?)}
│ Programmer⁺ = Programmer
│ Programmer' = Programmer⁺
│ Project⁺ = Project
│ Project' = Project⁺
└────────────────────────────────────────────────────────────────
```

The final part of the strategy simply requires us to hide all the variables in *(c)Move_ prog* that were introduced in steps (1) and (2) which means removing all variables v^+ from the declaration and using them to quantify the predicate existentially:

$$Move\_prog \triangleq (c)Move\_prog / \{Project\_Programmer^+\}$$

which gives:

```
┌─── Move_ prog ─────────────────────────────────────────────────
│ Project_Programmer
│ Project_Programmer'
│ Prognum? : Prog_Num
│ 'OldProjcode?, NewProjcode? : Proj_Code
├────────────────────────────────────────────────────────────────
│ ∃Project_Programmer⁺ •
│   (Prognum? ∈ dom(Programmer)
│   ∧ OldProjcode? ∈ dom(Project)
│   ∧ (Prognum?, OldProjcode?) ∈ Assignment
│   ∧ Prognum? ∈ dom(Programmer⁺)
│   ∧ NewProjcode? ∈ dom(Project⁺)
│   ∧ ¬((Prognum?, NewProjcode?) ∈ Assignment⁺)
│   ∧ Assignment⁺ = Assignment \ {(Prognum?, OldProjcode?)}
│   ∧ Assignment' = Assignment⁺ ∪ {(Prognum?, NewProjcode?)}
│   ∧ Programmer⁺ = Programmer
│   ∧ Programmer' = Programmer⁺
│   ∧ Project⁺ = Project
│   ∧ Project' = Project⁺)
└────────────────────────────────────────────────────────────────
```

If we expand the decorated schema *Project_Programmer*$^+$ and place those predicates not involving quantified variables outside the scope of the quantifier we get:

```
┌─── Move_ prog ──────────────────────────────────────────────
│ Project_Programmer
│ Project_Programmer′
│ Prognum? : Prog_Num
│ OldProjcode?, NewProjcode? : Proj_Code
├──────────────────────────────────────────────────────────────
│ Prognum? ∈ dom(Programmer)
│ OldProjcode? ∈ dom(Project)
│ (Prognum?, OldProjcode?) ∈ Assignment
│ ∃ Programmer⁺ : Prog_Num ↛ Prog_Name;
│    Project⁺ : Proj_Code ⤔ Proj_Name;
│    Assignment⁺ : Prog_Num ↔ Proj_Code •
│    (dom(Assignment⁺) ⊆ dom(Programmer⁺)
│    ∧ ran(Assignment⁺) ⊆ dom(Project⁺)
│    ∧ Prognum? ∈ dom(Programmer⁺)
│    ∧ NewProjcode? ∈ dom(Project⁺)
│    ∧ ¬((Prognum?, NewProjcode?) ∈ Assignment⁺)
│    ∧ Assignment⁺ = Assignment \ {(Prognum?, OldProjcode?)}
│    ∧ Assignment′ = Assignment⁺ ∪ {(Prognum?, NewProjcode?)}
│    ∧ Programmer⁺ = Programmer
│    ∧ Programmer′ = Programmer⁺
│    ∧ Project⁺ = Project
│    ∧ Project′ = Project⁺)
```

As we have already seen, such schemas can be simplified considerably by splitting the quantification and eliminating the variables decorated v^+ by substitution, using predicates such as $v^+ = v$ or $v' = v^+$. The schema therefore becomes:

```
┌─── Move_ prog ──────────────────────────────────────────────
│ Project_Programmer
│ Project_Programmer′
│ Prognum? : Prog_Num
│ OldProjcode?, NewProjcode? : Proj_Code
├──────────────────────────────────────────────────────────────
│ Prognum? ∈ dom(Programmer)
│ OldProjcode? ∈ dom(Project)
│ (Prognum?, OldProjcode?) ∈ Assignment
│ ∃ Programmer⁺ : Prog_Num ↛ Prog_Name;
│    Project⁺ : Proj_Code ⤔ Proj_Name;
│    Assignment⁺ : Prog_Num ↔ Proj_Code •
│    (dom(Assignment \ {(Prognum?, OldProjcode?)}) ⊆ dom(Programmer)
│    ∧ ran(Assignment \ {(Prognum?, OldProjcode?)}) ⊆ dom(Project)
│    ∧ Prognum? ∈ dom(Programmer)
│    ∧ NewProjcode? ∈ dom(Project)
```

$$\wedge \neg ((Prognum?, NewProjcode?) \in Assignment \setminus \{(Prognum?, OldProjcode?)\})$$
$$\wedge\ Assignment' = Assignment \setminus \{(Prognum?, OldProjcode?)\}$$
$$\cup \{(Prognum?, NewProjcode?)\}$$
$$\wedge\ Programmer' = Programmer$$
$$\wedge\ Project' = Project)$$

Elimination of the decorated variables has made the quantification vacuous and it can be removed. The *Move_ prog* schema therefore reduces to:

```
┌─ Move_ prog ──────────────────────────────────
│ Project_Programmer
│ Project_Programmer'
│ Prognum? : Prog_Num
│ OldProjcode?, NewProjcode? : Proj_Code
├────────────────────────────────────────────────
│ Prognum? ∈ dom(Programmer)
│ OldProjcode? ∈ dom(Project)
│ (Prognum?, OldProjcode?) ∈ Assignment
│ dom(Assignment \ {(Prognum?, OldProjcode?)}) ⊆ dom(Programmer)
│ ran(Assignment \ {(Prognum?, OldProjcode?)} ⊆ dom(Project)
│ NewProjcode? ∈ Project)
│ ¬((Prognum?, NewProjcode?) ∈ Assignment \ {(Prognum?, OldProjcode?)})
│ Assignment' = Assignment \ {(Prognum?, OldProjcode?)}
│                ∪ {(Prognum?, NewProjcode?)}
│ Programmer' = Programmer
│ Project' = Project
└────────────────────────────────────────────────
```

where the two occurrences of *Prognum?* ∈ dom(*Programmer*) have been replaced by one. There are some final simplifications which make this schema more acceptable. First, the declarations *Programmer, Programmer'* can be replaced by the familiar Δ*Project_Programmer*. Secondly, the predicates:

$$\text{dom}(Assignment \setminus \{(Prognum?, OldProjcode?)\}) \subseteq \text{dom}(Programmer)$$
$$\text{ran}(Assignment \setminus \{(Prognum?, OldProjcode?)) \subseteq \text{dom}(Project)$$

can be shown to be redundant. Taking the first of these predicates we proceed as follows:

$$\text{dom}(Assignment \setminus \{(Prognum?, OldProjcode?)\}) =$$
$$\text{dom}(Assignment) \setminus \text{dom}(\{(Prognum?, OldProjcode?)) = \text{dom}(Assignment) \setminus \{Prognum?\}$$

hence the first predicate becomes:

$$\text{dom}(Assignment) \setminus \{Prognum?\} \subseteq \text{dom}(Programmer)$$

If we apply union with {*Prognum?*} to both sides of this predicate we do not change its result but we can make further simplification:

$$(\text{dom}(Assignment) \setminus \{Prognum?\}) \cup \{Prognum?\} \subseteq \text{dom}(Programmer) \cup \{Prognum?\}$$

but

$$(\text{dom}(Assignment) \setminus \{Prognum?\}) \cup \{Prognum?\} = \text{dom}(Assignment)$$

and because we must have $Prognum? \subseteq \text{dom}(Programmer)$ it follows that:

$$\text{dom}(Programmer) \cup \{Prognum?\} = \text{dom}(Programmer)$$

so that the predicate reduces to:

$$\text{dom}(Assignment) \subseteq \text{dom}(Programmer)$$

By using a similar argument we can show that:

$$\text{ran}(Assignment \setminus \{(Prognum?, OldProjcode?)\}) \subseteq \text{dom}(Project)$$

can be replaced by:

$$\text{ran}(Assignment) \subseteq \text{dom}(Project)$$

and because these predicates are already implied by the presence of *Project-Programmer* in the delta notation they can be eliminated. The final *Move_ prog* schema is therefore:

```
┌─── Move_ prog ─────────────────────────────────────────────
│ ΔProject_Programmer
│ Prognum? : Prog_Num
│ OldProjcode?, NewProjcode? : Proj_Code
├─────────────────────────────────────────────────────────────
│ Prognum? ∈ dom(Programmer)
│ OldProjcode? ∈ dom(Project)
│ NewProjcode? ∈ dom(Project)
│ (Prognum?, OldProjcode?) ∈ Assignment
│ ¬((Prognum?, NewProjcode?) ∈ Assignment \ {(Prognum?, OldProjcode?)})
│ Assignment' = Assignment \ {(Prognum?, OldProjcode?)} ∪ {(Prognum?, NewProjcode?)}
│ Programmer' = Programmer
│ Project' = Project
└─────────────────────────────────────────────────────────────
```

which describes an operation that accepts a programmer number, an old project code and a new project code then removes the programmer from the old project and assigns the programmer to the new project. Schema composition is therefore a useful mechanism that constructs new schema definitions from old ones. Some of the case studies following this chapter provide additional composition examples. Notice also the preconditions that composition has generated for *Move_Prog*.

The final operators, schema overriding and schema piping, are less frequently used. The *overriding* of a schema P by a schema Q is written $P \oplus Q$ and is read 'P overridden by Q'. The result of overriding is a schema that corresponds to Q whenever the precondition for Q is true but elsewhere corresponds to P. Schema overriding can be thought of as applying operation Q wherever we can, but where Q is *not* applicable we apply P.

Schema piping is written $P \gg Q$. This operation is similar to composition with the difference that, rather than identifying the afterstate components of P with the before state components of Q, the *output* components of $S(!)$ are identified with the *input* components of $Q(?)$ that have the same base name. The result of the piping is a schema with the signatures of P and Q merged, a property that is the conjunction of those of P and Q, but those output components of P that match to input components of Q are renamed as input components and hidden. A use for piping will be illustrated shortly.

16.7 GENERIC CONSTRUCTIONS IN Z

The *Project–Programmer* case study described a situation where programmers were assigned to projects. In most organizations, however, other resources may well be associated with a project. For example, projects may have access to a number of database tables, printers or disk units, while human resources might involve project managers or analysts. If we imagine the case study to represent just one aspect of a resource management system (RMS)[2] then, clearly, the abstract state of the system will have to be extended considerably to include associations with the other human and physical resources. In many cases, however, the nature of the relationship between the project and the resource is the same as that between projects and programmers, for example.

- An analyst works on a number of different projects; a project employs a number of analysts.
- A disk unit is used by a number of projects; a project uses a number of disk units.
- A table is used in a number of projects; a project has access to a number of tables.

In each of these cases a relation can be used to reflect the relationship between the project and the resource in the same way as *Assignment* did for projects and programmers. The abstract state for the RMS can therefore be described (in part) by a schema constructed from the inclusion of a number of other schemas, each having a similar structure but tailored to describe an individual aspect. In short, a family of schema definitions is required. To deal with situations like this Z provides the *generic schema*. To explain its role we need to extend the case study somewhat to reflect an RMS. Imagine the given sets to now include.

[*PROJ_CODE, PROJ_NAME, EMP_NUM, EMP_NAME, TABLE_NO, TABLE_NAME, DISK_NO, DISK_UNIT, PRINTER_NUM, PRINTER_NAME, ...*]

and where now we have general sets of employee names and numbers which can be used to identify programmers, analysts and any other human resource. The relationship between a project and its name is again regarded as a partial injection from *PROJ_CODE* to *PROJ_NAME*, while for the human resources the relationships between the identifiers and their names will always be modelled as partial functions. For the physical resources, however, the relationships might vary so if we use the symbol ♠ to represent any one of the mathematical objects then we can introduce a number of abbreviation definitions to be used in the schema constructions, for example:

---

[2]Our model of an RMS is rather naïve but illustrates the role of generic schemas. Interested readers might like to look at the 'CAVIAR' RMS used by Flinn and Sorensen (Hayes, 1987) which is more sophisticated.

$$PROJECT \qquad == PROJ\_CODE \rightarrowtail PROJ\_NAME$$
$$PROGRAMMER == EMP\_NUM \nrightarrow EMP\_NAME$$
$$ANALYST \qquad == EMP\_NUM \nrightarrow EMP\_NAME$$
$$DISKS \qquad == DISK\_NO \spadesuit DISK\_UNIT$$
$$DICTIONARY \quad == TABLE\_NO \spadesuit TABLE\_NAME$$
$$PRINTERS \qquad == PRINTER\_NUM \spadesuit PRINTER\_NAME$$

where $\spadesuit$ has yet to be supplied. The generic construction that can be used to define the individual schemas for each resource in the abstract state is as follows:

─── *Project_Assignment* [*RESOURCE, OBJ*] ───────────────
Project : *PROJECT*
v_1 : *OBJ*
v_2 : *RESOURCE* $\leftrightarrow$ *PROJECT_CODE*
─────────────────────────────────────
$\mathrm{dom}(v_2) \subseteq \mathrm{dom}(v_1)$
$\mathrm{ran}(v_2) \subseteq \mathrm{dom}(Project)$
─────────────────────────────────────

Here the schema accepts two *formal generic parameters RESOURCE* and *OBJ* and introduces the variables v_1 and v_2 defined in terms of the types these parameters represent. When the schema is used, *actual generic parameters* will be supplied to instantiate the schema. Thus if the instantiation took the form *Project_Assignment* [*EMP_NUM, PROGRAMMER*] the parameter *EMP_NUM* replaces every instance of *RESOURCE*, while *PROGRAMMER* replaces every instance of *OBJ*. The schema resulting from this instantiation is therefore:

─── *Project_Assignment* [*EMP_NUM, PROGRAMMER*] ───────────────
Project : *PROJECT*
v_1 : *PROGRAMMER*
v_2 : *EMP_NUM* $\leftrightarrow$ *PROJECT_CODE*
─────────────────────────────────────
$\mathrm{dom}(v_2) \subseteq \mathrm{dom}(v_2)$
$\mathrm{ran}(v_2) \subseteq \mathrm{dom}(Project)$
─────────────────────────────────────

which corresponds exactly to the schema describing the abstract state of the *Project– Programmer* case study including the invariant that only known programmers can be assigned to known projects.

SAQ 16.4 Write out the schemas resulting from:

$$Project\_Assignment\ [EMP\_NUM, ANALYST]$$

and:

$$Project\_Assignment\ [TABLE\_NUM, DICTIONARY]$$

The answers to SAQ 16.4 show that a whole family of schemas can be defined for each of the resources by appropriate instantiations of the generic schema, and each case ensures that only known resources are associated with known projects. The obvious extension of this argument is to define (part of) the abstract state of the RMS by combining each of the separately instantiated generic schemas. This is done as follows, where the rename operator of the schema calculus is used to avoid the clashes between the variables v_1 and v_2 in each schema:

$A_1 \triangleq$ *Project_Assignment* [*EMP_NUM, PROGRAMMER*]
$\qquad\qquad\qquad$ [*Programmer* \ v_1, *Prg-Prj* \ v_2]
$A_2 \triangleq$ *Project_Assignment* [*PROG_NUM, ANALYST*] [*Analyst* \ v_1, *Anal-Prj* \ v_2]
$A_3 \triangleq$ *Project_Assignment* [*TABLE_NUM, DICTIONARY*] [*Dictionary* \ v_1, *Dict-Prj* \ v_2]
$\vdots$

RMS $\triangleq [A_1 ; A_2 ; A_3 ; \ldots]$

Of course, there will be other components in the abstract state and other restrictions on the combinations that state objects can assume, e.g. the RMS invariant might be extended to include:

$$\text{dom}\mathit{Programmer} \cap \text{dom}\mathit{Analyst} = \{\,\}$$

such that programmers and analysts always remain separate resources. The generic schema, however, can be seen as yet another technique that permits the separation of concerns that make Z specifications more manageable and readable.

Useful though generic schemas are, an even more useful construction is the *generic constant* which can be used within Z specifications to introduce constants (such as functions) that are applicable across a wide spectrum of types. Like the schema, the generic constant definition is just another in the series of the formal paragraphs of a Z document and takes the following general form:

$$
\boxed{
\begin{array}{l}
[X] \\
\hline
x : X \\
\hline
P_X
\end{array}
}
$$

The distinctive box notation defines a whole family of variables x that satisfy some predicate P_X. As with the generic schema, at the point where we wish to use x we have to replace the formal generic parameter(s) with actual generic parameters(s) thereby instantiating the variable.

As usual, new ideas are always best illustrated with an example. Recall that in Sec. 6.3.3 the question was raised of whether we needed to distinguish between (say) an empty set of *Cars* and an empty set of *Books*. Strictly speaking we do, because the two sets are of different types and it would offend the rules of typed set theory to have a member ({ } or $\emptyset$) that could belong to both. If, however, we define the empty set generically then we can instantiate it as a member of any type we wish. The definition follows from our informal discussion in Chapter 6:

$$
\boxed{
\begin{array}{l}
[X] \\
\hline
\{\,\} : \mathbb{P}X \\
\hline
\{\,\} = \{x : X \mid x \neq x\}
\end{array}
}
$$

$\{\,\}$ [*Cars*] and $\{\,\}$ [*Books*] therefore represent empty sets of *Cars* and *Books* respectively.

The empty set, however, is so familiar that explicit instantiation is rarely used; rather the type of { } is usually inferred from its context.

Many other examples of generic definitions appear in Spivey (1992)—the Z basic library—which includes definitions of objects such as *Sets, Relations, Functions* and the operations that can be performed upon them. Notice also that the library frequently defines a collection of operators in one generic construction, e.g. the set operators *intersection, union* and *difference*. The generic definitions for these are:

$$
\begin{array}{|l}
\hline
\rule{0pt}{1em}[X] \\
\hline
\_\cup\_,\ \_\cap\_,\ \_\backslash\_ : \mathbb{P}X \times \mathbb{P}X \to \mathbb{P}X \\
\hline
\forall S,T : \mathbb{P}X \bullet S \cup T = \{x : X \mid x \in S \vee x \in T\} \wedge \\
\quad\quad\quad\quad S \cap T = \{x : X \mid x \in S \wedge x \in T\} \wedge \\
\quad\quad\quad\quad S \backslash T = \{x : X \mid x \in S \wedge \neg(x \in T)\} \\
\hline
\end{array}
$$

The notation used in the signature (e.g. $\_\cup\_$) is meant to describe union, intersection and difference as binary operators that accept two arguments—both sets of type X— each operator returning a set of the same type as a result. The predicates define the effect of the operators and these largely follow from Chapter 5.

Generic definitions are clearly useful and adaptable concepts but authors of a specification should be aware of a restriction that applies if these definitions are to be mathematically sound, namely that the definition uniquely determines a value for the constant *for every possible value of the formal parameter(s)*. In this respect, the following generic definition is incorrect:

$$
\begin{array}{|l}
\hline
\rule{0pt}{1em}[X] \\
\hline
not\_empty : \mathbb{P}X \\
\hline
\#(not\_empty) \neq 0 \\
\hline
\end{array}
$$

for when X is an empty set the instantiated predicate fails. As an example of the use of both generic schemas and generic constants we return to the specification of the *Sort* operation discussed in the case study in Chapter 12. The important point to recall is that to sort the items belonging to some set X, the set must have a total order defined upon it. Recall that a total order is a particular relation that relates items of the set to one another, i.e. it is a homogeneous relation of type $R : X \leftrightarrow X$ which has the following properties:

- $\forall x : X \bullet xRx$ The relation is reflexive, relating elements to themselves.
- $\forall x, y, z : X \bullet xRy \wedge yRx \Rightarrow x = y$ The relation is antisymmetric such that either x comes earlier than y in the order or y comes earlier than x but not both.
- $\forall x, y, z : X \bullet xRy \wedge yRz \Rightarrow xRz$ The relation is transitive such that if x is earlier than y and y is earlier than z then x is earlier than z.
- $\forall x, y : X \bullet xRy \vee yRx$ Every pair of elements of the set X is related.

Therefore, given some set X, when we form $X \leftrightarrow X$ the only relations in this set that are total orders are those that satisfy the predicates above. In general then, the set of total orders that can be defined upon X is given by the following generic definition:

$$\underline{\quad[X]\quad}$$

$total\_order : \mathbb{P}(X \leftrightarrow X)$

$\forall R : X \leftrightarrow X \bullet R \in total\_order \Leftrightarrow$
$\qquad (\forall x : X \bullet xRx) \land$
$\qquad (\forall x, y, z : X \bullet xRy \land yRz \Rightarrow x = y) \land$
$\qquad (\forall x, y, z : X \bullet xRy \land yRz \Rightarrow xRz) \land$
$\qquad (\forall x, y : X \bullet xRy \lor yRx)$

From the signature, *total_order* is a set of relations over X (i.e. it is of type $\quad(X \times X)$) and each relation in this set is a total order on X, e.g. if X were the set of integers then the relations $\leq$ and $\geq$ would be members of *total_order*. We can now specify the sort operation using a generic schema that describes the operation as accepting a sequence of $X(in?)$ and a particular total order (say $\leq_X?$ or $\geq_X?$) and producing a sequence of $X(out!)$ that has the same number of elements in the same frequency as *in?* and which is ordered according to the input order. The following schema sorts in ascending order[3] based on the input relation $\leq_X$. The equivalent schema *Sort_Descending[X]* can easily be constructed.

$$\underline{\quad Sort\_Ascending[X]\quad}$$

$in?, out! : \text{seq } X$
$\leq_X : X \leftrightarrow X$

$\leq_X? \in total\_order[X]$
$\forall i, j : \text{dom } out! \bullet i < j \Rightarrow out! \, i \leq_X out! \, j$
$items \, (in?) = items \, (out!)$

As a final point, it might now be well worth revisiting the *Project–Programmer* case study to re-examine the *Prognames_ona_ proj* operation that lists the names of programmers on a particular project. With reference to Chapter 9 the Z schema for this operation can be written as follows:

$$\underline{\quad Prognames\_ona\_project\quad}$$

$\Xi Project\_Programmer$
$Projcode? : PROJ\_CODE$
$Progs! : \mathbb{P} \, PROG\_NAME$

$Projcode? \in \text{dom}(Project) \land$
$Progs! = \text{ran}((\text{dom}(Assignment \triangleright \{Projcode?\})) \lhd Programmer)$

We noted in the case study that the problem with this specification is that since the output (*Progs!*) is a set, it cannot contain duplicate names. If a project employs a number of programmers with the same name then the operation does not distinguish them. This difficulty can be avoided if we modify the operation as follows:

---

[3]Because of the possibility of duplicates in the input sequence, some authors prefer to call this 'non-decreasing' order. I feel this confuses rather than enlightens.

```
┌── Prognames_ona_ project ────────────────────────────────────────
│ ΞProject_Programmer
│ Projcode? : PROJ_CODE
│ Progs! : PROG_NUM ↛ PROG_NAME
├────────────────────────────────────────────────────────────────
│ Projcode? ∈ dom(Project)
│ Progs! = (dom(Assignment ▷ {Projcode?})) ◁ Programmer
└────────────────────────────────────────────────────────────────
```

which now outputs a set of pairs—programmer numbers followed by programmer names—for each programmer on the project. However, with a little more adventure we could specify an operation that produces an *ordered list* of programmer names (including duplicates) for any target project. If we redefined *PROG_NUM* as a set of strictly positive natural numbers, e.g. $PROG\_NUM == \{1 \ .. \ 5000\}$, then the schemas involved are:

```
┌── Prognames_ona_ project-1 ──────────────────────────────────────
│ ΞProject_Programmer
│ Projcode? : PROJ_CODE
│ Progs! : seq PROG_NAME
├────────────────────────────────────────────────────────────────
│ Projcode? ∈ dom(Project)
│ Progs! = squash ((dom(Assignment ▷ {Projcode?})) ◁ Programmer)
└────────────────────────────────────────────────────────────────
```

$$Prognames\_ona\_ project \triangleq Prognames\_ona\_ project\text{-}1 \gg Sort \ [PROG\_NAME]$$

In *Prognames_ona_ project-1* the output is a sequence of programmer names produced by *squash*ing the function. Using the generic definition, the output from the first schema is piped directly to a customized *Sort* which then yields a sequence of programmer names in ascending order. For piping to be defined, the *Progs!* output component from *Prognames_ona_ project-1* must match the input component of *Sort* in base name and type. We therefore rename *Progs!* to *in?* and hide the variable in the final schema. The piping is therefore defined in terms of the equivalent expression:

$$Prognames\_ona\_ project \triangleq ((Prognames\_ona\_ project\text{-}1[in?/Progs!]$$
$$\wedge \ Sort \ [PROG\_NAME]) \backslash \{in?\}$$

SAQ 16.5 Deduce the definition of the schema *Prognames_ona_ project*.

As a final comment, interested readers might like to re-examine the *Project–Programmer* case study to see if other operations could benefit from the sort, e.g. *Projnames_withno_ progs*. These could be similarly respecified.

16.8 SUMMARY

This long chapter has defined and illustrated almost all the operators of Z schema calculus. Schemas represent the basic structuring mechanism within a Z specification and they have a number of important features:

- Schemas are a characteristic feature of Z.
- The formal aspect of a Z specification is described in terms of schemas. They have a distinctive box-like notation which distinguishes them from other parts of the document.
- Schemas consist of a declaration part and a predicate part—called the 'property' of the schema.
- Schemas are not tuples; consequently they can be manipulated in a more flexible fashion especially with regard to their combination.
- Schema calculus defines a series of operators that can be used to manipulate schemas. The operators of the calculus affect both the declaration and predicate parts.
- Schemas can be quantified.
- Schemas are used to describe abstract states, initial states and operations.
- Combined schemas can often be simplified using the laws of ordinary predicate calculus. Useful laws (see Chapter 5) are:

$$\exists x : X \bullet P_y \wedge Q_x \dashv\vdash P_y \wedge \exists x : X \bullet Q_x$$
$$P_y \dashv\vdash \exists x : X \bullet x = y \wedge P_x$$
$$\exists a,b,c,\ldots : X \bullet P_a \wedge P_b \wedge P_c \wedge \ldots can\ be\ written$$
$$\exists a : X \bullet P_a \wedge \exists b : X \bullet P_b \wedge \exists c : X \bullet P_c \ldots$$

- Schemas can be defined generically so that they can be used with a wide variety of different types.

The schema calculus is unique to Z. The specification language VDM (see Parts 6 and 7), however, has some parallels with schema composition and schema precondition calculations. In the latter case these emerge as *implementability proof obligations* and when we look at these later you should note some remarkable similarities with the exercises conducted in Z.

PART FIVE

Z Case Studies

Example is the school of mankind, and they will learn at no other.
Edmund Burke (1729–97), British politician, *Letters on a Regicide Peace*

INTRODUCTION

This part of the book presents three case studies which illustrate the overall structure of
a Z document and the various techniques used in its construction. The objects specified
are:

- Stacks and queues
- Symbol tables
- A simple drinks dispensing machine

while the techniques employed include:

- Generic definitions
- Alternative specification models
- Theorem proofs for initial states and specification properties
- Precondition calculations
- Total operation specifications
- Precondition summaries

The symbol table is commonly used in introductory texts on Z and the discussion
presented here is really only a variation on a generally accepted theme. The specification is included so that the reader may compare the approach used by Z with that of
the approach taken by VDM later in the book. In addition, there are case studies in the
literature where the symbol table specification has been modified to deal with block
structured languages and also included as part of the specification of a simple
assembler. The reader is again encouraged to review these (Hayes 1987).

Stacks and queues are almost invariably included in texts on VDM but rarely in texts
on Z. (See Lightfoot (1991) where a very simple stack is specified.) A primary purpose

of this book is to enable the reader to review the approaches taken by the various techniques, and with this end in mind a full Z specification for these objects is also developed.

The final specification for the drinks dispensing machine illustrates some interesting aspects of Z but is included primarily to permit a more detailed comparison with the VDM approach in particular. The drinks machine is similar to the cash dispenser problem which is again commonly used in introductory specifications.

Although comparison with other specification techniques is important, it is equally important to use the case studies to illustrate the techniques of Z *per se*. In this respect the studies show how Z specifications are structured through the definition and combination of schemas, and how Z deals with a variety of generic definitions, constructs theorems to discharge proof obligations and calculates preconditions to describe total operations. In all cases the proofs are conducted rigorously rather than strictly formally and are therefore rather more readable. The first two case studies also show how alternative models for objects can often be constructed in model-based specification techniques and examine the influence the choice of model has on the subsequent workload—especially in the area of proof.

17

GENERIC STACKS AND QUEUES

17.1 INTRODUCTION

In this first case study we present the Z specifications for two very familiar and frequently used objects: stacks and queues. Stacks and queues should be familiar to everyone involved in computing; it is therefore unnecessary to explain the behaviour of these objects here.

There are three technical features of this example which the reader should appreciate. First, the objects are defined generically so that they can be subsequently used in a variety of specifications with a range of different stack types. In this respect, the role of the generic notation throughout the specification should be carefully noted. Secondly, stacks and queues are frequently described as lists[1] and this observation leads naturally to the use of the sequence as the most appropriate mathematical model. Finally, although the sequence may be appropriate, it is not the only model that can be used. The case study therefore suggests an alternative specification which models these objects as sets of time-stamped items; top of stack corresponds to the item associated with the latest time stamp while the first in the queue is the item with the earliest time stamp. An important feature of Z—and other constructive specification techniques—is that designers are free to investigate the merits of a wide range of possible models. Readers are free to develop this second model as an exercise.

17.2 THE GIVEN SETS, ABBREVIATION DEFINITIONS AND AXIOMATIC DESCRIPTIONS

The given sets are introduced by the paragraph [$X, BOOLEAN$]. Stacks and queues can be constructed for any items of interest. The given set X therefore represents any set which the specifier may care to use. This set is used in the generic definitions and instantiated when the objects and their operators are used. $BOOLEAN$ represents the set of logical constants {$true, false$}. The simple data type $Message$ is introduced to provide a range of error messages appropriate to stacks and queues:

$Message ::= OK \mid the\ Stack\ is\ full \mid the\ Stack\ is\ empty \mid the\ Queue\ is\ full \mid the\ Queue\ is\ empty$

---

[1] A stack is a last in first out (LIFO) list while a queue is a first in first out (FIFO) list. Both are lists, but they are managed in different ways to give their characteristic behaviour.

In the specifications, the variable *Report!* : *Message* is universally used to convey an exception report. Our stacks and queues are *bounded,* i.e. upper limits exist to the population of each. We use the following axiomatic descriptions to introduce global constants *StackMax* and *QueueMax*; however the notation *QueueMax* = ... is meant to convey the fact that the actual population limits are user supplied:

$$
\begin{array}{|l}
\hline
StackMax : \mathbb{N} \\
\hline
StackMax = \dots \\
\end{array}
\qquad \text{and} \qquad
\begin{array}{|l}
\hline
QueueMax : \mathbb{N} \\
\hline
QueueMax = \dots \\
\end{array}
$$

The only abbreviation definitions used are those defined in the Z basic library.

17.3 THE ABSTRACT STATE OF THE STACK

$$
\begin{array}{|l}
\hline
\_\_ Abs\_Stack\_State \ [X] _____ \\
Stack : \text{seq } X \\
\hline
0 \le \#Stack \\
\#Stack \le StackMax \\
\hline
\end{array}
$$

The stack is modelled as a sequence of some given set X. Legal states for the stack correspond to those where the stack population lies between zero and the population limit *StackMax* (inclusive). This constraint on the state data is reflected by the predicates in the schema which represents the state invariant. The predicates record the following facts:

- The stack population cannot fall below zero.
- The stack population is less than or equal to *Stackmax*.

17.4 THE DELTA AND XI NOTATIONS

$$
\begin{array}{|l}
\hline
\_\_ \Delta Stack\_State[X] _____ \\
Abs\_Stack\_State \ [X] \\
Abs\_Stack\_State' \ [X] \\
\hline
\end{array}
$$

$$
\begin{array}{|l}
\hline
\_\_ \Xi Stack\_State[X] _____ \\
\Delta Stack\_State \ [X] \\
\hline
Stack' = Stack \\
\hline
\end{array}
$$

These are the conventional definitions in Z; $\Delta Stack\_State[X]$ will be included in the schema for any operation that brings about a state change. $\Xi Stack\_State[X]$ will be included in the schema for any operation that leaves the state unchanged.

17.5 THE INITIAL STATE OF THE STACK

Initially the stack is empty, which presents an obligation to show that this initial state satisfies the state invariant. The proof is in Theorem 17.1.

Theorem 17.1   The initialization theorem

$$\vdash \exists Abs\_Stack\_State' \, [X] \bullet Initial\_Stack\_State[X]$$

This theorem has no premises and simply demands that some after state $Abs\_Stack\_State'[X]$ exists that satisfies the requirements of $Initial\_Stack\_State[X]$. If we expand the quantified schema the statement of theorem becomes:

(Th17.1.1) $\vdash \exists Stack' : \text{seq } X \mid 0 \leq \#Stack' \wedge \#Stack' \leq StackMax \bullet Stack' = \langle \rangle$

Rewriting the restricted quantifier (see Chapter 5) gives:

(Th17.1.2) $\vdash \exists Stack' : \text{seq } X \bullet 0 \leq \#Stack' \wedge \#Stack' \leq StackMax \wedge Stack' = \langle \rangle$

By assuming $Stack' = \langle \rangle$ is *true* (i.e. the initialization works as intended) the existential quantifier can be made vacuous by substitution and the expression reduces to:

(Th17.1.3) $0 \leq \# \langle \rangle \wedge \# \langle \rangle \leq StackMax \wedge true$

The remaining proof proceeds as follows:

(Th17.1.4) $\# \langle \rangle = 0$ (fact about sequences)
(Th17.1.5) $0 \leq \# \langle \rangle$ is *true*
(Th17.1.6) $\# \langle \rangle \leq StackMax$ is *true* (since 0 is the minimum element of $StackMax$)
              hence
(Th17.1.7) $0 \leq \# \langle \rangle \wedge \# \langle \rangle \leq StackMax \wedge true$ is *true*

QED

Our initial state is therefore legal and acceptable because it satisfies the state invariants.

17.6 PARTIAL OPERATIONS FOR THE STACK

There are four classic operations that can be performed on stacks: *Push*, *Pop*, *Top* and *Stack_Empty*.

17.6.1 The *Push* operation

This operation adds a new item to the stack and brings about a state change. The operation accepts an item of type X, forms a sequence from it and concatenates it with the stack. The predicates demand:

- The state invariants are maintained.
- The new item is placed at the head of the sequence, i.e. on top of the stack.

17.6.2 The *Pop* operation

```
┌─── Pop[X] ──────────────────────────────────────────
│ ΔStack_State[X]
├─────────────────────────────────────────────────────
│ Stack' = tail Stack
└─────────────────────────────────────────────────────
```

This operation removes an item from the stack and brings about a state change. The predicate demands that:

- The state invariants are maintained.
- The item removed is the head of the sequence, i.e. the one on the top of the stack.

17.6.3 The *Top* operation

```
┌─── Top[X] ──────────────────────────────────────────
│ ΞStack_State[X]
│ i! : X
├─────────────────────────────────────────────────────
│ i! = head Stack
└─────────────────────────────────────────────────────
```

This operation returns a copy of the item that is currently at the top of the stack; the stack, however, remains unchanged and so the operation does not bring about a state change. The predicates demand that:

- The state invariants are maintained.
- No state changes occur.
- The item output is a copy of the current top of the stack.

17.6.4 The *Stack_Empty* operation

```
┌─── Stack_Empty[X] ──────────────────────────────────
│ ΞStack_State[X]
│ b! : BOOLEAN
├─────────────────────────────────────────────────────
│ b! = (#Stack = 0)
└─────────────────────────────────────────────────────
```

The operation determines whether or not a stack is empty. The stack remains unchanged and so the operation does not bring about a state change. The predicates demand that:

- The state invariants are maintained.
- No state changes occur.
- The output is determined by whether or not the stack is empty.

17.7 PRECONDITION CALCULATIONS

The preconditions for an operation determine those states of the system upon which the operation can be legally applied. When we establish a precondition for an operation we are really proving that:

- The operation can be applied without offending the state invariants;
- A legal final state is guaranteed so that the operation is implementable in practice.

Given some operation OP, the calculation and simplification of $preOP$ really establishes that:

$$\exists State'; Outs! \bullet OP$$

where $Outs!$ is the set of declarations of the output variables of OP and $State$ is the abstract state of the system for which OP is defined. In this respect establishing $preOP$ determines OP to be applicable for those combinations of before states and inputs such that there exists an after state and outputs satisfying the relationships among the variables involved.

For the stack, the state invariant represents a precondition for every operation. But in the previous part of the book the term was used to refer to those predicates that characterized a particular operation. In order to deduce these preconditions for each operation we have to calculate $PrePush$, $PrePop$, $PreTop$ and $PreStack\_Empty$. These schema are calculated by expanding the delta and xi notations and hiding all after states and output variables by removing them from the declaration list and existentially quantifying them in the predicate, that is:

__ *PrePush*[*X*] _____

$Abs\_Stack\_State[X]$
$i? : X$

$\exists Abs\_Stack\_State'[X] \bullet (Stack' = \langle i? \rangle \,^\wedge Stack)$

__ *PrePop*[*X*] _____

$Abs\_Stack\_State[X]$

$\exists Abs\_Stack\_State'[X] \bullet (Stack' = tail\ Stack)$

__ *PreTop*[*X*] _____

$Abs\_Stack\_State[X]$

$\exists Abs\_Stack\_State'[X]; i! : X \bullet (i! = head\ Stack \wedge Stack' = Stack)$

```
┌─── PreStack_Empty[X] ─────────────────────────────────────────
│ Abs_Stack_State[X]
├───────────────────────────────────────────────────────────────
│ ∃Abs_Stack_State' [X]; b! : BOOLEAN • (b! = (#Stack = 0) ∧ Stack' = Stack)
```

Each schema needs to be simplified to eliminate the quantification and we use the *Push* operation as an example. If we expand the *Abs_Stack_State'[X]* schema in *PrePush[X]* we get:

```
┌─── PrePush[X] ────────────────────────────────────────────────
│ Abs_Stack_State[X]
│ i? : X
├───────────────────────────────────────────────────────────────
│ ∃ Stack' : seq X • (0 ≤ #Stack' ∧ #Stack' ≤ StackMax ∧ Stack' = ⟨i?⟩ ^ Stack)
```

By assuming the operation behaves as intended and substituting $\langle i? \rangle$ ^ *Stack* for *Stack'* the quantification becomes vacuous so we can write:

```
┌─── PrePush[X] ────────────────────────────────────────────────
│ Abs_Stack_State[X]
│ i? : X
├───────────────────────────────────────────────────────────────
│ 0 ≤ #(⟨i?⟩ ^ Stack)
│ #(⟨i?⟩ ∧ Stack) ≤ StackMax
```

Now, $\#(\langle i? \rangle$ ^ *Stack*$) = \#Stack + 1$ because the concatenation increases the population of the sequence by 1, so that these predicates can be written:

$$0 \le \#Stack + 1 \text{ and } \#Stack + 1 \le StackMax$$

Because $\#Stack$ cannot be less than 0 (property of sequences), the first predicate is always true while the second predicate simplifies to $\#Stack < StackMax$. The final precondition schema is therefore:

```
┌─── PrePush[X] ────────────────────────────────────────────────
│ Abs_Stack_State[X]
│ i? : X
├───────────────────────────────────────────────────────────────
│ #Stack < StackMax
```

which of course demands that the stack can be pushed only if there is room for at least one more item!

SAQ 17.1 Perform the calculations necessary for *PrePop*.

The answer to SAQ 17.1 shows that the precondition for *Pop* demands that $0 < \#Stack$ so that the stack can be popped only if it is non-empty and this fits perfectly with our intuitive understanding of the object.

Finally, we can calculate the precondition schema for *Stack_Empty* which turns out to be interesting. If we expand *Abs_State_Stack'* in the schema we get:

```
___ PreStack_Empty[X] _____
  Abs_Stack_State[X]
_____
  ∃Stack' : seq X; b! : BOOLEAN • (0 ≤ #Stack' ∧
                                    #Stack' ≤ StackMax ∧
                                    Stack' = Stack ∧
                                    b! = (#Stack = 0))
_____
```

By assuming the truth of the postcondition, substituting *Stack* for *Stack'* and splitting the quantification the schema becomes:

```
___ PreStack_Empty[X] _____
  Abs_Stack_State[X]
_____
  ∃Stack' : seq X • (0 ≤ #Stack ∧ #Stack ≤ StackMax)
  ∃b! : BOOLEAN • (b! = (#Stack = 0))
_____
```

The quantification in the first predicate is vacuous and can be removed. The predicate that results is simply a repetition of the state invariant in *Abs_Stack_State*[X] and is therefore redundant. We can also assume that the final predicate is true because once again it really would be pointless to try to establish preconditions if we do not start with the premise that the operation performs properly! The final schema therefore becomes:

```
___ PreStack_Empty[X] _____
  Abs_Stack_State[X]
_____
  true
_____
```

which simply means that the *Stack_Empty* operation is always successful because it has *no precondition whatsoever* other than the state invariant. The preconditions for each of the stack operations appear in Table 17.1.

Table 17.1 Inputs, outputs and preconditions for the total operations of the simple stack

Operation	Inputs/outputs	Preconditions(s)
Push	i? : X Report! : Message	#Stack < StackMax
Pop	none	0 < #Stack
Top	i? : X Report! : Message	0 < #Stack
Stack_Empty	b! : BOOLEAN Report! : Message	true

SAQ 17.2 Complete the precondition calculations by determining *PreTop*. What comments would you make regarding the use of the sequence operator *head* in the specification of *Top*?

At first glance, the specifications for *Push*, *Pop* and *Top* appeared not to contain a precondition, yet the calculations revealed that in each case one existed. Whereas this should be taken as evidence of the importance of precondition calculations, it could equally well be taken as suggesting that the original specification be modified to include explicit reference to the precondition. Thus, *Push*[*X*] for example could be rewritten as:

Push[X]

$\Delta Stack\_State[X]$
$i? : X$

$\#Stack < StackMax$
$Stack' = \langle i? \rangle ^\wedge Stack$

---

with similar appropriate modifications for *Pop*[*X*] and *Top*[*X*]. The additional predicates are really redundant because, as the precondition calculations show, they are all implied. However, the specification conveys more information about the behaviour of each operation.

17.8 THE TOTAL OPERATIONS FOR THE STACK

The total operations can be defined by negating the precondition(s) for each of the partial operations and constructing a schema for the operation that should be effected when the precondition is offended. In each case this operation preserves the status quo. Since *Stack_Empty* has no preconditions, this exercise affects only *Push, Pop* and *Top*. The negated preconditions are:

- *Push* $\neg(\#Stack < StackMax)$, i.e. $\#Stack \geq StackMax$ or simply $\#Stack = StackMax$ because the stack population cannot exceed *StackMax*.
- *Pop* and *Top* $\neg(0 < \#Stack)$, i.e. $0 \geq \#Stack$ or simply $0 = \#Stack$ because the stack population cannot fall below 0 (property of sets).

The corresponding error operations are shown as follows:

Push_Error[X]

$\Xi Stack\_State[X]$
$Report! : Message$

$\#Stack = StackMax$
$Report! = the\ Stack\ is\ full$

Pop_Error[X]

$\Xi Stack\_State[X]$
$Report! : Message$

$\#Stack = 0$
$Report! = the\ Stack\ is\ empty$

```
┌─── Top_Error[X] ──────────────────────────────────────
│ ΞStack_State[X]
│ Report! : Message
├───────────────────────────────────────────────────────
│ #Stack = 0
│ Report! = the Stack is empty
└───────────────────────────────────────────────────────
```

If we now define a schema *Success* that simply reports *OK*:

$$Success \triangleq [Report! : Message \mid Report! = OK]$$

then each total operation can be described as below:

$$Total\_Push[X] \triangleq (Push[X] \wedge Success) \vee Push\_Error[X]$$
$$Total\_Pop[X] \triangleq (Pop[X] \wedge Success) \vee Pop\_Error[X]$$
$$Total\_Top[X] \triangleq (Top[X] \wedge Success) \vee Top\_Error[X]$$
$$Total\_Stack\_Empty[X] \triangleq (Stack\_Empty[X] \wedge Success)$$

Notice, however, that in the case of *Total_Top[X]* no constraint is placed on the value of *i!* returned in the event of an error. This is quite a common feature in the treatment of total operations in Z.

17.9 PROPERTIES OF THE STACK SPECIFICATION

From the specifications we would expect that if we *Push* the stack and then immediately *Pop* it the stack will remain unchanged, i.e. *Push[X]* ; *Pop[X]* represents the *identity operation*. Theorem 17.2 and its proof show that this is indeed true.

Theorem 17.2

$$Push[X] \; ; \; Pop[X] \vdash Stack' = Stack$$

In order to prove this theorem we need to perform the composition and show that the final predicate contains the clause on the right-hand side. Readers should by now be familiar with the composition mechanism and so the steps are presented below with minimal comment.

(Th17.2.1) $Push[X] [Abs\_Stack\_State^+/Abs\_Stack\_State'][Stack^+/Stack']$

```
┌─── Push[X] ───────────────────────────────────────────
│ Abs_Stack_State[X]
│ Abs_Stack_State⁺[X]
│ i? : X
├───────────────────────────────────────────────────────
│ Stack⁺ = ⟨i?⟩ ⌢ Stack
└───────────────────────────────────────────────────────
```

(Th17.2.2) $Pop[X] [Abs\_Stack\_State^+/Abs\_Stack\_State] [Stack^+/Stack]$

```
┌─── Pop[X] ──────────────────────────────────────────
│ Abs_Stack_State⁺[X]
│ Abs_Stack_State'[X]
├──────────────────────────────────────────────────────
│ Stack' = tail Stack⁺
└──────────────────────────────────────────────────────
```

(Th17.2.3) $Push\_Pop[X] \triangleq Push[X] [Abs\_Stack\_State^+/Abs\_Stack\_State']$
$[Stack^+/Stack'] \wedge Pop[X] [Abs\_Stack\_State^+/$
$Abs\_Stack\_State] [Stack^+/Stack]$

```
┌─── Push_Pop[X] ─────────────────────────────────────
│ Abs_Stack_State[X]
│ Abs_Stack_State⁺[X]
│ Abs_Stack_State'[X]
│ i? : X
├──────────────────────────────────────────────────────
│ Stack⁺ = ⟨i?⟩ ^ Stack
│ Stack' = tail Stack⁺
└──────────────────────────────────────────────────────
```

(Th17.2.4) $Push\_Pop[X] \backslash (Abs\_Stack\_State^+)$

```
┌─── Push_Pop[X] ─────────────────────────────────────
│ Abs_Stack_State[X]
│ Abs_Stack_State'[X]
│ i? : X
├──────────────────────────────────────────────────────
│ ∃Abs_Stack_State⁺ • (Stack⁺ = ⟨i?⟩ ^ Stack ^ Stack' = tail Stack⁺)
└──────────────────────────────────────────────────────
```

(Th17.2.5) Expand the $Abs\_Stack\_State^+$ schema.

```
┌─── Push_Pop[X] ─────────────────────────────────────
│ Abs_Stack_State[X]
│ Abs_Stack_State'[X]
│ i? : X
├──────────────────────────────────────────────────────
│ ∃Stack⁺ : seq X • (0 ≤ #Stack⁺ ∧
│                    Stack⁺ ∧
│                    Stack⁺ = ⟨i?⟩ ^ Stack ∧
│                    Stack' = tail Stack⁺)
└──────────────────────────────────────────────────────
```

(Th17.2.6)   Substitute for $Stack^+$ throughout the schema.

```
┌─── Push_Pop[X] ──────────────────────────────────────
│ Abs_Stack_State[X]
│ Abs_Stack_State'[X]
│ i? : X
├──────────────────────────────────────────────────────
│ ∃Stack⁺ : seq X • (0 ≤ #(⟨i?⟩ ^ Stack) ∧
│                      #(⟨i?⟩ ^ Stack) ≤ StackMax ∧
│                      Stack' = tail (⟨i?⟩ ^ Stack))
└──────────────────────────────────────────────────────
```

(Th17.2.7)   Remove the vacuous quantification and simplify by noting that $tail (\langle i?\rangle \,^\wedge Stack)) = Stack$.

```
┌─── Push_Pop[X] ──────────────────────────────────────
│ Abs_Stack_State[X]
│ Abs_Stack_State'[X]
│ i? : X
├──────────────────────────────────────────────────────
│ 0 ≤ #(⟨i?⟩ ^ Stack) ∧
│ #(⟨i?⟩ ^ Stack) ≤ StackMax ∧
│ Stack' = Stack
└──────────────────────────────────────────────────────
```

$$QED$$

At this point the proof is complete, for the final schema contains the predicate that shows the system state remains unchanged. However, the first two predicates can be simplified:

$$0 \le \#(\langle i?\rangle \,^\wedge Stack)$$

can be written:

$$0 < (\#Stack + 1) \lor 0 = (\#Stack + 1)$$

Because $0 = (\#Stack + 1)$ cannot be *true* for sequences, $0 < (\#Stack + 1)$ suggests that this predicate reduces to:

$$0 \le \#Stack$$

Similarly, $\#(\langle i?\rangle \land Stack) \le StackMax$ simplifies to $\#Stack < StackMax$, so the final schema becomes:

```
┌─── Push_Pop[X] ──────────────────────────────────────
│ ΞStack_State[X]
│ i? : X
├──────────────────────────────────────────────────────
│ 0 ≤ #Stack
│ #Stack < StackMax
└──────────────────────────────────────────────────────
```

Notice that as a 'side-effect' of this proof we have developed a schema where the preconditions have been made explicit, so that if we were to conduct a precondition calculation then $PrePush\_Pop[X]$ would appear as:

```
┌─── PrePush_Pop[X] ────────────────────────────
│ Abs_Stack_State[X]
│ i? : X
├───────────────────────────────────────────────
│ #Stack < StackMax
│ 0 ≤ #Stack
└───────────────────────────────────────────────
```

Notice also that whereas Pop requires that $0 < \#Stack$, the $Push\_Pop$ operation simply demands that $0 \leq \#Stack$. This is because the $Push$ (which occurs first—see the composition order) will always ensure that even an empty stack will be populated before the Pop. Once again, these explicit preconditions are really redundant but their presence does make the specification much more understandable.

17.10 THE QUEUE

The queue is really only a variation on the general theme of the stack. The abstract state of the queue, the delta and xi notations and the initial state all remain the same. The schemas therefore are:

```
┌─── Abs_Queue_State[X] ────────────────────────
│ Queue : seq X
├───────────────────────────────────────────────
│ 0 ≤ #Queue
│ #Queue ≤ QueueMax
└───────────────────────────────────────────────
```

```
┌─── Queue_State[X] ────────────────────────────
│ Abs_Queue_State[X]
│ Abs_Queue_State'[X]
└───────────────────────────────────────────────
```

```
┌─── ΞQueue_State[X] ───────────────────────────
│ ΔQueue_State[X]
├───────────────────────────────────────────────
│ Queue' = Queue
└───────────────────────────────────────────────
```

```
┌─── Initial_Queue_State[X] ────────────────────
│ Abs_Queue_State'[X]
├───────────────────────────────────────────────
│ Queue' = ⟨⟩
└───────────────────────────────────────────────
```

The operations of course differentiate the queue from the stack. The following schemas for each characteristic partial operation are shown, accompanied by a brief explanation:

```
___ Addtoqueue[X] _____
ΔQueue_State[X]
i? : X
_____
Queue' = Queue ^ ⟨i?⟩
```

This operation adds a new item to the queue and brings about a state change. The operation accepts an item of type X, forms a sequence from it and concatenates it with the queue. The predicates demand that:

• The state invariants are maintained.
• The new item is made the last in the sequence, i.e. placed at the back of the queue.

```
___ Deletefromqueue[X] _____
ΔQueue_State[X]
_____
Queue' = tail Queue
```

This operation removes an item from the queue and brings about a state change. The predicate demands that:

• The state invariants are maintained.
• The item removed is the head of the sequence, i.e. the one at the front of the queue.

```
___ Front[X] _____
ΞQueue_State[X]
i! : X
_____
i! = head Queue
```

This operation returns a copy of the item that is currently at the head of the queue; the queue, however, remains unchanged and so the operation does not bring about a state change. The predicates demand that:

• The state invariants are maintained.
• No state changes occur.
• The item output is a copy of the current head of the queue.

```
___ Queue_Empty[X] _____
ΞQueue_State_[X]
b! : BOOLEAN
_____
b! = (#Queue = 0)
```

This operation is really the same as that for the stack and determines whether or not a queue is empty. The queue remains unchanged and so the operation does not bring about a state change. The predicates demand that:

• The state invariants are maintained.
• No state changes occur.
• The output is determined by whether or not the queue is empty.

It is left as an exercise for readers to prove the initialization theorem, define the total operations and precondition schemas and to discharge the obligations concerning the properties of the queue.

17.11 AN ALTERNATIVE MODEL FOR STACKS AND QUEUES

Stacks and queues are ordered structures that benefit from a specification model that is itself ordered. The model we have used is the sequence which corresponds closely to the list. The sequence imposes order through its index value, which acts as a placement indicator for the position of an element in the list. There are, however, other ways of imposing order among some population of interest, and as an alternative approach to the specification we consider a mechanism that time-stamps elements as they enter the structure. Thus, the top of the stack is that element associated with the latest time stamp, while the head of the queue is the element associated with the earliest time stamp. Stacks and queues are therefore modelled as sets of ordered pairs $\{\ldots, (t_i, i), \ldots\}$ where t_i represents the time element i entered the structure.

Clearly, different stamps can be associated with the same element—this mechanism permits duplicate elements to appear in the stack or queue—but different elements cannot have the same time stamp because this would not permit us to determine which was the current head of queue or top of stack. All this suggests that these structures can be modelled as partial functions from a set of times to a set of items—not the other way around. Because this mapping is functional, a time can be associated with one item at most but an item may be associated with several different times. In order to compare this new specification to that using sequences, we must be careful to preserve continuity across the operators. The *Push* operator, for example, must not accept an item *and* a time, for that would make it a different specification to that using sequences. Therefore, although we need to introduce another given set *TIME*, the time stamp must be determined by the system. The given sets and the declaration abbreviation for the set of partial functions from *TIME* to *X* are as follows (in keeping with earlier comments concerning given sets, we need not provide any detail of what 'time' is):

$$[TIME, X, BOOLEAN]$$

$$TIME \leftrightarrow X == \{R : TIME \leftrightarrow X \mid \forall t : TIME; x, y : X \bullet (t,x) \in R \land (t,y) \in R \Rightarrow x = y\}$$

The schemas for the abstract state of the stack, the delta and xi notations, the initial stack state and the *Stack_Empty* operation are as follows:

```
┌─── Abs_Stack_State[X] ──────────────────────────────
│ Stack : TIME ⇸ X
├─────────────────────────────────────────────────────
│ 0 ≤ #Stack
│ #Stack ≤ StackMax
└─────────────────────────────────────────────────────
```

```
┌─── ΔStack_State[X] ─────────────────────────────────
│ Abs_Stack_State[X]
│ Abs_Stack_State'[X]
└─────────────────────────────────────────────────────
```

```
___ ΞStack_State[X] _____
ΔStack_State[X]
_____
Stack' = Stack
```

```
___ Initial_Stack_State[X] _____
Abs_Stack_State'[X]
_____
Stack' = { }
```

```
___ Stack_Empty[X] _____
Ξ Stack_State [X]
b! : BOOLEAN
_____
b! = (#Stack = 0)
```

These schemas should (by now) be quite understandable, while the obligation to prove the *Initial State* theorem can be discharged in a fashion similar to that for sequences. This is left as an exercise for the reader. The specifications for the remaining operators, however, are directly concerned with the time stamping mechanism and differ quite considerably from those developed previously. Each specification will now be discussed. For simplicity the existence of the orders $>$ and $\geq$ on the items of the set *TIME* has been assumed. (See Part 3 for a discussion of orders.)

```
___ Push[X] _____
ΔStack_State[X]
i? : X
_____
```
$$\exists t_i : TIME \bullet ((\forall t_s : TIME \mid t_s \in \text{dom } Stack \bullet t_i > t_s) \land$$
$$Stack' = Stack \oplus \{(t_i, i?)\})$$

The functionality of the *Push* is exactly as it was before; it accepts an item and places it on top of the stack. The predicate demands that:

- Some new time (t_i) exists, which is greater than any of the times currently used in the stack. The item $i?$ is stamped with this time and the pair $\{(t_i, i?)\}$ added to the stack. Because $i?$ is associated with the latest time stamp it becomes the current top of the stack.

To *Pop* the stack we have to reverse this process and build a predicate that finds the element associated with the latest time stamp. The stack is popped by removing this pair from the set. The specification is:

```
___ Pop[X] _____
ΔStack_State[X]
_____
```
$$\exists_1 t_i : TIME; i : X \mid (t_i, i) \in Stack \bullet ((\forall t_s : TIME; s : X \mid (t_s, s) \in Stack \bullet t_i \geq t_s) \land$$
$$Stack' = Stack \setminus \{(t_i, i)\})$$

The predicate demands that:

- There is exactly one ($\exists_1$) pair in the stack which has a time stamp greater than all the others (but of course equal to itself). This must be the pair with the latest time stamp and hence the associated item is the current top of the stack. This pair is removed from the stack.

The specification for *Top* is very similar but rather than removing the pair we simply isolate the item and output a copy. The stack is therefore unchanged.

$Top[X]$

$\Xi Stack\_State[X]$
$i! : X$

$\exists_1 t_i : TIME; i : X \mid (t_i,i) \in Stack \bullet ((\forall t_s : TIME; s : X \mid (t_s,s) \in Stack \bullet t_i \geqslant t_s) \land$
$$i! = \mathrm{ran}\{(t_i,i)\})$$

With these specifications we can calculate the precondition schemas, define the total operations and construct theorems to prove properties of the stack as we did before. However, because we have used a different model we must expect the effort involved in all this to be influenced by our choice. Modelling stacks as sets of ordered pairs is certainly less intuitive than modelling them as lists using sequences. Consequently, the reasoning involved when determining precondition schemas and proving properties is rather more difficult, and this observation promotes the general suggestion that the simplest model is often the most appropriate and usually the easiest to reason about. We therefore complete this case study by illustrating the point by calculating the pre-condition schema for *Push—PrePush*

We begin by expanding the delta notation:

$Push[X]$

$Abs\_Stack\_State[X]$
$Abs\_Stack\_State'[X]$
$i? : X$

$\exists t_i : TIME \bullet ((\forall t_s : TIME \mid t_s \in \mathrm{dom}\ Stack \bullet t_i > t_s) \land Stack' = Stack \oplus \{(t_i,i?)\})$

---

and hiding all the after state variables (there are no outputs), i.e. $PrePush \triangleq Push[X] \backslash \{Abs\_Stack\_State'[X]\}$. The schema is:

$PrePush[X]$

$Abs\_Stack\_State[X]$
$i? : X$

$\exists Abs\_Stack\_State'[X] \bullet (\exists t_i; TIME \bullet ((\forall t_s : TIME \mid t_s \in \mathrm{dom}\ Stack \bullet t_i > t_s) \land$
$$Stack' = Stack \oplus \{(t_i,i?)\}))$$

By expanding the $Abs\_Stack\_State'[X]$ schema we have a rather more formidable predicate to simplify:

___ *PrePush*[*X*] _____

Abs_Stack_State[*X*]
i? : *X*

$\exists Stack' : TIME \nrightarrow X \bullet (0 \leq \#Stack' \wedge \#Stack' \leq StackMax \wedge$
$\qquad\qquad (\exists t_i : TIME \bullet$
$\qquad\qquad ((\forall t_s : TIME \mid t_s \in \text{dom } Stack \bullet t_i > t_s) \wedge$
$\qquad\qquad Stack' = Stack \oplus \{(t_i, i?)\})))$

We begin the simplification by splitting the inner existentially quantified predicate using the following sequent (see Chapter 5):

$$\exists x : X \bullet (P_x \wedge Q_x) \vdash (\exists x : X \bullet P_x) \wedge (\exists x : X \bullet Q_x)$$

___ *PrePush*[*X*] _____

Abs_Stack_State[*X*]
i? : *X*

$\exists Stack' : TIME \nrightarrow X \bullet (0 \leq \#Stack' \wedge \#Stack' \leq StackMax \wedge$
$\qquad\qquad \exists t_i : TIME \bullet (\forall t_s : TIME \mid t_s \in \text{dom } Stack \bullet t_i > t_s) \wedge$
$\qquad\qquad \exists t_i : TIME \bullet Stack' = Stack \oplus \{(t_i, i?)\})$

then separately quantifying all the inner predicates by applying the same sequent:

___ *PrePush*[*X*] _____

Abs_Stack_State[*X*]
i? : *X*

$\exists Stack' : TIME \nrightarrow X \bullet (0 \leq \#Stack' \wedge \#Stack' \leq StackMax)$
$\exists Stack' : TIME \nrightarrow X \bullet (\exists t_i : TIME \bullet (\forall t_s : TIME \mid t_s \in \text{dom } Stack \bullet t_i > t_s))$
$\exists Stack' : TIME \nrightarrow X \bullet (\exists t_i : TIME \bullet Stack' = Stack \oplus \{(t_i, i?)\})$

The quantified predicate:

$$\exists Stack' : TIME \nrightarrow X \bullet \exists t_i : TIME \bullet (\forall t_s; TIME \mid t_s \in \text{dom } Stack \bullet t_i > t_s)$$

is vacuous because it does not involve the quantified variable *Stack'* and so the outer quantification can be removed. We must also assume that the final predicate is *true* because there is really little point in trying to find preconditions for *Push* if we do not start with the premise that the operation behaves as it should! If we establish preconditions by assuming the truth of this final predicate then we prove that a guaranteed final state can be reached when these are satisfied. Because $Stack' = Stack \oplus \{(t_i, i?)\}$ is *true* it can remain as part of the specification and be used to eliminate *Stack'* from the first predicate by substitution. Eliminating *Stack'* allows us to drop the quantification so that the schema becomes:

```
┌─── PrePush[X] ─────────────────────────────────────────────
│ Abs_Stack_State[X]
│ i? : X
├────────────────────────────────────────────────────────────
│ (0 ≤ #(Stack ⊕ {(t_i,i?)}) ∧ #(Stack ⊕ {(t_i,i?)}) ≤ StackMax)
│ ∃t_i : TIME • (∀t_s : TIME | t_s ∈ dom Stack • t_i > t_s)
└────────────────────────────────────────────────────────────
```

Adding a pair to the stack of course increases the cardinality of the set by 1 and so the first predicate can be written:

$$(0 \le \#Stack + 1) \wedge (\#Stack + 1 \le StackMax)$$

which reduces to $\#Stack < StackMax$. Our final precondition schema is therefore:

```
┌─── PrePush[X] ─────────────────────────────────────────────
│ Abs_Stack_State[X]
│ i? : X
├────────────────────────────────────────────────────────────
│ #Stack < StackMax
│ ∃t_i : TIME • (∀t_s : TIME | t_s ∈ dom Stack • t_i > t_s)
└────────────────────────────────────────────────────────────
```

The preconditions for the operation are therefore that the stack is not full and some new time stamp can be found which is greater than all those currently used in the stack. The remaining precondition calculations, the total operation definitions, the property proof and the corresponding specification for the queue are left as an exercise. Take care.

17.12 SUMMARY OF THE STACK SPECIFICATION

This case study has used stacks and queues to familiarize readers with the structure of a small Z document and to demonstrate a number of important features of Z specifications: generic definitions, the initial state theorem, precondition calculations, property proofs and the influence of the particular specification model. The use of stacks and queues was a deliberate choice simply because of their familiarity—even though some readers may be getting thoroughly fed up with the saturation coverage of these structures by authors! In this way the reader is free to concentrate on techniques without having to refresh themselves continually with the behaviour of the object which we are specifying.

Throughout the specification, schemas have been defined generically so that stacks and queues of any sort can be described. Indeed, we could even add these definitions to our customized basic library if we so wished, thereby making these objects available to the whole community.

The proofs undertaken have used a number of techniques introduced in the previous part of the book: splitting quantifications, assuming certain predicates are *true*, substitutions and removing vacuous quantifications. All of these permit quite formidable predicates to be reduced to simpler and more meaningful forms.

A hallmark of model-based specifications is that the specifier is free to choose the most appropriate model. The case study illustrates, however, that the most appropriate models are often the simplest ones and that the choice of model critically affects the work required in the various areas of proof. Sets of time-stamped items are really quite similar to sequences but do not benefit from the range of operators defined for the latter. As a consequence we take on much more work than is strictly necessary.

18

THE SYMBOL TABLE

18.1 INTRODUCTION

Symbol tables are used by language processors such as assemblers, compilers and interpreters to associate a particular user-defined symbol with a value that represents some property that the symbol possesses, e.g. the address in store corresponding to the symbolic variable or label. The information held in the symbol table is used to check the syntax of programs and to generate object code.

A symbol table is superficially similar to a stack or a queue in that we have to specify operations that initialize the structure, add entries to it and remove entries from it. However, unlike stacks and queues, the functionality of this object does not necessarily require that its entries be ordered in some fashion. The simplest model to use, therefore, would be one that more closely reflects the property of sets than sequences, with the added feature that given a symbol we can determine the (single) value associated with it. This suggests that a partial function from a set of symbols to a set of values would be appropriate: partial because not all possible symbols permitted by the language would necessarily be mapped; and functional to permit the association of the symbol with a single value. The simplest view of the symbol table therefore models it as a set of (*symbol*, *value*) pairs.

Symbol tables, however, are very heavily used in practice and the overall performance of some translator may well depend on the efficiency with which symbols in the table can be retrieved and their properties used. In this sense a specification may well have to reflect the more practical consideration of retrieval efficiency and so we examine an alternative model; where the table is regarded as a sequence of (*symbol*, *value*) entries kept in order of frequency of access. Here the table keeps commonly used entries at the head of the table which permits a simple linear search to be more efficient. In our first case study the alternative specification was used to reflect the effect of a more difficult model on the clarity of the specification and the workload involved in reasoning about it. In this study the alternative model reflects a process whereby the specification is moving closer to the ultimate program by considering practical issues in an incremental fashion.

18.2 THE BASIC SYMBOL TABLE SPECIFICATION

The basic symbol table is really quite a simple structure and this discussion presents the specification with minimum comment because all of the techniques have been previously covered. The various proofs and properties are indicated but left as exercises for the reader. The operations specified include:

- *Insert*   Adds a new (*symbol*, *value*) pair to the table.
- *Find*   Determines the value associated with a particular symbol in the table.
- *Delete*   Removes an entry from the table.

18.2.1 The given sets, abbreviation definitions and axiomatic descriptions

We can assume two given sets, [*SYM*, *VAL*], representing respectively the set of all possible user-defined symbols for the language being considered and the set of all possible values that can be associated with symbols. In keeping with the nature of given sets we need not supply any information concerning these elements in these sets at this point in the specification.

In order to make the operations of the symbol table total we will need a simple data type *Message* to hold the various messages that the system can issue. *Message* is defined as follows:

$$Message ::= OK \mid the\ symbol\ is\ not\ in\ the\ table \mid symbol\ already\ present$$

We will not consider the case where the symbol table becomes full (we would not want the translation process for a perfectly legal program halted simply because we run out of memory for the table!) and so the specification is unbounded and we have no need for an axiomatic definition for *TableMax*. No abbreviation definitions are used other than those accepted as part of the Z notation.

18.2.2 The abstract state of the basic symbol table

The abstract state is modelled as a partial function from symbols to values. For such a simple state we can beneficially use the horizontal schema form:

$$Abs\_SymT\_State \triangleq [Table : SYM \nrightarrow VAL]$$

Notice that because we place no restrictions on the table other than it is functional, the predicate part of the schema is empty.

18.2.3 The delta and xi notations

$$\Delta SymT\_State \triangleq [Abs\_SymT\_State \; ; \; Abs\_SymT\_State']$$
$$\Xi SymT\_State \triangleq [\Delta SymT\_State \mid Table' = Table]$$

As usual, $\Delta SymT\_State$ will be included in the schema definitions for those operations that alter the state of the symbol table, while the inclusion of $\Xi SymT\_State$ reflects the fact that an operation leaves the state unchanged.

18.2.4 The initial state of the basic symbol table

Initially the symbol table is empty:

$$Initial\_SymT\_State \triangleq [Abs\_SymT\_State' \mid Table' = \{\ \}]$$

Our first obligation should be to show that this initial state satisfies the state invariants.

Theorem 18.1   The initialization theorem

$$\vdash \exists Abs\_SymT\_State' \bullet Initial\_SymT\_State$$

In this case, however, because there are no explicit invariants, this obligation is trivial for it simply requires that the empty set is functional!

18.2.5 Partial operations for the basic symbol table

Partial operations describe the behaviour of operations under normal circumstances. Each of the characteristic operations on the symbol table is shown below accompanied with a brief explanation of their predicates:

$$Find \;\widehat{=}\; [\Xi SymT\_State \;;\; s? : SYM \;;\; v! : VAL \mid s? \in \mathrm{dom}(Table);\; v! = Table\; s?]$$

- The input symbol must be a member of the symbol table.
- The output from the operation is the value associated with the symbol in the table.
- The table remains unchanged.

$$Insert \;\widehat{=}\; [\Delta SymT\_State \;;\; s? : SYM;\; v? : VAL \mid \neg(s? \in \mathrm{dom}(Table));$$
$$Table' = Table \oplus \{(s?,v?)\}]$$

- The symbol must not be present in the table.
- The symbol and the value associated with it are added to the table.
- The operation changes the state of the table.

$$Delete \;\widehat{=}\; [\Delta SymT\_State;\; s? : SYM \mid s? \in \mathrm{dom}(Table);\; Table' = \{s?\} \lhd Table]$$

- The input symbol must be a member of the table.
- The symbol and the value associated with it are removed from the table.
- The operation changes the state of the table.

18.2.6 Precondition calculations for the basic symbol table

The precondition schemas for each operation are as follows:

```
┌─── PreFind ──────────────────────────────────────────────────
│ Abs_State_SymT
│ s? : SYM
├──────────────────────────────────────────────────────────────
│ ∃Abs_SymT_State'; v! : VAL • (s? ∈ dom(Table) ∧ v! = Table(s?))
```

```
┌─── PreInsert ────────────────────────────────────────────────
│ Abs_SymT_State
│ s? : SYM
│ v? : VAL
├──────────────────────────────────────────────────────────────
│ ∃Abs_SymT_State' • (¬(s? ∈ dom(Table)) ∧ Table' = Table ⊕ {(s?, v?)})
```

```
┌─── PreDelete ─────────────────────────────────────────────────
│ Abs_SymT_State
│ s? : SYM
├───────────────────────────────────────────────────────────────
│ ∃Abs_SymT_State' • (s? ∈ dom(Table) ∧ Table' = {s?} ◁ Table)
└───────────────────────────────────────────────────────────────
```

SAQ 18.1   Complete the calculations by simplifying each of the precondition schemas.

The preconditions for each of the simple symbol table operations appear in Table 18.1.

Table 18.1 Inputs, outputs and preconditions for the total operations of the simple symbol stack

Operation	Inputs/outputs	Preconditions(s)
Insert	s? : SYM, v? : VAL, Report! : Message	¬(s? ∈ dom(Table))
Find	s? : SYM, v! : VAL, Report! : Message	s? ∈ dom(Table)
Delete	s? : SYM, Report! : Message	s? ∈ dom(Table)

18.2.7 The total operations for the basic symbol table

Find and *Delete* are defined only if the symbol is present in the table. Both of these operations can be made total by the use of the following schemas and schema expressions:

$$Success \triangleq [Report! : Message \mid Report! = OK]$$
$$Total\_Find \triangleq (Find \wedge Success) \vee NotPresent$$
$$Total\_Delete \triangleq (Delete \wedge Success) \vee NotPresent$$

Insert, on the other hand, is successful only if the symbol is not in the symbol table. The operation can be made total by means of the following schema expression:

$$Total\_Insert \triangleq (Insert \wedge Success) \vee Present$$

SAQ 18.2   Write the specifications for the schemas *Present* and *NotPresent*.

18.2.8 The properties of the basic symbol table specification

When a symbol is added to the table and then the same symbol is deleted from the table the state of the table should remain the same.

Theorem 18.2

$$Insert; Delete \mid s?_{in} = s?_{del} \vdash Table' = Table$$

SAQ 18.3   Prove Theorem 2. (Follow the techniques used in the case study on stacks and queues.)

18.3 AN ALTERNATIVE MODEL FOR THE SYMBOL TABLE

This second model recognizes the fact that in a practical environment the performance of the overall translation process will depend heavily on the speed with
which entries in the symbol table can be accessed and their property values
retrieved. The table is therefore described as an ordered structure; ordered according
to how many times a symbol has been accessed. Frequently needed symbols will
appear at the head of the table and therefore will be retrieved more quickly by a
simple linear search. The functionality of this specification should remain exactly the
same as the simple symbol table, including the property that the table be
'unbounded'. However, because of the explicit consideration of practicalities, such
as support for a linear search, it can be regarded as being one step closer to an
implementation.

Because the symbol table must now be ordered, it is modelled as a sequence of
entries where each entry is a (*symbol, value*) pair and where a symbol can occur at most
once in a table entry. (Because sequences are based on finite partial functions the table
must be physically 'bounded' but we regard this as large enough to accommodate any
translation process.) An additional functional structure will be supported that
maintains an access count for every symbol defined in the table. The count is
incremented by one each time the symbol is looked up in the symbol table. These two
structures are kept in correspondence at all times.

Operations must exist to *Insert* and *Delete* entries from the structures and to *Find* the
value associated with a particular symbol. *Insert* adds a new symbol to the table and
associates it with an access count of zero, reflecting the fact that a new symbol cannot yet
have been looked up. The new symbol is added to the logical end of the ordered table
because this places it in the correct relative position with respect to its frequency of access.

Delete removes corresponding entries from the table and the access structure, leaving
the relative order in the table unchanged. *Find* looks up a symbol, outputs the value
associated with it and increases its frequency count.

18.3.1 General theories concerning the specification

As a result of the *Find* operation the symbol table must be reorganized so that the order
of its entries properly reflects the new count for the accessed symbol. A *Sort_Table*
function is therefore introduced whose purpose is to organize table entries according to
their current access frequency—a natural number. *Sort_Table* accepts a symbol table
and the access frequencies of the symbols and returns a sorted table. In the specification we accept the existence of the total order $\geq$ on the natural numbers as this
ordering should be particularly familiar and understood. Total order and sorting was
reviewed earlier (Chapter 12).

18.3.2 The given sets, abbreviation declarations and axiomatic descriptions

The given sets remain as before—[*SYM, VAL*]—while a new set called *Entries* is
introduced using the following abbreviation definition:

$$Entries == \{s : SYM\,;\,v : VAL \bullet (s,v)\}$$

This set reflects the nature of the individual entries in the symbol table, i.e. (*symbol, value*) pairs. We can never know of course which symbols and values will be associated and so *Entries* simply represents all possible combinations, i.e. the Cartesian product over the two sets. The functional structure that records the access frequencies for each symbol is a mapping from *SYM* to $\mathbb{N}$, the set of natural numbers. This structure is a partial function whose type is introduced by the abbreviation definition:

$$Access == SYM \nrightarrow \mathbb{N}$$

With the symbol table modelled as seq *Entries*, the function *Sort_Table* is defined as a global constant in terms of the following axiomatic description:

$Sort\_Table : (\text{seq } Entries \times Access) \rightarrow \text{seq } Entries$

$Sort\_Table = \{in, out : \text{seq } Entries ; A : Access \,|$
$\qquad\qquad \text{dom}(\text{ran } in) \subseteq \text{dom } A \,\wedge$
$\qquad\qquad \forall i,j : \text{dom } out \bullet (i < j \Rightarrow A(\textit{first } (out\ i)) \geq A(\textit{first } (out\ j)) \,\wedge$
$\qquad\qquad items(in) = items(out)) \bullet ((in, A), out)\}$

This is a total function from pairs of symbol tables and access structures to symbol tables. The declaration together with the first predicate show that the function is defined only for situations where all the symbols in the table are present in the access structure where each is associated with just *one* frequency count. It would not be possible to order the table if there were more than one access frequency per symbol or if such frequencies were absent. The second predicate shows that the output table is organized such that the frequency count associated with any particular entry is greater than or equal to all those entries that come after it, i.e. the table is in descending order in this respect. The final predicate ensures that the output table contains exactly the same entries as the input table; the ordering process cannot gain or lose entries. The function could also order tables where the same symbol occurs in more than one entry but because of the restrictions on symbol tables this situation will never arise. Notice also that in this definition (and in much of the specification that follows) the argument for a function application has often been enclosed in parentheses. When the argument is complex this makes the specification more readable.

18.3.3 Abstract state of the alternative symbol table

_____ Abstract_SymT_State_____

$Freq\_Tab : Access$
$Table : \text{seq } Entries$

$\text{dom } Freq\_Tab = \text{dom}(\text{ran } Table)$
$\forall i, j : \text{dom } Table \bullet (i \neq j \Rightarrow \textit{first } (Table\ i) \neq \textit{first } (Table\ j) \,\wedge$
$\qquad\qquad i < j \Rightarrow Freq\_Tab(\textit{first } (Table\ i)) \geq Freq\_Tab(\textit{first } (Table\ j)))$

The predicates record the following facts:

- *Freq_Tab* is a function and therefore a symbol cannot occur twice, but there must be an entry in *Freq_Tab* for every unique symbol in the *Table*.
- No two entries in the table have the same symbol.
- The table is ordered with respect to the number of times the symbol in an entry has been accessed.

18.3.4 The delta and xi notations

```
┌─── ΔSymT_State ─────────────────────────────────
│ Abstract_ SymT_State
│ Abstract_ SymT_State'
└──────────────────────────────────────────────────
```

```
┌─── ΞSymT_State ─────────────────────────────────
│ ΔSymT_State
├──────────────────────────────────────────────────
│ Table'  =  Table
│ Freq_Tab'  = Freq_Tab
└──────────────────────────────────────────────────
```

18.3.5 The initial state of the symbol table

```
┌─── Initial_SymT_State ───────────────────────────
│ Abstract_SymT_State'
├──────────────────────────────────────────────────
│ Table' = ⟨⟩
│ Freq_Tab' = { }
└──────────────────────────────────────────────────
```

Initially both the symbol table and the frequency table are empty. As usual there is a proof obligation to show that this condition is a legal state of the system:

Theorem 18.2   The initialization theorem

$$\vdash \exists Abstract\_SymT\_State' \bullet Initial\_SymT\_State$$

If we expand the quantified schema *Abstract_SymT_State'* the statement of the theorem becomes:

$$\vdash \exists Freq\_Tab' : Access\ ;\ Table' : seq\ Entries\ |$$
$$\quad \mathrm{dom}\ Freq\_Tab' = \mathrm{dom}(\mathrm{ran}\ Table')$$
$$\quad \forall i,j : \mathrm{dom}\ Table'\ \bullet\ (i \neq j \Rightarrow first\ (Table'\ i) \neq first\ (Table'\ j) \wedge$$
$$\qquad\qquad i < j \Rightarrow Freq\_Tab'(first\ (Table'\ i)) \geq Freq\_Tab'(first\ (Table'\ j))$$
$$\qquad\qquad Table' = \langle\rangle$$
$$\qquad\qquad Freq\_Tab'\ =\ \{\}$$

With *Table'* and *Freq_Tab'* both empty the first predicate in the state invariant reduces to:

$$\mathrm{dom}\ (\{\}) = \mathrm{dom}\ (\{\})$$

which is clearly *true*. The second and third predicates require proof only when we have *i* and *j* that are members of dom *Table'*. For an empty sequence there is nothing to prove here and so the initial state can be regarded as satisfying the state invariant.

18.3.6 The partial operations for the alternative symbol table

There are three operations defined for the alternative model of the symbol table and these correspond exactly (in terms of their functionality) to those of the basic model.

The *Delete* operation

─── *Delete* ───

$\Delta SymT\_State$
$s? : SYM$

──

$\exists i \in \text{dom}(Table) \bullet (\textit{first } (Table\ i) = s? \wedge$
$\exists j \in \{0\} \cup \text{dom } Table' \bullet \{1 .. j\} \upharpoonright Table' \frown \langle Table\ i \rangle \frown \{(j+1) .. \#Table'\} \upharpoonright Table' = Table)$
$Freq\_Tab' = \{s?\} \lhd Freq\_Tab$

──

Delete changes the state of the system. The operation accepts a symbol and removes its entry from the symbol table *and* the frequency table. Deletion from the symbol table must maintain the order of the entries. The predicates demand that:

- The symbol is present in the symbol table; the index associated with the target symbol is used in the remaining predicate.
- After the operation, the table does not contain the symbol but some value *j* exists such that if we concatenate the first *j* entries of the after table with the sequence formed from the entry we deleted, and then concatenate this with the remaining entries of the after table, we will reform the original table. The existence of a value for *j* shows that the after table has the same entries in the same order as the initial table but does not contain the entry we wanted to delete. If the value of *j* is zero it simply means that the entry we deleted was the first in the original table. This predicate uses index restriction on the sequence.
- The symbol is removed from the frequency table.

The *Insert* operation

─── *Insert* ───

$\Delta SymT\_State$
$s? : SYM$
$v? : VAL$

──

$\neg (s? \in \text{dom}(\text{ran } Table))$
$Table' = Table \frown \langle (s?,v?) \rangle$
$Freq\_Tab' = Freq\_Tab \oplus \{(s?,0)\}$

──

Insert changes the state of the system. The operation places a new (*symbol, value*) pair at the end of the symbol table and adds a corresponding entry (*s?*,0) to *Freq_Tab* indicating, of course, that a new symbol cannot yet have been looked up. New entries can be added to the end of the symbol table because this places them in the correct order with respect to their access count. The insertion therefore does not require a reorganization of the table. The predicates demand that:

- The entry does not already exist in the table.
- The new entry is added to the logical end of the symbol table.
- The access frequency for this symbol is set to zero in the frequency table.

The *Find* operation

```
┌─── Find ──────────────────────────────────────────────
│ ΔSymT_State
│ s? : SYM
│ v! : VAL
├───────────────────────────────────────────────────────
│ s? ∈ dom(ran Table)
│ Freq_Tab' = Freq_Tab ⊕ {(s?, Freq_Tab(s?) + 1)}
│ Table' = Sort_SymT (Table, Freq_Tab')
│ ∃i : dom Table' • (first(Table' i) − s? ∧ v! − second(Table' i))
└───────────────────────────────────────────────────────
```

Find changes the state of the system. The operation increments the access count for the symbol by 1, reorganizes the symbol table accordingly, then outputs the value associated with the symbol. *Table'* is defined in terms of the application of the function *Sort_Table* with the pair (*Table, Freq_Tab'*) as argument where *Freq_Tab'* is the newly updated frequency table. The predicates demand that:

- The symbol must be in the table.
- The entry for the symbol in the frequency table is incremented by one.
- The table is sorted with respect to the updated access frequencies.
- The value associated with the symbol in the reorganized table is output.

Notice that the output value is taken from the reorganized table. This is again a practical consideration. Because its frequency count has been increased by one it will be found more quickly (by a linear search) than if we had output it from the old table. The final predicate is therefore better than the possible alternative:

$$\exists i : \text{dom } Table • (first(Table\ i) = s? \land v! = second(Table\ i))$$

18.3.7 Precondition calculations

The precondition schemas for each of the partial operations are shown below:

```
┌─── PreDelete ─────────────────────────────────────────
│ Abstract_SymT_State
│ s? : SYM
├───────────────────────────────────────────────────────
│ ∃Abstract_SymT_State' • (
│     ∃i ∈ dom(Table) • ( first (Table i) = s? ∧
│     ∃j ∈ {0} ∪ dom Table' • {1 .. j} 1 Table' ^ ⟨(Table i)⟩ ^
│         {(j + 1) .. #Table'}1 Table' = Table)
│ Freq_Tab' = {s?} ◁ Freq_Tab)
└───────────────────────────────────────────────────────
```

___ *PreInsert* _____

Abstract_SymT_State
s? : SYM
v? : VAL

_____

$\exists$*Abstract_SymT_State'* • (
$\neg$(*s?* $\in$ dom(ran(*Table*))) $\wedge$
Table' = *Table* $^\wedge$ $\langle$(*s?,v?*)$\rangle$ $\wedge$
Freq_Tab' = *Freq_Tab* $\oplus$ {(*s?*,0)})

_____

___ *PreFind* _____

Abstract_SymT_State
s? : SYM

_____

$\exists$*Abstract_SymT_State'* ; *v!* : *VAL* • (
s? $\in$ dom(ran(*Table*)) $\wedge$
Freq_Tab' = *Freq_Tab* $\oplus$ (*s?*, *Freq_Tab*(*s?*) + 1) $\wedge$
Table' = *Sort_SymT* (*Table*, *Freq_Tab'*) $\wedge$
$\exists i$: dom *Table'* • (*first*(*Table'* *i*) = *s?* $\wedge$ *v!* = *second*(*Table'* *i*)))

_____

As usual the precondition schemas can be simplified considerably. As an example, the simplified schema for *PreFind* shows some interesting influences from the invariant. We begin by removing predicates not involving variables quantified by $\exists$*Abstract_SymT_State'* ; *v!* : *VAL*:

___ *PreFind* _____

Abstract_SymT_State
s? : SYM

_____

s? $\in$ dom(ran(*Table*))
$\exists$*Abstract_SymT_State'*; *v!* : *VAL* • (
Freq_Tab' = *Freq_Tab* $\oplus$ (*s?*, *Freq_Tab*(*s?*) + 1) $\wedge$
Table' = *Sort_SymT* (*Table*, *Freq_Tab'*) $\wedge$
$\exists i$: dom *Table'* • (*first*(*Table'* *i*) = *s?* $\wedge$ *v!* = *second*(*Table'* *i*)))

_____

The predicate $\exists$*Abstract_SymT_State'* ; *v!* : *VAL* • (...) must be assumed to be *true* because it describes the proper outcome of the operation. There is little point in finding preconditions if we do not assume that the operation behaves as intended. If this predicate is *true* it can be omitted so that *PreFind* reduces to:

___ *PreFind* _____

Abstract_SymT_State
s? : SYM

_____

s? $\in$ dom(ran(*Table*))

_____

Preconditions of course must satisfy the state invariants, i.e. we cannot start from a state that is illegal. We can check this if we expand the *Abstract_SymT_State* schema:

```
┌─── PreFind ──────────────────────────────────────────────
│ Freq_Tab : Access
│ s? : SYM
├──────────────────────────────────────────────────────────
│ s? ∈ dom(ran(Table)
│ dom Freq_Tab = dom(ran Table)
│ ∀i,j : dom Table • (i ≠ j ⇒ first (Table i) ≠ first (Table j) ∧
│                      i < j ⇒ Freq_Tab(first (Table i)) ≥ Freq_Tab(first (Table j)))
```

The first two predicates demand that :

$$s? \in \text{dom}(\text{ran } Table) \land \text{dom } Freq\_Tab = \text{dom}(\text{ran } Table)$$

which requires that:

$$s? \in \text{dom } Freq\_Tab$$

showing that the explicit precondition and the invariant combine to suggest another precondition if a final state is to be guaranteed; the symbol must be present not only in the symbol table but also in the frequency table. The final precondition schema is therefore:

```
┌─── PreFind ──────────────────────────────────────────────
│ Abstract_SymT_State
│ s? : SYM
├──────────────────────────────────────────────────────────
│ s? ∈ dom(ran Table)
│ s? ∈ dom Freq_Tab
```

This observation also acts as a handy check on the properties of the specification because it is the obligation of *Insert* to ensure that the symbol is in *Freq_Tab*. We examine the properties shortly while the remaining precondition calculations and their summary are left as an exercise.

18.3.8 The total operations

Find and *Delete* are defined only if the symbol is present in both the symbol and frequency tables. Both of these operations can be made total by the following schemas and schema expressions:

$$Success \mathrel{\hat=} [Report! : Message \mid Report! = OK]$$
$$Total\_Find \mathrel{\hat=} (Find \land Success) \lor NotPresent$$
$$Total\_Delete \mathrel{\hat=} (Delete \land Success) \lor NotPresent$$

Insert, on the other hand, is successful only if the symbol is not present in the symbol table. The operation can be made total by means of the following schema expression:

$$Total\_Insert \triangleq (Insert \wedge Success) \vee Present$$

The *NotPresent* and *Present* schemas are only variations on those developed in SAQ 18.4. We leave the definition of these as an exercise.

18.3.9 Properties of the specification

There are some interesting properties concerning the specification that we might like to try to prove most of which depend upon a proper correspondence between the symbol and frequency tables. The theorems are presented as follows:

- Theorem 18.3 *Insert* ; *Delete* $| s?_i = s?_d \vdash \Xi SymT\_State$
- Theorem 18.4 *Delete* ; *Insert* $| s?_d = s?_i \vdash \Xi SymT\_State$
- Theorem 18.5 *Insert* ; *Find* $| s?_i = s?_f \vdash v! = v?$
- Theorem 18.6 *Find* ; *Find* $| s?_{f1} = s?_{f2} \vdash Freq\_Tab' \, s?_{f2} = Freq\_Tab \, s?_{f1} + 2$

In Theorem 18.3 we try to prove that if we insert a symbol and then immediately delete the *same* symbol the system state remains unchanged. In Theorem 18.4 we perform the operations in reverse order. Theorem 18.3 should be relatively straightforward to prove, whereas Theorem 18.4 needs some careful consideration.

SAQ 18.4 What extra condition must be assumed before Theorem 18.4 can be proven?

In Theorem 18.5, if we insert a symbol and then find it, we recover the value that we just added, while in Theorem 18.6, finding the same symbol twice increases its frequency count by two.

SAQ 18.5 Theorem 18.6 can be phrased as:

$$Find \, ; \, Find \, | \, s?_{f1} = s?_{f2} \vdash Freq\_Tab' \, s?_{f2} = Freq\_Tab \, s?_{f1} + 2$$

Prove this theorem.

18.4 SUMMARY

In this example the emphasis has been on the effect of the alternative model used as a basis for the specification. In particular we note the appearance of many more theorems, which is necessary because the added complexity generates many more specification properties. This complexity also extends to the precondition calculations which become rather more difficult to deduce.

This case study once again reminds us that when reading a formal specification in Z, we are often benefiting from the considerable amount of thought put into the selection of the most appropriate model by the author(s). This choice critically affects both the communication of our ideas and the effort involved in subsequent proofs.

SAQ 18.6 Once the symbol table has been completed, the *Find* operation extracts values that can be used to construct object code. When the object code has been generated, any symbol entry in the table associated with a frequency count of zero means that a variable has been declared but has never been referenced in the program. Such variables are redundant but they should be presented so that the programmer can be satisfied that they are no longer needed. Write the specification for an operation that can be used as a diagnostic to determine those symbolic variables—if any.

19

A DRINKS DISPENSING MACHINE

19.1 INTRODUCTION

This final case study examines the specification of a drinks dispensing machine, the control panel for which is shown in Fig 19.1. Coins are inserted to (at least) the value of the drink and the drink chosen by pressing an appropriate combination of the selection buttons. The drink is then served by pressing button D. Unlike tea and coffee, chocolate is served only white *and* sweet (commercial chocolate powder contains whitener and sweetener). If for some reason the drink cannot be dispensed the customer can obtain a full refund by pressing button R. The machine accepts any coin that is legal tender in the United Kingdom and the correct change is issued (if necessary) once a drink has been dispensed.

The machine has a number of displays which are useful to the customer and to those who maintain it. The service light is illuminated if the machine needs to be serviced. Servicing will be required when ingredients for certain drinks are exhausted. However, the machine is fully functional for drinks that do not need those ingredients. The only occasion when the machine is effectively out of use (apart from initialization) is when the ingredients for all the drinks have been exhausted. The two other displays are the coin display and the report display. The coin display shows the current value (in pence) of the coins inserted into the machine. This is a simple LED display with the word BAL (for balance) and the letter P permanently part of the display. Immediately below this is the report display which is used to give instructions to the customers. On the real machine this would be designed in some eye-catching way.

Machines like this are quite commonplace and frequently driven by microchips which contain the logic for deducing the outcome of a particular machine situation. This case study is therefore an exercise in the specification of the ROM programs. The study follows the now familiar pattern but omits the various proofs, precondition calculations and indexes in an attempt to make it more manageable and readable. These are left as exercises. This study concentrates instead on the techniques of Z and, in particular, the use of bags.

19.2 THE GIVEN SETS, ABBREVIATION DEFINITIONS AND AXIOMATIC DESCRIPTIONS

There are a number of sets and functions to be defined in this section. We begin by providing simple data types for the selection buttons on the control panel and the ingredients of the various drinks:

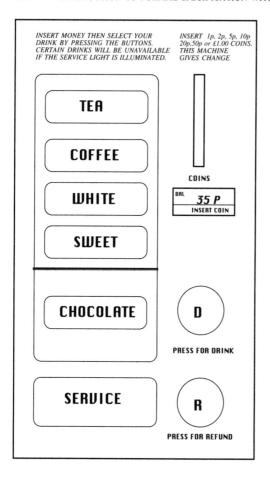

Fig 19.1   Control panel for the simple drinks dispenser

$Selection\_buttons ::= TEA \mid COFFEE \mid WHITE \mid SWEET \mid CHOCOLATE$
$Ingredient ::= Milk\_powder \mid Chocolate\_powder \mid Tea\_bag \mid Coffee\_granules \mid Sugar \mid Water$

The information displayed in the report display is provided by the data type *Message*:

Message ::= this drink is unavailable | insert more money and select drink again |
correct change unavailable | no cups in machine | try another coin | not in use | insert coin

while the condition of the service light is indicated using the data type *Onoff*:

$$Onoff ::= on \mid off$$

We will further assume that there is a 'universe' of coins which contains the accepted British coin set. All other coins are regarded as 'foreign' and are not differentiated. A foreign coin is unacceptable to the machine. The data type *Coin* summarizes this universe from a British perspective:

$Coin ::= One\_Penny \mid Two\_Pence \mid Five\_Pence \mid Ten\_Pence \mid Twenty\_Pence \mid$
$\qquad Fifty\_Pence \mid One\_Pound \mid Unacceptable\_coin$

The set of British coins is therefore easily defined through the following abbreviation definition:

$$British\_Coin == \{c : Coin \mid c \neq Unacceptable\_coin\}$$

Having introduced the set of selection buttons we are now in a position to define those combinations of button presses that represent a recognized drink. This information is provided by simple enumeration in the abbreviation definition for *Drink*. Notice that the choice of drink is represented by a *set of buttons* which means that the order in which the buttons are pressed is irrelevant. Notice also that odd combinations such as $\{TEA, COFFEE, CHOCOLATE\}$ are not members of this set and therefore represent unavailable drinks (thank goodness!):

$$Drink == \{\{TEA\}, \{COFFEE\}, \{CHOCOLATE\}, \{TEA, WHITE\},$$
$$\{TEA, SWEET\}, \{TEA, WHITE, SWEET\}, \{COFFEE, WHITE\},$$
$$\{COFFEE, SWEET\}, \{COFFEE, WHITE\ SWEET\}\}$$

The final abbreviation definition provides the list of ingredients for each one of the drinks:

$List\_of\_ingredients ==$
$\{\{Tea\_bag, Water\}, \{Coffee\_granules, Water\}, \{Chocolate\_powder, Water\}, \{Tea\_bag,$
$Water, Milk\_powder\}, \{Tea\_bag, Water, Sugar\}, \{Tea\_bag, Water, Sugar,$
$Milk\_powder\}, \{Coffee\_granules, Water, Milk\_powder\}, \{Coffee\_granules, Water,$
$Sugar\}, \{Coffee\_granules, Water, Sugar, Milk\_powder\}\}$

SAQ 19.1 Write definitions for these two sets by set comprehension.

We now turn our attention to the various constants and functions that will be required. First, we have to be able to associate a particular drink with the set of ingredients required to make it. The ingredient set is unique to a drink and each drink must have a set of ingredients so we define *Recipe* as a total injection from *Drinks* to *List_of_ingredients*. Clearly, *Recipe* represents a fixed mapping which is simply used to look up the ingredients associated with a particular combination of selection buttons. We therefore declare *Recipe* as a global constant through an axiomatic description:

$Recipe : Drink \rightarrowtail List\_of\_ingredients$

$Recipe = \{\{TEA\} \mapsto \{Tea\_bag, Water\}$
$\qquad \{COFFEE\} \mapsto \{Coffee\_granules, Water\}$
$\qquad \{CHOCOLATE\} \mapsto \{Chocolate\_powder, Water\}$
$\qquad \{TEA, WHITE\} \mapsto \{Tea\_bag, Water, Milk\_powder\}$
$\qquad \{TEA, SWEET\} \mapsto \{Tea\_bag, Water, Sugar\}$
$\qquad \{TEA, WHITE, SWEET\} \mapsto \{Tea\_bag, Water, Sugar, Milk\_powder\}$
$\qquad \{COFFEE, WHITE\} \mapsto \{Coffee\_granules, Water, Milk\_powder\}$
$\qquad \{COFFEE, SWEET\} \mapsto \{Coffee\_granules, Water, Sugar\}$
$\qquad \{COFFEE, WHITE, SWEET\} \mapsto \{Coffee\_granules, Water, Sugar, Milk\_powder\}\}$

A similar argument applies to *Worth*, the function that associates a coin with its value. This must be a total injection from *British_Coin* to its value in pence because all coins have a unique value. We will therefore again define the function as a global constant.

The machine is assumed to have a number of coin hoppers or tubes where each denomination is separately stored. The machine can store only a certain number of coins in each hopper and so we define a total function called *HopperMax* which determines the maximum number of coins of each denomination that can be held. Similarly, *StockMax* is a total function that associates each ingredient with the maximum number of units (tea bags, sugar lumps, etc.) that the machine can store, while *CupMax* represents the maximum number of plastic cups the machine can hold. Water is assumed to be inexhaustible because all machines are connected to the main supply. The individual limits for coins, cups and ingredients will be supplied later by the manufacturer of the machine. All these points are reflected in the following axiomatic description:

$Worth : British\_Coin \rightarrowtail \mathbb{N}$
$HopperMax : British\_Coin \rightarrow \mathbb{N}_1$
$StockMax : Ingredient \rightarrow \mathbb{N}_1$
$CupMax : \mathbb{N}$

$Worth = \{One\_Penny \mapsto 1, Two\_Pence \mapsto 2, Five\_Pence \mapsto 5, Ten\_Pence \mapsto 10,$
$\qquad\qquad Twenty\_Pence \mapsto 20, Fifty\_Pence \mapsto 50, One\_Pound \mapsto 100\}$
$HopperMax = \{One\_Penny \mapsto .., ..., One\_Pound \mapsto ..\}$
$StockMax = \{Tea\_bag \mapsto .., ..., Water \mapsto \infty\}$
$CupMax = ...$

Value is a total function that computes the value (in pence) of a bag of British coins. Bags are used extensively in this specification because they conveniently associate each coin in a collection with the number of times it occurs. A recursive definition of this total function is:

$Value : bag\ British\_Coin \rightarrow \mathbb{N}$

$Value\ [\![\ ]\!] = 0$
$\forall c : British\_Coin\ ;\ n : \mathbb{N} \bullet Value\ [\![c \mapsto n]\!] = Worth\ c * n$
$\forall b_1, b_2 : bag\ British\_Coin \bullet Value\ (b_1 \uplus b_2) = Value\ b_1 + Value\ b_2$

The value of an empty bag of coins is 0. The value of a bag containing coins of just one denomination is the worth of the coin times the number that we have in the bag. Finally, we make the observation that a bag containing coins of more than one denomination can be regarded as formed by the union of two other bags; one containing coins of only one denomination, the other containing the rest of the coins. We find the value of this first bag and continually apply the observation to the other bag, keeping a running total as we proceed. Recursive calls are terminated by the fact that the value of an empty bag is zero.

We also need to decide whether one bag is a subset of another. This is important because we can issue the correct change only if the coins needed are currently part of the collection of coins that make up the machine's takings. In the following example the first bag is a subset of the second because the second bag contains the first:

$$\{One\_Penny \mapsto 6\} \sqsubseteq \{One\_Penny \mapsto 7, Five\_Pence \mapsto 6, One\_Pound \mapsto 3\}$$

while in the next example the first bag is *not* contained in the second bag and is therefore not a subset:

$$\neg(\{One\_Penny \mapsto 8\} \sqsubseteq \{One\_Penny \mapsto 7, Five\_Pence \mapsto 6, One\_Pound \mapsto 3\})$$

Bag subset is simply a relation like 'less than' or 'equal to' over the numbers. We define this relation as a generic constant so that it can be used on any bag not just bags of *British_coins*, thereby permitting easy migration of the specification to another country. The following definition says that one bag is a subset of another if for each element, the *count* in the first bag is less than or equal to the *count* in the second. This of course ensures that all elements in the first bag are also in the second.

$[X]$

$\_ \sqsubseteq \_ : bag\ X \leftrightarrow bag\ X$

$b_1 \sqsubseteq b_2 \Leftrightarrow (\forall x : X \bullet count\ b_1\ x \le count\ b_2\ x)$

19.3 THE ABSTRACT STATE OF THE MACHINE

The abstract state of the machine is described by the following schema:

Abs_State_Machine

Balance, Takings : bag *British_coin*
Stock : bag *Ingredient*
Cups : $\mathbb{N}$
Prices : *Drink* $\rightarrow \mathbb{N}$
Service_light : *Onoff*
Coin_display : $\mathbb{N}$
Report_display : *Message*

$\forall c : dom\ Takings \bullet 0 \le count\ Takings\ c \le HopperMax\ c$
$\forall i : dom\ Stock \bullet 0 \le count\ Stock\ i \le StockMax\ i$
$0 \le Cups \le CupMax$
$Coin\_display = Value\ Balance$

Balance and *Takings* are both bags of *British_coin* enforcing the point that no other coins are permitted in the machine. *Balance* simply records the combination of coins that has been inserted by the current customer. Inserted coins are immediately added to *Takings*, which always represents the total amount of money in the machine.

Stock is a bag that records the current stock levels of each of the ingredients, while *Cups* records the number of plastic cups in the machine. *Prices* is a total function from *Drink* to $\mathbb{N}$ showing that all drinks have an associated price. This function can be updated if required to reprice the drinks. *Service_light* is a state variable which is either *on* or *off*, while *Coin_display* and *Report_display* correspond to the displays on the front of the machine (see Fig 19.1). Both *Coin_display* and *Report_display* are taken as state variables to convey the notion of 'persistence' associated with an LED.

In this design we need separate state variables for *Balance* and *Coin_display* even though they always represent the same amount. *Balance* is kept as a separate variable to permit the machine to keep track of the combination of coins the customer inserted. This bag is returned intact when the refund button is pressed. Customers would not be happy if after inserting, say, a 20 pence coin for a drink and then asking for a refund they received twenty 1 pence coins!

The invariants record the following facts:

- For each British coin there will be a maximum number that the machine can store in its coin tube.
- For each ingredient there will be some maximum stock value that can be stored in the machine.
- There is a maximum number of cups which the machine can hold.
- The coin display always shows the value of the current balance.

19.4 THE DELTA AND xi NOTATIONS

```
┌─── ΔMachine_State ─────────────────────────────────
│ Abs_State_Machine
│ Abs_State_Machine'
├────────────────────────────────────────────────────
│
└────────────────────────────────────────────────────
```

```
┌─── ΞMachine_State ─────────────────────────────────
│ Abs_State_Machine
│ Abs_State_Machine'
├────────────────────────────────────────────────────
│ Balance' = Balance
│ Stocks' = Stocks
│ Takings' = Takings
│ Cups' = Cups
│ Prices' = Prices
│ Service_light' = Service_light
│ Coin_display' = Coin_display
│ Report_display' = Report_display
└────────────────────────────────────────────────────
```

Once again these are the conventional Z definitions but in this specification there is little use for the xi schema because almost all operations write to the report display LED and thereby change it (but see *No_refund* later).

19.5 THE INITIAL STATE OF THE MACHINE

```
__ Initial_Machine_State _____
Abs_State_Machine'
_____
Balance' = [[ ]]
Stocks' = [[ ]]
Takings' = [[ ]]
Cups' = 0
Prices' = {d : Drink • (d, 0)}
Service_Light' = on
Report_display' = not in use
```

In the initial state all the bags are empty, the machine has no cups, the drinks have not been priced, the report display LED says *not in use* and the service light is *on* indicating that a service is required.

19.6 PARTIAL OPERATIONS FOR THE DRINKS MACHINE

The partial operations are:

- *Service_Machine*
- *Insert_coin*
- *Get_drink*
- *Refund*
- *Take_ profit*

In all of these the condition of *Coin_display* is always determined by the state invariant:

$$Coin\_display = Value\ Balance$$

This predicate migrates to all operations through schema inclusion and therefore no explicit reference is made to the display in any of the schemas that follow.

19.6.1 Servicing the machine

```
__ Service_Machine _____
ΔAbs_State_Machine
new_stocks? : bag ingredient
new_cups? : N
new_takings? : bag British_coin
new_ prices? : Drinks ⇸ N₁
_____
Balance' = Balance
Stocks' = Stocks ⊎ new_stocks?
Cups' = Cups + new_cups?
Takings' = Takings ⊎ new_takings?
Prices' = Prices ⊕ new_ prices?
Service_Light' = off
Report_display' = insert coin
```

There are no preconditions to a service; the machine can be serviced at any time. The service light does not have to be illuminated nor do we have to run out of ingredients. The role of the service light is simply to indicate when the machine *must* be serviced. Servicing is therefore an operation that always succeeds.

When we service the machine we can add to the number of cups, the stocks of ingredients and to the takings already in the machine. Adding to the takings means that the machine is more likely to be able to give correct change so the service improves its functionality. In the schema bag union is used to deal with these aspects. It should also be pointed out that during a service the levels of any of these items could be left alone. This would be effected by using inputs such as *new_cups?* $= 0$ or *new_stocks?* $= [\![\ ]\!]$. The prices of the drinks can also be changed during a service if required by overriding the old *Prices* function with *new_prices?* Leaving prices unchanged on a service is indicated by using *new_prices?* $= \{\ \}$.

Servicing does not alter the *Balance* in the machine. If someone puts in money without pressing for a drink or a refund then the next person gets some good fortune. Because servicing can only *add* to the machine, servicing is distinguished from profit taking, which is regarded as a separate operation (see Sec. 19.6.5). Finally, once the machine has been serviced the service light is *off* and the report display LED reads *insert coin* indicating its readiness for use.

19.6.2 Inserting coins

```
┌─── Insert_Coin ─────────────────────────────────
│ Δ_Abs_State_Machine
│ c? : Coin
├──────────────────────────────────────────────────
│ c? ≠ Unacceptable_coin
│ count Takings c? < HopperMax c?
│ Balance' = Balance ⊎ {(c? ↦ 1)}
│ Takings' = Takings ⊎ {(c? ↦ 1)}
│ Stocks' = Stocks
│ Cups' = Cups
│ Prices' = Prices
│ Service_light' = Service_light
│ Report_display' =insert coin
└──────────────────────────────────────────────────
```

The schema *Insert_coin* describes the process of inserting a single coin into the machine. The process of building a balance is therefore seen as the repeated application of the insert coin operation. An alternative (and more abstract) approach would be to model this process in terms of the machine accepting a bag of coins in a single operation but this is a somewhat less intuitive solution. The precondition(s) for this operation demand(s) that:

- The coin is British.
- The coin tube (hopper) for the coin is not full.

If the coin is accepted both the balance and the takings are increased, while the report display LED prompts for another coin. All other aspects of the system state remain the same. In this specification therefore, all inserted (acceptable) coins go straight to *Takings*, while *Balance* is simply a variable used to keep track of the combination of coins tendered so far. Consequences of this specification are that *Takings* alone records how much money is in the machine at any point in time, *Value Balance* records how much the current customer is in credit, while all change has to be taken from *Takings*.

19.6.3 Getting a drink

```
___ Get_Drink _____
ΔAbs_State_Machine
choice? : ℙSelection_buttons
d! : Drink
Change! : bag British_coin
_____
choice? ∈ Drink
Value Balance ≥ Prices choice?
∀i : Recipe choice? • count Stock i > 0
Cups > 0
∃b : bag British_coins • (b ⊑ Takings ∧ Value Balance = Value b + Prices choice?)
Balance′ = ⟦ ⟧
Stock′ ⊎ {i : Recipe choice? • i ↦ 1} = Stock
Cups′ = Cups − 1
Change! ⊑ Takings ∧ Value Balance = Value Change! + Prices choice?
Takings′ ⊎ Change! = Takings
Prices′ = Prices
Service_light′ = Service_light
Report_display′ = insert coin
d! = choice?
```

Drinks are chosen by pressing some combination of the selection buttons. The input *choice?* is therefore a set of button presses indicating that the order in which they are pressed is irrelevant. Once a drink has been dispensed the machine issues correct change (if necessary). The preconditions demand that:

- The combination of button presses corresponds to a known drink.
- The balance in the machine is at least enough to pay for the chosen drink.
- All the ingredients are available to make the drink.
- A cup is available.
- The machine can issue correct change if necessary.

This last precondition is interesting and again illustrates a useful technique when handling bags of money. The predicate that has to be satisfied if the correct change is to be issued is:

$$\exists b : bag\ British\_coins • (b ⊑ Takings ∧ Value\ Balance = Value\ b + Prices\ choice?)$$

which demands that all the coins necessary to make the change are already part of the machine's takings and that the value of the balance in the machine includes the price of the drink and the value of the change. Although this is a funny way of putting it, it avoids our having to make any commitment to the composition of the bag of coins returned to the customer. This is determined by the machine alone, dependent upon the mix of coins currently in the coin tubes, but at this level of abstraction we do not have to address how this is achieved.

Dispensing a drink is, of course, a physical act and the nearest we can describe it in the specification is by making the output variable $d!$ equal to the input $choice?$ Once the drink has been dispensed the balance becomes empty, the stock levels of each of the ingredients are reduced by one, the machine has one less cup, the change is issued, the takings have been reduced to reflect the change issued and the report display LED prompts for another coin. The service light and the drink prices are unaffected.

Notice how the specification deals with the reductions in the *Stock* and *Takings* bags. The predicate:

$$Stock' \uplus \{i : Recipe\ choice? \bullet i \mapsto 1\} = Stock$$

is a postcondition that describes the relationship between the input and the stock levels before and after the operation. The condition expressed is that bag union between the stock after and a bag where each of the ingredients of the chosen drink occurs exactly once, is equal to the stock before. This is the same as saying that the stock level of every ingredient of the chosen drink has been reduced by one after the operation. The predicate:

$$Takings' \uplus Change! = Takings$$

describes the reduction in takings in similar fashion.

19.6.4 The refund

```
┌─── Refund ────────────────────────────────────────────
│ ΔAbs_State_Machine
│ Refund! : bag British_Coin
├────────────────────────────────────────────────────────
│ Balance ≠ [[ ]]
│ Refund! = Balance
│ Refund! ⊑ Takings
│ Takings' ⊎ Refund! = Takings
│ Balance' = [[ ]]
│ Stocks' = Stocks
│ Cups' = Cups
│ Prices' = Prices
│ Service_light' = Service_light
│ Report_display' = insert coin
└────────────────────────────────────────────────────────
```

Customers can demand a refund from the machine at any time. The operation has just one precondition:

• The balance is not empty.

which really corresponds to customers inserting coins and then changing their minds. It is important from a user-friendly point of view that the machine returns the same bag of coins that the customer input and this is reflected by the predicate:

$$Refund! = Balance$$

The refund is issued from the takings in the machine which, of course, contains all the coins the customer inserted (see *Insert_coin* earlier). The predicate:

$$Refund! \sqsubseteq Takings$$

is therefore really superfluous but remains for the sake of clarity. Once a refund has been issued, the balance is reset and the report display LED prompts for another coin. Stocks, cups, prices and the service light remain unaffected, while the *Takings* are reduced to reflect the refund given.

19.6.5 Taking profit

```
┌─── Take_ profit ──────────────────────────────────
│ ΔAbs_State_Machine
│ Profit! : bag British_Coin
├────────────────────────────────────────────────────
│ Takings' ⊎ Profit! = Takings
│ Balance' = [[ ]]
│ Stocks' = Stocks
│ Cups' = Cups
│ Prices' = Prices
│ Service_light' = Service_light
│ Report_display' = insert coin
└────────────────────────────────────────────────────
```

Taking profit, like servicing, has no preconditions and will always succeed. However, unlike servicing, this operation 'profiteers' in the sense that any balance owing to the customer is removed by including it in the takings, i.e. *Balance'* = [[ ]]. We cannot remove money that is not in the machine for our bag operators are not defined on negative occurrences (however see Hayes and Jones (1989)) and a profit of zero is possible if no one has used the machine in between the profit-taking operations.

When taking profit we can remove all the money in the machine but this will prevent the machine from being used if the next customer does not tender the exact money.

SAQ 19.2 How would you express this property as a theorem?

Taking profit leaves cups, stocks, prices and the service light unchanged but writes the message *insert coin* to the report LED. Notice again how the first predicate defines the takings afterwards by demanding that the bag union for *Takings'* and *Profit!* equals the original *Takings*. Once again this technique does not dictate any particular coin composition for the profit.

19.7 TOTAL OPERATIONS FOR THE DRINKS MACHINE

As usual the total operations are formed from the partial operations by considering what happens when their preconditions are offended. Previous case studies used the schema *Success* as part of the definition of the total operations. This study departs from this practice because the report display LED really achieves the same thing in that the *insert coin* prompt shows that the previous operation has been successful. Similarly, the usual role for the output variable *Report!* has been assumed by the LED.

There are no preconditions for *Service* or *Take_ profit* and so these operations are already total. The preconditions for the *Insert_coin* operation, however, show that it can fail in a number of ways:

- The coin inserted is unacceptable (i.e. it is not British).
- The coin tube (hopper) for the coin is full.

The following schemas describe what happens in these circumstances:

```
┌─── Reject_coin ──────────────────────────────────────────
│ ΔAbs_State_Machine
│ c?, c! : Coin
├───────────────────────────────────────────────────────────
│ c? = Unacceptable_coin
│ Takings' = Takings
│ Balance' = Balance
│ Stocks' = Stocks
│ Cups' = Cups
│ Prices' = Prices
│ Service_light' = Service_light
│ Report_display' = try another coin
│ c! = c?
└───────────────────────────────────────────────────────────
```

```
┌─── Hopper_full ──────────────────────────────────────────
│ ΔAbs_State_Machine
│ c?, c! : Coin
├───────────────────────────────────────────────────────────
│ count Takings c? = HopperMax c?
│ Takings' = Takings
│ Balance' = Balance
│ Stocks' = Stocks
│ Cups' = Cups
│ Prices' = Prices
│ Service_light' = Service_light
│ Report_display' = try another coin
│ c! = c?
└───────────────────────────────────────────────────────────
```

and so the total operation of inserting a coin is defined by:

$$Total\_Insert\_coin \triangleq Insert\_coin \lor Reject\_coin \lor Hopper\_full$$

Notice that the *Hopper_full* operation does not signal a service. Because the machine gives change, it is capable of reducing the contents of popular coin tubes by being biased towards certain coinage mixes. In the total operation coins are rejected ($c! = c?$) and returned to the customer if the preconditions fail.

By examining the preconditions for the *Get_drink* operation we see that it too can fail in a number of ways:

- The combination of selection buttons pressed by the customer does not correspond to a known drink.
- The customer has not inserted enough money.
- The machine is out of stock(s) for the chosen drink.
- The machine has run out of cups.
- The exact change is unavailable.

The schemas that deal with each of these events are as follows:

Drink_not_known

$\Delta Abs\_State\_Machine$
$choice? : \mathbb{P} Selection\_buttons$

$\neg (choice? \in Drink)$
$Takings' = Takings$
$Balance' = Balance$
$Stocks' = Stocks$
$Cups' = Cups$
$Prices' = Prices$
$Service\_light' = Service\_light$
$Report_display' = $ this drink is unavailable

Not_enough_money

$\Delta Abs\_State\_Machine$
$choice? : \mathbb{P} Selection\_buttons$

$Value\ Balance < Prices\ choice?$
$Takings' = Takings$
$Balance' = Balance$
$Stocks' = Stocks$
$Cups' = Cups$
$Prices' = Prices$
$Service\_light' = Service\_light$
$Report_display' = $ insert more money and select drink again

---

```
┌─── Out_of_stock(s) ──────────────────────────────────
│ ΔAbs_State_Machine
│ choice? :  Selection_buttons
├──────────────────────────────────────────────────────
│ ∃i : Receipe choice? • count Stock i = 0
│ Takings' = Takings
│ Balance' = Balance
│ Stocks' = Stocks
│ Cups' = Cups
│ Prices' = Prices
│ Service_light' = on
│ Report_display' = this drink is unavailable
└──────────────────────────────────────────────────────
```

```
┌─── Out_of_cups ──────────────────────────────────────
│ ΔAbs_State_Machine
│ choice? : ℙSelection_buttons
├──────────────────────────────────────────────────────
│ Cups = 0
│ Takings' = Takings
│ Balance' = Balance
│ Stocks' = Stocks
│ Cups' = Cups
│ Prices' = Prices
│ Service_light' = on
│ Report_display' = no cups in machine
└──────────────────────────────────────────────────────
```

```
┌─── No_change_available ──────────────────────────────
│ ΔAbs_State_Machine
│ choice? :  Selection_buttons
├──────────────────────────────────────────────────────
│ (Value Balance ≥ Prices choice? ∧
│ ¬∃b : British_coins • (b ⊑ Takings ∧ Value Balance = Value b + Prices choice?))
│ Takings' = Takings
│ Balance' = Balance
│ Stocks' = Stocks
│ Cups' = Cups
│ Prices' = Prices
│ Service_light' = Service_light
│ Report_display' = correct change unavailable
└──────────────────────────────────────────────────────
```

Most of the schemas are fairly straightforward but some comment may be appropriate for the preconditions of *Out_of_stock(s)* and *No_change_available*. The predicate:

$$\exists i : Recipe\ choice? \bullet count\ Stock\ i = 0$$

says that there exists at least one ingredient of the drink which is out of stock, while:

> $Value\ Balance \geq Prices\ choice?\ \wedge$
> $\neg \exists b : British\_coins \bullet (b \sqsubseteq Takings \wedge Value\ Balance = Value\ b + Prices\ choice?)$

says that although the balance is sufficient to pay for the drink there is no bag of coins which is currently part of the machine's takings and is of value equal to the change required.

Finally, the total operation can be related to the process of pressing button D on the control panel such that the non-deterministic definition of this operation becomes:

$$Press\_button\_D \triangleq Get\_drink \vee Drink\_not\_known$$
$$\vee\ Not\_enough\_money$$
$$\vee\ Out\_of\_stock(s)$$
$$\vee\ Out\_of\_cups$$
$$\vee\ No\_change\_available$$

All of the total operations so far leave the balance in the machine if the preconditions fail. To recover money the customer must press button R for a refund. However, the precondition for *Refund* requires that the balance is *not* empty. If a customer requests a refund when the balance is empty the status quo is preserved. Thus:

_____ *No_refund* _____

$\Xi Machine\_State$

$Balance = [\![\ ]\!]$

The total operation for a refund can therefore related to pressing button R:

$$Press\_button\_R \triangleq Refund \vee No\_Refund$$

19.8 SUMMARY

In this case study the emphasis has been centred largely on the use of bags to specify the properties of a familiar real-world object. Bags are rather neglected members of the mathematical toolkit but in many circumstances—especially where monetary amounts or stock levels are concerned—they present an ideal model. The real drinks dispensing machine would have to have quite sophisticated coin recognition mechanisms and elaborate algorithms to determine optimum coin compositions for change given current machine takings. Using bags we are able to capture the essential behaviour of these aspects without committing ourselves to particular implementations. A number of these are well known within the automatic catering industry and the manufacturer is free to employ the most appropriate given the intended operating characteristics of the machine. The next part of the book reviews the complementary method VDM. The drinks dispenser will be visited again so that direct comparison can be made between the two approaches.

PART SIX

VDM-SL: The Vienna Development Method-Specification Language

The ability to simplify means to eliminate the unnecessary so that the necessary may speak.

Hans Hofmann (1880–1966), German-born US painter

INTRODUCTION

The Vienna Development Method (VDM) was conceived at the IBM Vienna laboratory from academic research carried out by a number of different workers in the general areas of programming language definition during the 1960s and early 1970s. The foundation work provided by the academics was then moulded into a coherent methodology by the Viennese industrial researchers around 1973–5 of whom Cliff Jones and Dines Bjørner are probably the most well known. This early phase is often termed 'classical' VDM and it predates Z as a formal systematic method for the development of software systems. However, like Z, the involvement of industrial researchers was seen as critical in moving the method from academia to the real world, where it could be used to find practical solutions to a wide variety of software engineering problems. It is a credit to the method that its success in the industrial sector since the early 1980s has generated a number of supporting textbooks and considerable academic research such that VDM is now seen as an industry mature product.

Like Z, VDM provides a specification language which acts as a notation for recording specifications, together with a series of proof obligations that permit a designer to reason about the correctness of a design and to justify particular design steps. The use of VDM, however, does not guarantee an optimum or best design solution. Like Z, this insight always has to be provided by the designer. A specification written in VDM is a mixture of formal mathematical statements and informal explanatory text. The role of these two components is exactly the same as before, but whereas Z bases its formal descriptions firmly on typed set theory, VDM employs the same areas of discrete mathematics but in a less rigid fashion. We can therefore expect differences between the two methods; we shall see, for example, that a VDM specification is somewhat closer to the program environment than one written in Z and that the strong typing of Z is less vigorously applied in VDM. What really needs emphasis, however, are the similarities and not the differences and this is what this part of the book tries to achieve.

There have been a number of major developments marking what could be called the consolidation of *VDM*. The first of these was the publication of *The Vienna Development Method—the Meta Language* (Bjørner and Jones, 1978) and *Formal Specification and Software Development* (Bjørner and Jones, 1982) which refer to the classical VDM developed over the period 1973–8. In 1980, *Software Development: a rigorous approach* (Jones, 1980) was published, which dealt with the program development aspects of VDM and this text became well known as a result of its use on a number of industrial courses. In 1986 *Systematic Software Development Using VDM* (Jones, 1986) appeared, while *Case Studies in Systematic Software Development* (Jones and Shaw, 1990) describes a wide range of industrial case studies aimed at establishing the maturity of the method. A second edition of Jones (1986) appeared in 1991. Like Z, the issue of standardization is being actively addressed. The rather more mature VDM has had longer to develop its variations and these are being brought together in a unified form by the British Standards Institution VDM-SL standardization panel (BSI IST/5/50). In this part of the book the VDM described is essentially that proposed by the BSI and published in the VDM-SL reference guide by Dawes (1991).

20

ESSENTIAL VDM

CHECKLIST OF OBJECTIVES

After reading this chapter you should be able to:

- Understand the structure of a specification written in VDM.
- Appreciate the similarities between the mathematical objects of VDM and those of Z.
- Understand the typing mechanism of VDM.
- Compare the abstract state schema of Z with the state definition of VDM.
- Realize that the proof obligations of VDM correspond to many of the theorems of Z.

20.1 INTRODUCTION

We have seen that Z uses a basic library containing generic definitions of mathematical objects together with their operators and the laws governing their behaviour. This has been referred to as the 'toolkit' and its contents are referenced freely by those using the method. VDM has an equivalent toolkit serving precisely the same purpose as that of Z, with a very similar collection of objects. In this respect the mathematical aspects of VDM present us with very little that is really new. Rather, we will find that it is its use of the mathematics, its emphasis and notation that largely distinguish it from Z. This chapter reviews the toolkit of VDM and the general structure of a VDM specification, drawing parallels with Z wherever appropriate. This discussion begins from a position which emphasizes that which is common across the two methods rather than that which differs.

20.2 THE MATHEMATICAL OBJECTS OF VDM

Z is based on a theory of sets which evolve to define relations, functions, sequences and bags. At the lowest level of consideration each of these objects is a set and can always be treated as such. Whereas the set is the atomic mathematical object for Z, the fundamental compound object is the relation, for all the other objects are simply special kinds of relation. In Z, therefore, there is a simple smooth progression in mathematical complexity with new object types being created by the application of just two type constructors. VDM is also founded upon set theory but unlike Z its evolution is not based on variations of the relation. Indeed, relations are never referred to as separate types in VDM, often being regarded simply as particular sort of sets or as structures called *maps* (see later).

Apart from sets (and tuples), one of the most fundamental objects in VDM is the function. In common with Z the function is regarded as a mathematical abstraction for the familiar concept of a mapping between two sets of interest. The domain of the function is the set of values to which it can be applied, while the application of the function to an element in its domain yields a single result. The range of the function is therefore regarded simply as a set of values which contains the results of function application. As in Z, the function provides a *fixed mapping* from argument to result, i.e. it can be regarded as a constant which is simply a set of pairs. In Z, however, we have become used to dealing with functions in two contexts, either as variables belonging to particular function types, or as constants introduced by axiomatic descriptions. When we declare a variable to belong to a particular function type in Z, e.g. $f : X \rightarrow Y$, we are really allowing f to range over any one of the values embodied in the type so that application of f with an argument at one instant might not yield the same result as its application with the same argument at some other time because the value of the variable might have been changed in between. When we declare the function through an axiomatic description, however, we confine the function to a single constant value within its type, and in such cases application of the function with the same argument *always* gives the same result. It is this latter context that is most often reflected by the function in VDM and so functions and function definitions serve much the same purpose as finite functions in typed set theory and certain axiomatic descriptions in Z.

The definition of a function in VDM can be achieved in different ways: *directly* (explicitly), *implicitly* or as a *polymorphic* definition. A direct definition provides a rule or expression for the evaluation of the result from the argument(s). In this respect the definition shows *how* the result is computed. This approach suffers from the disadvantage that for many situations the description becomes too algorithmic and this removes a degree of freedom with regard to the choice of the final implementation. Implicit specification of functions, on the other hand, are concerned with *what* has to be achieved and not how. In such cases the behaviour of the function is expressed in terms of pre- and postconditions and we have become familiar with the use of these in Z. Generally speaking, these descriptions are more concise and postpone our commitment to an implementation until later in the software engineering process where such considerations are more appropriate. In this sense, VDM functions are often referred to as *loosely specified* in that they do not define a particular occurrence but a whole class of occurrences, any one of which satisfies the specification. At some point, however, an implicit definition must be made explicit in order that it be implemented on a real machine, and this will generate a proof obligation which requires us to show that the direct definition satisfies its implicit specification. Function definitions can also be Polymorphic and these simply correspond to the generic constants of Z (see Chapter 16).

Although functions in VDM are useful, the nature of their fixed mapping and the need to provide either a rule or a postcondition to deduce their result renders them inappropriate as models in many areas of reality. For example, in the *Project–*

Programmer scenario (see Chapter 9), the relationship between the sets *Prog_Num* and *Prog_Name* is dynamic, continually capturing and releasing pairs as the programmers come to and go from the organization. Using the set of partial functions in Z we can declare a variable *Programmer:Prog_Num* $\twoheadrightarrow$ *Prog_Name* that admirably reflects the qualities and properties of this relationship, but the function of VDM does not convey the notion of change, nor can we easily devise a rule or postcondition for its result in a situation such as this. Because of these difficulties VDM introduces the *map* and map *types*, which can be regarded as one stage further in the evolution of the function, yet which possess properties that distinguish them and make them more appropriate models for dynamic situations. Indeed, we shall see that the map type is really the VDM analogue of the function type in Z.

A map is a structure that expresses a relationship between two sets of interests; the sets again being referred to as the *from-set* and the *to-set*. The elements of the *from-set* for which the map is defined are the *domain* of the map, while those of the *to-set* that are associated with elements of the domain are the *range* of the map. Figure 20.1 shows some map *M* that associates personal identifier numbers with names, and in this sense the map can be regarded as a set of ordered pairs with a restriction applied to the mapping that an element in the domain can map at most to one in the range. Application of the map with an element from the domain yields an element of the range, e.g. $M(P5) = Jocasta$, or $M(P4) = Jack$.

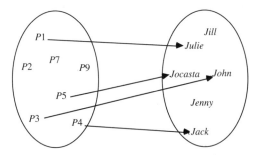

Figure 20.1 A map constructed between sets of personal identifier numbers and names.

Of course, given two sets a whole host of different maps could be constructed. A map type in VDM describes just such a collection of individual map values. A map, however, is not a set in the normal sense and the set operators cannot be applied to it. Neither is the map a function. Despite its description as a collection of ordered pairs, the pairs that constitute the map cannot be deduced from some rule or postcondition governing map application. Rather, the argument–result relationship is explicitly constructed and pairs are *dynamically* managed using operators that permit entries to be added to or removed from the map. In short, a map in VDM is a mathematical object with its own operators distinct from sets and functions.

In VDM a variable can be declared using a particular map type. At any time this variable can assume any map value embodied in the type. Using the map operators the value of this variable can be changed so that the map can act as a persistent object retaining (through its current state) a history of the transformations carried out upon it. Jones and Shaw (1990) draw the parallel that managing a map is like building and maintaining a table of pairs with map application corresponding to a table 'lookup'. In this sense the map must also be finite and objects in VDM are often seen to retain this link with reality. Jones and Shaw's comparison, however, is somewhat tenuous in that whereas a table has a first, second, ..., and last entry, a map (regarded simply as a collection of pairs) supports no such notion of order among its entries. In computer systems, access to information via unique *keys* is one of the most common activities and poses significant implementation difficulties. The map can be regarded as a set of *key–value* pairs and provides a powerful abstraction for this process leading to precise specifications. This observation, together with persistence, means that maps are the most common structure used in large VDM specifications.

The concept of the map type in VDM parallels the function type in Z and the operators that characterize and distinguish the map are very similar to those discussed earlier in Chapter 8. However, in Z functions evolved from relations but this is not the case in VDM. Indeed, VDM sees no need to introduce the relation as a structure with a distinguishing type within its specifications. A relation represents a many-to-many association where a single item in the domain can identify several items in the range. In VDM one way to accommodate this characteristic is by using a map that relates elements of the domain to *single* items in the range but where each item in the range is itself a set. Relations in VDM are therefore often simply particular types of map, although the most usual way of modelling them is as sets of pairs; subsets of some Cartesian product over the two sets. Using a map representation, however, may have an advantage in that we inherit a whole host of useful operators which cannot be applied to VDM sets. This means that the object we would naturally regard as a single discrete type in Z can be represented as two distinct types in VDM. This seems quite unusual but is a natural consequence of the typing emphasis in VDM.

VDM also supports a separate type for sequences. The operators that characterize these objects are much same as in Z. Sequence types can be regarded as variations of the general map type, but these objects are not maps and the map operators do not strictly apply. VDM has no specific type constructor for bags (sometimes called multisets) but these can be modelled as maps from the elements to their multiplicity in the multiset.

The remaining mathematical objects of VDM are composite values (*records*) and union types. Composite values resemble schema types in Z, however composite values are much more frequently used within a VDM specification than schema variables are in a Z specification. Union types have no direct counterpart in Z other than a super-ficial similarity to simple data types. The analogy however is a dangerous one, for union types in VDM essentially permit the union of two different types to form a new type containing all the values of the old types. This, of course, is illegal in Z, which never permits elements of one type to appear in another. Union types like relations again suggest that the typing mechanism in VDM is less vigorous than in Z. As in Z, all mathematical objects in VDM can be named and these names are again called identifiers. Identifiers in VDM must begin with a letter (plain English or Greek) but can optionally contain digits, hyphens (not underscores) and primes.

Finally, notice that in VDM, sets, functions, maps, sequences, bags and records are quite distinct types and the operators that characterize one often cannot be applied to another. In Z, however, every structure evolves from the set. Consequently, set operators can be applied (with care) to relations or functions. Indeed we have seen that the latter share many common operators. The qualification 'with care' implies that in certain cases application of these operators may destroy the qualities that make (say) a function a function. In Z the type declaration is used to predicate membership to define sets of particular flavours and represents the mechanism by which the nature of the different sets is distinguished and preserved. The type mechanism of VDM and its consequences are discussed shortly.

20.3 THE STRUCTURE OF A VDM SPECIFICATION

The main components of a VDM specification are:

- Type definitions
- Value definitions and a
- State definition, together with
- Function definitions and
- Operation definitions

Proof obligations also exist that correspond to the theorems of Z and ensure the 'well formedness' of the specification.

20.3.1 Type definitions in VDM

Type definitions appear at the head of a specification in a *type definition block* preceded by the keyword `types` and introduce the various types to be used throughout the specification. All types introduced in this way have global scope. In VDM, as in Z, a type is simply a collection of values distinguished by the operations that can be performed upon them. VDM provides a number of predefined *basic* and *fundamental basic types* together with a number of type constructors that can be used to form *compound types* from existing ones. Types can also be formed by restricting the membership of other types by some *invariant* or by forming a *union-type* from two or more types which contains all the values from the participants. Apart from the last method, all this is familiar from Z. Indeed we shall see that the types definition block of VDM serves much the same purpose as the given sets, simple data types and abbreviation definitions of Z

The case for a type system has already been argued (Chapter 15) as a mechanism that avoids certain paradoxes and enables a degree of consistency checking. However, VDM is not a strongly typed language in the sense we have come to expect from our study of Z. The ability to model the relation as either a set or a map shows that a relation could be present in a specification in two quite distinct forms. Although this is possible in Z it is far less likely. Similarly, elements from a number of different types can form a union type which means that it is not always possible in VDM to assign each expression and each context a unique type and to derive rules on that basis. Indeed, in VDM we sometimes have to test to see if a value belongs to a particular type because sometimes two values might look the same but are really of different types.

In Z we have only two type constructors for the mathematical objects—$\mathbb{P}$ and $\times$—and whereas it is possible to apply power set to a relation in Z (because a relation is simply a set) it is not always possible to apply power set to a 'relation' in VDM because it may be modelled as a map which is not a set. Because sets are not maps which are not composite values, VDM has to introduce a number of customized type constructors that have to be applied to the basic types to build the new compound ones. In VDM, therefore, there is no notion of underlying type while the possibility of subtypes exists. Examples of these will be introduced as we progress through the chapter; readers may like to come back to this introduction where a further reading might be more meaningful.

Type definitions in VDM take the form:

$$id = T$$

where `id` is an identifier with global scope and `T` is a type expression involving the various type constructors or explicit enumeration. Each type definition statement is separated from the next by a semicolon (;). Most of the constructors are introduced in the following chapters.

Types can also formed by using the union type operator·(|). Thus:

$$\texttt{types}$$
$$Type\text{-}1 = ;$$
$$Type\text{-}2 = ;$$
$$Type\text{-}n = ;$$
$$Union\text{-}type = Type\text{-}1 \mid Type\text{-}2 \mid \ldots \mid Type\text{-}n ;$$

where *union-type* is a set that now contains all the values of types *Type*-1 to *Type-n* with 'common' elements appearing only once. The union type operator is associative and commutative so that *union-type* is the same type irrespective of the order used in the union. A special type, the *nil-type* also exists containing the single value `Nil`. `Nil` is conventionally taken to stand for the absence of a value so that when a variable is assigned to a type such as:

$$Type\text{-}with\text{-}Nil = Type \mid \texttt{Nil}$$
$$\vdots$$
$$X : Type\text{-}with\text{-}Nil$$

Assignments such as $X = \texttt{Nil};$ are perfectly legal and suggest that no value has yet been obtained for X.

A type can also be defined by restricting the members of some other type using an invariant:

$$Type\text{-}2 = Type\text{-}1$$
$$\texttt{inv } T \triangleq \textbf{B};$$

Here *Type*-2 is the name of the new type, while `T` acts as an identifier for this type in the Boolean expression **B**. This expression acts as an invariant; it limits the values of *Type*-2 to only those of *Type*-1 for which the expression **B** is `true`.

Finally, in VDM a type can be introduced and named but not defined by an *incomplete type definition* of the form:

$$Undefined\text{-}Type \texttt{ is not yet defined} \qquad (\text{or simply } Undefined\text{-}Type = \ldots)$$

suggesting that the definition will be supplied later, while the type of a value can always be tested for using a *type membership expression* of the form:

$$is\text{-}T(E)$$

Here T is a type identifier (predefined or named) while E is an expression that yields a value. If that value belongs to T the expression returns true, e.g. is -$\mathbb{Z}($) determines whether the expression in parentheses is an integer.

20.3.2 Declaring variables in VDM specifications

The type identifier id is used to distribute the type throughout the specification through variable declarations such as:

$$v : \text{id}$$
$$a,b,c : \text{id} \qquad \text{or}$$
$$a,b : \text{id}_1, c : \text{id}_2$$

which is similar to Z except that the comma rather than a semi-colon separates variables of different types in the declaration list. The rules for variable identifiers are the same as for type identifiers. Declarations can appear in various parts of the specification and the variables introduced may have either *global* or *local* scope depending on the nature of the declaration. The remainder of this chapter discusses these distinctions where appropriate.

20.3.3 Predefined, token and quote types in VDM

The basic and fundamental basic types are predefined and part of the VDM toolkit or basic library of definitions. The fundamental basic types include:

- $\mathbb{R}$ The set of real numbers
- $\mathbb{B}$ The set of Booleans {true, false}
- char   The set of characters
- token   The set of *tokens*

The basic types are simply regarded as subsets of the reals:

- $\mathbb{Q}$ The set of rational numbers
- $\mathbb{Z}$ The set of integers
- $\mathbb{N}$ The set of non-negative integers or natural numbers
- $\mathbb{N}_1$ The set of strictly positive integers

The usual operators are also defined for these types. A further type exists which is a *quote type* consisting of a single constant value or *quote literal*. Most of these types are already quite familiar but we notice that reals, rationals and characters are not part of the Z basic library, while token and quote types are peculiar to VDM.

The type token consists of an infinite number of distinct values having no predefined properties other than equality and inequality. Tokens are used to define types with the minimum of specified properties. In this respect token is often used in the same context as a *given set*, e.g. the Z paragraph:

$$[STUDENT, PROGRAMMER]$$

in VDM could become:

$$
\begin{aligned}
&\texttt{types}\\
&STUDENT = \texttt{token}_1;\\
&PROGRAMMER = \texttt{token}_2;
\end{aligned}
$$

where $\texttt{token}_1$, $\texttt{token}_2$, etc., are used when more than one such set is required. Most types introduced in this manner are used by the type constructors in the specification to build more complex compound types, and this parallels Z exactly. The use of $\texttt{token}$ should not be confused with an incomplete type definition $\texttt{is not yet defined}$. Token types are those whose properties will never be needed during development of the specification, while incomplete definitions are used when the definition will be required, but not just yet. Type membership expressions cannot be used with $\texttt{token}$.

A quote type is a type containing a single value that is user defined and not part of the VDM language. It is therefore not a basic type. A quote type has no identifier other than the literal value itself and, like tokens, quote values have no properties other than equality and inequality. Some examples might be:

$$
\texttt{RED, BLUE, GREEN, YELLOW, WHITE, BLACK}
$$

which describe six separate quote types, while the new types *Colours*, *Primary-colours* and *Non-colours* can be made with a type expression using the type union operator (|):

$$
\begin{aligned}
&\texttt{types}\\
&Colours = \texttt{RED | BLUE | GREEN | WHITE | BLACK};\\
&Primary\text{-}colours = \texttt{RED | BLUE | GREEN};\\
&Non\text{-}colours = \texttt{WHITE | BLACK};
\end{aligned}
$$

Quote types are almost invariably used in this fashion and superficially the types generated using them resemble the simple data type of Z. Notice, however, that $\texttt{WHITE}$ (say) is a member of two different types and this would not be permitted in Z. Type membership expressions cannot be used with quote types.

20.3.4 Values and value definitions

Values are introduced in a *values definition block* preceded by the keyword $\texttt{values}$. The most usual form of a value definition is $\texttt{id:T = E}$ which introduces some variable $\texttt{id}$ of type $\texttt{T}$ and associates it with the value provided by the expression $\texttt{E}$. Value definitions are used to introduce global constants into the specification and in some ways fulfil the role of axiomatic descriptions in Z. A very common use for $\texttt{values}$ therefore would be to introduce constants such as *CupMax*, *StackMax*, *HopperMax*, *Recipe* or *Worth* into the specification, for example:

$$
\begin{aligned}
&\texttt{values}\\
&CupMax : \mathbb{N} = 100;\\
&StackMax : \mathbb{N} = 500
\end{aligned}
$$

In cases where the value of the constant has yet to be determined VDM provides the *incomplete value definition:*

$$
StackMax : \mathbb{N} \texttt{ is not yet defined};
$$

20.3.5 State definitions and operation definitions

State definitions in VDM correspond to the *abstract state schema* in Z. In VDM the state is persistent and represents the mechanism by means of which the system retains a history of the operations that have been performed upon it. The state is described by collection of mathematical objects whose combinations may be restricted by a predicate that acts as a state invariant and this parallels Z exactly, except that in VDM the state definition can optionally refer to the initial state of the system which in Z is provided by a separate *Initial_State* schema. The general form of the *state definition block* in VDM is:

```
state VDM-State of
  A : id₁
  B : id₂
  N : idₙ
inv   mk-VDM-state (a,b,..n) ≜ ...
init mk-VDM-state (a',b',..n) ≜ ...
end
```

Operations in VDM serve precisely the same purpose as in Z and are introduced in the *operation definition block* which is preceded with the keyword `operations`.

Because abstract states and operations are very closely related all of Chapter 22 is devoted to them. There we examine their structure and relationship by revisiting the *Homework* problem.

20.3.6 Function definitions

Functions are introduced in the *function definition block* which is preceded by the keyword `functions`. Functions are one of the many mathematical objects that can be defined in VDM. Chapter 21 discusses their definitions in detail.

20.4 MODULES

All the various definitions in a VDM specification are collected together in a *module* which corresponds to the document of Z. The simplest form of a module is one which consists of a series of definition blocks:

```
module VDM-module
definitions
  types
    ⋮
  values
    ⋮
  state
    ⋮
  functions
    ⋮
  operations
    ⋮
end VDM-module
```

The same module identifier (in this case VDM-*module*) must appear at the beginning and the end of the module. It is possible to write complete VDM specifications in a monolithic style where the whole specification is embodied in one single module. However, VDM-SL has facilities by means of which large specifications can be organized into smaller modules whose various definitions can be exported and used by others. In this respect, VDM-SL has partially addressed the major weakness of 'classical VDM' when compared to Z, namely, the lack of a structuring tool which permits large specifications to be managed through logically self-contained units which are then assembled using operators similar to those of the schema calculus. In this respect, the more complete description of the module in VDM takes the following form:

```
module VDM-module
parameters
            ⋮
imports from
            ⋮
exports
            ⋮
instantiation
            ⋮
definitions
            ⋮
end VDM-module
```

The `definitions` part remains largely as before but the preceding section—the *interface part*—describe the external or visible properties of the module, i.e. those aspects of the specification that permit its features to be used by others. The `parameters` section is the VDM analogue of the formal parameter list of a generic schema definition in Z. The entities defined in the definition section of a 'parametrized' module will in general depend upon the module parameter section, and these cannot be declared for use in other modules in the `exports` section until they are *instantiated* with actual parameters. This is the purpose of the `instantiation` block in the interface part which generates actual instances from generic definitions. The `imports from` section of course describes the types, functions, operations, etc., that this module receives from others. The detail of module definitions in VDM will be discussed in later chapters.

As a final comment, it should be pointed out that the module in VDM-SL is really the manifestation of the abstract data type and that the terminology used by VDM in constructing modules is very similar to certain programming languages that have explicit object support, e.g. Ada or Modula-2. VDM is therefore frequently seen as being closer to a programming environment than Z but still sufficiently abstract to fulfil the purpose(s) of a specification language. The next chapter discusses other aspects of VDM that preserve a link with reality.

20.5 PROOF OBLIGATIONS

The static constraints of a VDM specification, i.e. the requirements of the language syntax and typing mechanism, are generally readily checked. The term 'proof obligation' refers to those aspects of the well formedness of the specification that cannot be easily statically checked. Proof obligations appear in VDM as in Z generally addressing the problems of implementability, specification properties and satisfiability. The implementability obligation provides the assurance that it is possible to have a system in the real world that corresponds to the specification, i.e. that for a given set of arguments that satisfy the precondition of an operation, a result exists that satisfies the postcondition. Formal reasoning can also show that specifications enjoy particular properties, while explicit definitions of functions and ultimately actual program (pseudo) code has to be shown to satisfy the specification for which it is written.

As in Z, proof obligations are in the form of sequents (implications) to be proved. The formality of VDM makes these obligations quite precise; the level of detail to be employed when discharging the obligation, however, is a matter of judgement and this again parallels the activity in Z. Finally, in VDM the type rules often generate proof obligations especially when union types are used; this is not a feature of Z however. The style and notation employed by VDM when constructing proof obligations is illustrated in some of the chapters that follow.

20.6 SUMMARY

This chapter has outlined the basic character of a VDM specification, drawing parallels with Z whenever appropriate. The two approaches are really very similar but their differing philosophies lead to differences of emphasis, the most notable being the typing system, the closer relationship between the syntax of a VDM specification and a typical structured programming language such as Pascal and the lack of a specification calculus similar to the schema calculus of Z. The 'peculiarities' of the typing system in VDM should not be seen as a weakness but rather as a different approach, while the structure of the specification makes the migration from a VDM specification to actual code much more intuitive than in Z. The absence of an equivalent calculus, however, has been an area of major criticism in the past. VDM-SL introduces the 'module' to assist the structuring aspects of large specifications, and to some extent this makes specifications reusable within others. However, there are no real parallels in VDM to the conjunction, composition, etc., of schemas in Z which made the method so flexible.

21

THE MATHEMATICS OF VDM-SL

CHECKLIST OF OBJECTIVES

After reading this chapter you should be able to:

- Understand the close relationship between the mathematical objects of VDM and Z.
- Use the type constructors to introduce objects of different types into a VDM specification.
- Understand and apply the operators characterizing the various types.
- Use polymorphic definitions.

21.1 INTRODUCTION

Chapter 20 introduced the typing mechanism of VDM and the basic and fundamental basic types that come predefined and as part of the VDM library. All other types in VDM are *compound types* and are constructed from basic, token, union or indeed other compound types by means of specific *type constructors* which parallel the use of $\mathbb{P}$ and $\times$ in Z. This chapter discusses each compound type, the constructors used to create values for the type and the operators applicable to it. In particular, it is concerned with the compound types *sets, tuples, functions, maps, sequences, bags* and *records* (or *composite values*). Many of these types have direct parallels with objects in Z and in this respect the discussion makes every effort to relate the two so that the reader is made aware of the common basis these methods share.

21.2 SETS TYPES IN VDM-SL

We have seen that the definition of a set in Z is achieved by either enumeration or set comprehension, for example:

$$S == \{101, 102, 103, ..\} \qquad \text{or} \qquad S == \{n : \mathbb{Z} \mid n > 100 \bullet n\}$$

The definition is achieved using the *abbreviation definition* symbol ==; the left-hand side being defined to mean the same as the right. The declaration that an element s belongs to this set is then given by $s : S$ while the underlying type of the set itself naturally becomes the power set of its members, i.e. S : $\mathbb{P}S$.

In VDM all sets are assumed to be finite. The argument for this restriction is that when writing specifications for the real world, infinite sets are rarely met. Computer stores of course are themselves finite and so it is only ever possible to manipulate such sets through a finite representation. This relationship with reality is a common feature of modelling with VDM and arises repeatedly.

Sets other than the basic types in VDM can be defined by enumeration or comprehension in much the same way as in Z, for example:

```
types
S = {101, 102, 103, .. }      or
S = {n | n : Z • n > 100}
```

However, notice that the equality sign is used in the type definition, while comprehension follows the pattern:

$$\{expression \mid declaration \bullet predicate\}$$

rather than:

$$\{declaration \mid predicate \bullet expression\}$$

S is again an abbreviation for the set being defined and the declaration that an individual element belongs to a particular set is achieved by statements such as s : S. However, VDM employs a type construction mechanism for the sets themselves which varies significantly from that of Z.

In VDM, types are again simply collections of values distinguished by the operations that can be performed upon them. All sets created by enumeration or comprehension (all sets other than the basic or fundamental basic types) are regarded as compound types derived from the base type of the set elements themselves. The VDM set type constructor (or *generator*) is −set so that the notation T−set introduces a set type, i.e. a collection of values each one of which is a finite set of values of the type T. It therefore describes the set of all possible finite permutations of T and in this respect resembles the finite power set in Z. For example, returning to the *Homework* problem for a moment, given a collection of values that represents a *universe* of possible students:

```
types
Student = {Huw, Wyn, Deri, Marilyn, Suzanne, Mike, Jane, Mort}
```

each individual is of type *Student*, while the notation *Student*−set constructs a new collection which is effectively the set of all possible (finite) subsets of *Student*:

{{ }, {Huw}, {Wyn}, {Deri}, ..., {Huw, Wyn}, {Huw, Deri}, ...,
{Huw, Wyn, Deri}, ..., {Huw, Wyn, Deri, Marilyn, Suzanne, Mike, Jane, Mort}}

In VDM the type created by the generator is used within a type definition statement to assign the type to an identifier. Consequently, statements such as:

$$Stdset = Student\text{−set}$$

permit VDM to define a type once and distribute it throughout the specification by means of its identifier. Thus:

$$Class,\ Handed\text{-}in,\ Not\text{-}handed\text{-}in : Stdset$$

declares *Class*, *Handed-in* and *Not-handed-in* to each be *sets* of students while:

$$s : \textit{Student}$$

declares *s* to be an individual student.

21.3 THE SET OPERATORS

The set operators in VDM are largely defined as for Z but with the restriction that all sets are finite. Thus VDM supports *union, intersection, difference, distributed intersection and union, equality, inequality, subset, proper subset, membership* ($\in$) and *cardinality*. Some slight differences exist in symbolism however. The set difference operator is *minus* ($-$) while VDM uses the keyword `card` instead of $\#$ for set cardinality. Thus:

$$S_1 - S_2 \equiv S_1 \setminus S_2 \qquad \text{and} \qquad \text{card } S \equiv \#S$$

VDM replaces the subrange notation of typed set theory $\{m \mathrel{..} n\}$ with $\{m, \ldots, n\}$ while the finite subset operator of VDM ($\mathscr{F}$) takes a set as its operand and produces the set of all the subsets of the operand. Thus, $\mathscr{F}(S)$ is similar to the power set operator ($\mathbb{P}$) of Z but with the added restriction that the power set is finite. If the elements of S are of some type T, then the set itself is of type `T-set` and because $\mathscr{F}(S)$ returns a set of sets, the type of the result is therefore `(T-set)-set`. Unlike $\mathbb{P}$ in Z, $\mathscr{F}$ cannot be used as a type constructor.

   The majority of the notational differences between Z and VDM are simply annoying variations on an otherwise uniform theme. The constructor `-set`, however, is a notable exception and the subtleties involved in its different use need careful management when migrating from a specification based on Z to one involving VDM.

21.4 TUPLES OR PRODUCT TYPES

In VDM, the tuple is regarded as an ordered collection of two or more values called *components*, while the tuples themselves are sometimes referred to as *product values*. A product type expression takes a form partly familiar from Z in that the VDM type operator for tuples is $\times$. Thus:

$$\texttt{id} = T_1 \times T_2 \times T_3 \times \ldots \times T_n$$

describes a tuple type with component values t_1 of type $T_1, \ldots, t_n$ of type T_n ($n \geq 2$) and where `id` once again serves to distribute the type throughout the specification (e.g. *Var* : `id`). Actual tuple instances are built using the tuple constructor *mk*-(..) with arguments of the appropriate types. Thus, *mk*-$(2, a)$ produces a tuple instance of type $\mathbb{Z} \times$ `char`.

21.5 FUNCTIONS IN VDM-SL

In VDM a function is simply a way of defining a rule for obtaining a result from zero or more arguments. Although a function may not require any arguments for its application it must have a result otherwise it is meaningless. When the argument involves more than one parameter, the actual parameters are regarded as forming a tuple type. In this respect the function definition can still be regarded as describing a fixed mapping between two sets but where the *from-set* is a set of tuples. Functions in VDM-SL can be defined directly (explicitly), implicitly or as polymorphic functions.

21.5.1 The direct definition of functions in VDM

The general form of the direct definition of a function in VDM is as follows:

> *Function name* : *argument type*(*s*) → *result type*
> *function name*(*argument*(*s*)) $\triangle$ *E*
> pre **B**

The first line of the definition introduces the types of both the argument(s) and the result. (Another way of looking at this is that in the first line the domain and range sets are separated by an arrow →.) This line is frequently called the signature. The second line provides an explicit expression (*E*) that defines the application of the function with arguments of the type(s) provided, while the special symbol $\triangle$ is read 'is defined by'. The use of this notation is meant to distinguish the direct definition of a function from propositions which might involve equality (and should not be confused with the delta notation of Z). The final line of the definition introduces a Boolean expression (**B**) involving the argument(s) only that act as a precondition constraining the domain of the function. The precondition is optional. When it is omitted the Boolean defaults to true and the only obligation carried by the arguments is that they all correspond to the type(s) expressed in the signature. Such preconditions are *trivial* and are often omitted; in such circumstances the definition corresponds to that of a total function. The natural extension of this reasoning is that when a precondition is present the constraints on the domain define a partial function. Function applications are undefined for circumstances outside their precondition, while the application itself is expressed in the general form:

$$f(a_1, a_2, a_3, \ldots, a_n) = r$$

The following example illustrates the use of the notation in the definition of a function *max-int* which finds the larger of two integers:

> *max-int* : $\mathbb{Z} \times \mathbb{Z} \to \mathbb{Z}$
> *max-int* (i, j) $\triangle$ if $i \leq j$ then j else i

The signature shows that the function accepts some combination of integers (through the product type) and returns an integer. The application of the function takes the form *max-int*(i, j) with i and j corresponding to the integer arguments, while the definition of the function body itself is quite straightforward and employs a familiar conditional *if* ... *then* ... *else* expression to convey the result. The absence of a precondition defines *max-int* to be a total function.

Another simple example is that of a function that determines the absolute value of an integer:

> *abs* : $\mathbb{Z} \to \mathbb{Z}$
> *abs*(*i*) $\triangle$ if $i < 0$ then $-i$ else i

The function is again total. As an example of the use of a precondition, the following function finds the largest element in a set of (non-empty) positive integers. This definition corresponds to the *max* function of set theory:

$$max : \mathbb{N}_1 \text{-set} \rightarrow \mathbb{N}_1$$
$$max\ (S) \triangleq \texttt{let}\ i \in S\ \texttt{in}$$
$$\texttt{if card}\ S = 1\ \texttt{then}\ i$$
$$\texttt{else}\ max\text{-}int(i,\ max\ (S - \{i\}))$$
$$\texttt{pre card}\ S \neq 0$$

The presence of the precondition shows that the function is partial, being defined for non-empty sets only. The definition itself is recursive; the recursive calls being terminated when set cardinality reaches 1. The terminology used in the expression has been extended to introduce a local variable, namely i, based on the general format:

$$\texttt{let}\ local\text{-}variable = E_1\ \texttt{in}\ E_2$$

A local variable is one used within the body of the definition to help describe the result. It achieves this by assuming the value assigned in the expression E_1 when used in expression E_2. The variable has no role outside the function definition and in this respect resembles the local variable mechanism used in programming languages.

The terminology can also be extended to include any of the unary and binary operators of the mathematical objects in VDM, case statements and, as we have just seen, recursion and other function definitions. Indeed, the whole terminology of direct function definition is decidedly algorithmic such that they can really be regarded as implementations—a point we return to shortly. These extensions to the terminology are introduced where necessary, but some simple examples would be appropriate now. For example, assuming we have defined two sets:

$$Month = \{Jan, Feb, \dots, Dec\} \quad \text{and} \quad Year = \{1583, \dots, 2599\}$$

a function to deduce the number of days in a month could be written:

$$Days\text{-}in\text{-}month : Month \times Year \rightarrow \mathbb{N}_1$$
$$Days\text{-}in\text{-}month\ (m, y) \triangleq \texttt{cases}\ m :$$
$$Jan \rightarrow 31$$
$$Feb \rightarrow \texttt{if}\ is\text{-}leap\text{-}year(y)\ \texttt{then}\ 29\ \texttt{else}\ 28$$
$$Mar \rightarrow 31$$
$$Apr \rightarrow 30$$
$$\vdots$$
$$\texttt{end}$$

while a function to determine the absolute value of the product of two numbers might be defined:

$$absprod : \mathbb{Z} \times \mathbb{Z} \rightarrow \mathbb{Z}$$
$$absprod\ (i, j) \triangleq \texttt{let}\ k = i * j\ \texttt{in}$$
$$\texttt{if}\ k < 0\ \texttt{then}\ -k\ \texttt{else}\ k$$

Once again these functions are total because of the absence of preconditions. In the first example the result is determined by which of the case choices matches the month m; notice the use of a conditional expression and another function (*is-leap-year*) within the definition. The second example again uses a local variable definition. The conditional and case expressions are a generalization of the familiar form from programming languages.

A final point to bear in mind when defining functions directly in VDM is that a number of commonly used functions may not be easily understood when the normal parenthesized application format is used, e.g. if we defined the operator $+$ to add two integers, the prefix application $+(a,b)$ is much less familiar than $a + b$. In cases where an *infix* notation is more natural the signature of VDM functions can be modified. Thus, rather than:

$$+ : \mathbb{Z} \times \mathbb{Z} \to \mathbb{Z}$$
$$+(a,b) \underline{\Delta} \, a + b$$

we have:

$$\_+\_ : \mathbb{Z} \times \mathbb{Z} \to \mathbb{Z}$$
$$a + b \underline{\Delta} \, a + b$$

where a and b are the integer parameters. A similar argument clearly extends to prefix operators such as $-$. All this is familiar from Z where many generic definitions of the basic library are similarly modified. Direct definitions of functions in VDM often introduce auxiliary functions that are used frequently in a large specification. The case studies in the chapters on VDM provide some examples.

SAQ 21.1 Write a direct definition of the truth-valued function *is-leap-year* which accepts a year and returns a Boolean indicating whether or not that year is a leap year.

21.5.2 Implicit definitions of functions in VDM

Direct definitions are useful but even the examples above suggest that for complex functions the definitions become too algorithmic and resemble specific implementations rather than offering a range of possibilities. Direct definitions describe *how* a result is to be determined, implicit definitions, however, simply state *what* the function has to achieve. There are a number of advantages to this approach:

- Each implicit definition corresponds to a wide range of possible implementations.
- The definitions are usually much more concise than the implementations.
- Implicit definitions are usually far more understandable and amenable to a process of reasoning.

In VDM, implicit specification is achieved through the use of both pre- and postconditions, the postcondition replacing the expression of an explicit definition. The precondition again records assumptions about the arguments. It is a predicate over the initial state value(s) and embodies the circumstances under which the operator may be legally applied. The result of a function is not defined outside the scope of its precondition. The postcondition is a predicate over the initial *and* final state values and describes the relationship that must exist between the argument(s) and the result if the function has behaved properly. This mechanism conveys *what* has to be achieved without indicating *how* it can be computed. We have become used to pre- and postconditions in Z, but in VDM the keywords `pre` and `post` are used to introduce the conditions.

The implicit specification of a function in VDM takes the general form:

$$F\text{-name}\ (a : T_a, b : T_b, c : T_c, \ldots)\ r : T_r$$
$$\texttt{pre } \mathbf{B}$$
$$\texttt{post } \mathbf{B'}$$

The first line corresponds once again to the signature and it is charged with the responsibility to introduce the name of the function (*F-name*), an argument list (which we regard as a tuple if we have more than one argument) $a : T_a, b : T_b, c : T_c, \ldots$ (each of corresponding type) and a result r (of type T_r). The notation used is intentionally closer to that of a programming language such as Pascal. The pre- and postconditions are phrased in terms of Boolean expressions $\mathbf{B}$ and $\mathbf{B'}$ respectively. $\mathbf{B}$ is an expression involving only the argument(s), while $\mathbf{B'}$ is an expression involving both argument(s) and result. Both may therefore be regarded as if they explicitly defined two truth-valued functions thus:

$$\texttt{pre}\ \text{-}F\text{-name} : T_a \times T_b \times T_c \ .. \rightarrow \mathbb{B}$$
$$\texttt{pre}\ \text{-}F\text{-name}\ (a, b, c, \ldots) \underline{\Delta}\ \mathbf{B}$$

and

$$\texttt{post}\ \text{-}F\text{-name} : T_a \times T_b \times T_c \times \ldots \times T_r \rightarrow \mathbb{B}$$
$$\texttt{post}\ \text{-}F\text{-name}\ (a, b, c, \ldots, r) \underline{\Delta}\ \mathbf{B'}$$
$$\texttt{pre}\ \mathbf{B}$$

where a truth-valued function is simply one where the range is the set of Booleans so that explicit definitions are invariably expressed in terms of logical operators. This alternative method is illustrated by first using it to define the *abs* function which returns the absolute value of some integer:

$$abs\ (i : \mathbb{Z})\ r : \mathbb{Z}$$
$$\texttt{pre} = true$$
$$\texttt{post}\ 0 \leq r \wedge (r = i \vee r = -i)$$

In the example, the precondition is trivial in that the only requirement upon i is that it is an integer. Because the domain is therefore not restricted, trivial preconditions denote total functions. As with explicit definitions, trivial preconditions are often omitted. The converse of this argument is that once again non-trivial preconditions denote partial functions. Notice also that the postcondition simply relates argument to result in a fashion that conveys the intended meaning of *abs*, while the explicit definition earlier provided a rule for its evaluation.

The pre- and postcondition functions of *abs* are:

$$\texttt{pre}\ \text{-}abs : \mathbb{Z} \rightarrow \mathbb{B}$$
$$\texttt{pre}\ \text{-}abs : (i) \underline{\Delta}\ true$$
$$\texttt{post}\ \text{-}abs : \mathbb{Z} \times \mathbb{Z} \rightarrow \mathbb{B}$$
$$\texttt{post}\ \text{-}abs : (i, r) \underline{\Delta}\ 0 \leq r \wedge (r = i \vee r = -i)$$

The absence of a written precondition for $\texttt{post}$ -*abs* means that it defaults to true and this corresponds of course to the definition of $\texttt{pre}$ -*abs*.

A further example is that of *max* defined earlier (Part 3), the implicit specification being:

$$max : (S : \mathbb{N}_1 \text{-set}) \, r : \mathbb{N}_1$$
$$\text{pre card } S \neq 0$$
$$\text{post } r \in S \wedge \forall x \in S \bullet r \geq x$$

Notice again the distinction between this definition and the previous one given for *max*. The postcondition is now a Boolean expression (evaluating to true or false) relating argument to result, while the explicit definition provided an expression that evaluated to a *number*.

The precondition and postcondition functions of *max* are:

$$\text{pre -}max : \mathbb{N}_1 \text{-set} \rightarrow \mathbb{B}$$
$$\text{pre -}max(S) \underline{\Delta} \text{ card } S \neq 0$$

and:

$$\text{post -}max : \mathbb{N}_1 \text{-set} \times \mathbb{N}_1 \rightarrow \mathbb{B}$$
$$\text{post -}max(S,r) \underline{\Delta} \, r \in S \wedge \forall x \in S \bullet r \geq x$$
$$\text{pre card } S \neq 0$$

Finally, we can provide an implicit definition for the *max-int* function which determines the larger of two integers:

$$max\text{-}int : (i : \mathbb{Z}, j : \mathbb{Z}) \, r : \mathbb{Z}$$
$$\text{pre } true$$
$$\text{post } (r = i \vee r = j) \wedge i \leq r \wedge j \leq r$$

The pre- and postcondition functions for *max-int* are:

$$\text{pre -}max\text{-}int \; \mathbb{Z} \times \mathbb{Z} \rightarrow \mathbb{B}$$
$$\text{pre -}max\text{-}int(i,j) \underline{\Delta} \, true$$

$$\text{post -}max\text{-}int \; \mathbb{Z} \times \mathbb{Z} \times \mathbb{Z} \rightarrow \mathbb{B}$$
$$\text{post -}max\text{-}int(i,j,r) \underline{\Delta} \, (r = i \vee r = j) \wedge i \leq r \wedge j \leq r$$

Implicit definition offers considerable advantages over explicit definition leading to more manageable and readable specifications. The general form of implicit specification also extends beyond functions to the definition of operations in VDM and examples of this are introduced in the next chapter. Some examples of function definitions are to be found in the case studies.

21.5.3 Polymorphic function definitions

A polymorphic function definition is an explicit definition which is written generically using *type variables*. In this respect polymorphics in VDM correspond to certain generic schemas in Z. A type variable is denoted by an identifier beginning with the special symbol @; it may be used in no other context in VDM. Such functions have a polymorphic signature which contains the formal generic parameters; to obtain an actual function the definition has to be instantiated with actual parameters. Section 21.11 provides some examples of polymorphic function which are used to provide generic definitions of useful bag operators in VDM.

21.6 FUNCTION OPERATORS

Function definitions in VDM are loosely specified in that they represent all the functions that can take the type of the parameter and return the type of the result. In this sense the signature of a function denotes the function's type and as is usual with types there is a set of characteristic operators. In VDM there are just two function operators: function composition and function iteration. Function composition is written $F_2 \circ F_1$ where F_1 and F_2 are both function expressions. It yields a function which can be thought of as equivalent to that produced by applying first $F_1(a_1, a_2, a_3, \ldots, a_n)$ and then applying F_2 to the result. The result type of F_1 must therefore correspond to the parameter type of F_2. An example of function composition can be found on page 325. Function iteration takes the general form F^n or $F \wedge n$ where n is a non-negative integer and F^n is equivalent to the function produced by applying $F\, n$ times. The result type of F must of course correspond to its parameter type, while F^0 is the identity function that simply returns the value of its parameter.

21.7 FUNCTION TYPES

Every function defined in VDM belongs to a particular function type dictated by the type expression used in its signature. Such type expressions have one of two possible forms:

$$T_1 \to T_2 \quad \text{or} \quad (\,) \to T_2$$

where types T_1 and T_2 can be compound, reflecting the fact that the function receives many arguments and/or returns many results. If, however, T_1 is empty ( ), the function accepts no arguments. A function type describes all functions that accept a parameter of type T_1 and return a value of type T_2. Function types are used in the case studies later.

21.8 PROOF OBLIGATIONS AND FUNCTION DEFINITIONS

The ability to define functions implicitly in VDM has clear advantages from a specification point of view; however, every implicit function definition must be shown to be both implementable and satisfiable otherwise the specification itself is catastrophically damaged. Implementability means that given a particular precondition it is possible to achieve its postcondition; if this were not so the function could never be realized in practice. Satisfiability confirms this latter point—that an implementation (if you like an explicit definition) properly corresponds to the implicit definition. Later chapters illustrate the implementability problem for a number of specifications, so for now we concentrate on satisfiability and show how those defining functions in VDM are faced with a proof obligation such that:

> there must exist some explicit interpretation of the pre- and postconditions such that for any set of function parameters of the correct types which satisfy the precondition, there must be a result of the correct type which along with the parameters satisfies the postcondition.

It is therefore necessary to show that there exists *at least one* explicit function definition (i.e. an implementation) that satisfies the pre- and postcondition requirements of the implicit definition. To put this requirement more formally so that we can reason about it, we can generalize the properties of implicit and explicit function definitions. Let us assume that we define some function f both ways (where T_p could be a tuple type thereby corresponding to functions with 'many' arguments):

$$f(p : T_p)\, r : T_r$$
$$\mathtt{pre} \ldots p \ldots$$
$$\mathtt{post} \ldots p \ldots r \ldots$$

with pre- and postcondition function signatures:

$$\mathtt{pre}\text{-}f : T_p \to \mathbb{B} \quad \text{and} \quad \mathtt{post}\text{-}f : T_p \times T_r \to \mathbb{B}$$

while a direct definition will have the signature:

$$f : T_p \to T_r$$

and this will satisfy the implicit specification if we can show that:

$$\forall p \in T_p \bullet \mathtt{pre}\text{-}f(p) \Rightarrow f(p) \in T_r \wedge \mathtt{post}\text{-}f(p, f(p))$$

This implication relates the application of the explicit function (i.e. $f(p)$) to the requirements of the implicit specification and demands that for all parameters of the correct type ($\forall p \in T_p$), if the precondition function is indeed *true* for the parameter (i.e. $\mathtt{pre}\text{-}f(p)$) then the application of the explicit function must produce a result of the correct type (i.e. $f(p) \in T_r$) and the postcondition function must be *true* for the original parameter and the result (i.e. $\mathtt{post}\text{-}f(p, f(p))$).

As with Z, discharging proof obligations in VDM is an important but tedious exercise! We can illustrate the process and the format of its presentation by examining the relationship between the explicit and implicit definitions of the *max-int* functions:

$$max\text{-}int : \mathbb{Z} \times \mathbb{Z} \to \mathbb{Z}$$
$$max\text{-}int\,(i,j) \underline{\Delta} \text{ if } i \leq j \text{ then } j \text{ else } i$$

$$max\text{-}int : (i : \mathbb{Z}, j : \mathbb{Z})\, r : \mathbb{Z}$$
$$\mathtt{pre} \ true$$
$$\mathtt{post}\ (r = i \vee r = j) \wedge i \leq r \wedge j \leq r$$

Proofs and simplifications in Z were largely conducted in terms of schemas and because of the nature of these constructs each step in the argument could be easily delineated. There were occasions, however, when we conducted our arguments informally in terms of sequences of statements, hypotheses and laws, and the presentation of these became increasingly clumsy as the complexity of the argument increased (see, for example, Chapter 16 where we simplified precondition schemas). Proofs should be encouraged and proof conducted in any style is better than no proof at all! However, the style used here in discharging the proof obligation—the natural deduction style (see Chapter 5)—is rather more formal and frequently used by Jones (1991) to address this potentially untidy but necessary aspect of formal specifications. We have to show that the direct definition satisfies the implicit specification of *max-int*.

21.8.1 Proof obligation

$\forall i,j \in \mathbb{Z} \bullet \texttt{pre}\ \textit{-max-int}\ (i,j) \Rightarrow \textit{max-int}(i,j) \in \mathbb{Z} \land \texttt{post}\ \textit{-max-int}(i,j, \textit{max-int}(i,j))$

Proof

$\texttt{from}\ i,j \in \mathbb{Z}$

1	$i \leq j \lor i > j$	$\mathbb{Z}, h$
2	$\texttt{from}\ i \leq j$	
2.1	$\textit{max-int}(i,j) = j$	$\textit{max-int}(h, h2)$
2.2	$\textit{max-int}(i,j) \in \mathbb{Z}$	$2.1, h$
2.3	$(j = i \lor j = j) \land i \leq j \land j \leq j$	$\mathbb{Z}, h, h2, \land, \lor$
2.4	$\texttt{post}\ \textit{-max-int}(i,j,j)$	$\underline{\Delta}\ \texttt{subs}/\texttt{post}\ \textit{-max-int}(h, 2.3)$
2.5	$\texttt{post}\ \textit{-max-int}(i,j, \textit{max-int}(i,j))$	$=\ \texttt{t-subs}(2.4, 2.1)$

$\texttt{infer}$
$\textit{max-int}(i,j) \in \mathbb{Z} \land \texttt{post}\ \textit{-max-int}(i,j, \textit{max-int}(i,j))$

3	$\texttt{from}\ i < j$	
3.1	$\textit{max-int}(i,j) = i$	$\textit{max-int}(h, h3)$
3.2	$\textit{max-int}(i,j) \in \mathbb{Z}$	$3.1, h$
3.3	$(i = i \lor i = j) \land i \leq i \land i \leq j$	$\mathbb{Z}, h, h3, \land, \lor$
3.4	$\texttt{post}\ \textit{-max-int}(i,j,i)$	$\underline{\Delta}\ \texttt{subs}/\texttt{post}\ \textit{-max-int}(h, 3.3)$
3.5	$\texttt{post}\ \textit{-max-int}(i,j, \textit{max-int}(i,j))$	$=\ \texttt{t-subs}(3.4, 3.1)$

$\texttt{infer}$
$\textit{max-int}(i,j) \in \mathbb{Z} \land \texttt{post}\ \textit{-max-int}(i,j, \textit{max-int}(i,j))$

4	$\textit{max-int}(i,j) \in \mathbb{Z} \land \texttt{post}\ \textit{-max-int}(i,j, \textit{max-int}(i,j))$ (1, 2, 3)	

$\texttt{infer}$
$\forall i,j \in \mathbb{Z} \bullet \texttt{pre}\ \textit{-max-int}\ (i,j) \Rightarrow \textit{max-int}(i,j) \in \mathbb{Z} \land \texttt{post}\ \textit{-max-int}(i,j, \textit{max-int}(i,j))$

Each statement in the proof is taken as *true* either as a hypothesis (h) or as a result of some reasoning, the shorthand for which appears on the right-hand side of the statement. Hypotheses are introduced by the keyword $\texttt{from}$ and these are used within the proof by reference to the line positions where they were introduced. Thus h refers to the original hypothesis $i,j \in \mathbb{Z}$, while h2 refers to the hypothesis on line 2, i.e. $i \leq j$; similarly for h3. References such as $\mathbb{Z}$ simply use definitions and facts about the data types being manipulated, while appeals to the various direct definitions are shown as *max-int*, $\texttt{pre}$ *-max-int* and $\texttt{post}$ *-max-int*. Of the remaining terminology '= t-subs' simply means that given two equal terms (referenced by the line numbers in brackets) one can be substituted for the other. (The simplest interpretation of this notation is that '= t-subs' can be read 'equals true by substitution of ...'.) Notation such as '$\underline{\Delta}$ subs/ $\texttt{post}$ *-max-int*(h, 2.3)' refers to application of the function appealing not only to line 2.3 but also to the hypothesis h.

The proof begins with the hypothesis that both i and j are integers. Line 1 is *true* because of h and the properties of integers ($\mathbb{Z}$). Line 1 also permits the remaining proof to be conducted in terms of two subgoals $i \leq j$ and $i > j$ such that if the obligation is discharged for *each* hypothesis, it is discharged for *all* integers. Line 2 introduces the second hypothesis (h2) and establishes the first subgoal. Line 2.1 is *true* by appealing to the application of the direct definition of *max-int* and the hypotheses h and h2. Line 2.2 establishes that the function returns an integer result because of 2.1 and h, while using this result the Boolean expression defining the post *-max-int* function is *true* because of $\mathbb{Z}$, h, h3 together with the known properties of $\land$ and $\lor$. Line 2.4 establishes that the post *-max-int* function is *true* by appealing to the original hypothesis and line 2.3. By substituting line 2.1 for *i* in line 2.4, line 2.5 shows that the post *-max-int* function is *true* when applied to the original parameters and the result from the application of the direct definition. Finally, we infer that the proof obligation has been discharged for this particular subgoal. The second part of the proof addresses the second subgoal in an analogous fashion. At line 4 the proof is complete for all integers because of lines 1, 2 and 3. The final inference completes the proof. Normally, of course, such a narrative would not accompany the proof and with experience many of the steps in a proof can be performed on a single line. Dawes (1991) summarizes all the properties of functions in VDM.

21.9 MAPS AND MAP TYPES

The map as a distinct type is introduced into a VDM specification in the types definition block using the notation:

$$\texttt{types}$$
$$M = D \xrightarrow{\text{m}} R$$

with subsequent distribution of the type throughout the specification by declarations such as:

$$m_1, m_2 : M$$

The notation $D \xrightarrow{\text{m}} R$ is the (general) map *type constructor* and introduces a compound type (in this case M) whose values are all the possible maps that can be constructed from subsets of the types D and R. The notation $m_1, m_2 : M$ consequently declares variables m_1 and m_2 to be (at any time) one of these maps. As an example, if we had earlier defined two set types:

$$Prog\text{-}Num = \{P1, P2, P3, \dots\}$$
$$Prog\text{-}Name = \{Julie, Jocasta, John, Jenny, Jack, Jill\}$$

part of a company's personnel file might be modelled by the map type *Prog* where:

$$Prog = Prog\text{-}Num \xrightarrow{\text{m}} Prog\text{-}Name$$

The type includes values such as:

$\{\mapsto\}$ the empty map—see below
$\{P1 \mapsto Jack\}$
$\{P2 \mapsto Jack\,\}$
$\{P3 \mapsto Jack\,\}$
$\{P4 \mapsto Jack, P1 \mapsto Jocasta\}$
$\{P5 \mapsto John, P5 \mapsto Jill, P6 \mapsto Jack, P2 \mapsto Jocasta, P9 \mapsto Julie\}\dots$

and the declaration *Programmer* : *Prog* permits the variable *Programmer* to assume any one of these values at any time. Clearly these observations draw very close parallels between the map type *Prog* and the partial function type *Prog_Num* ⇸ *Prog_Name* in the *Project–Programmer* scenario of Part 3. In particular:

- Each map value in the type is a pair, each pair represented by maplet notation. The special notation {↦} and not { } represents the empty map because a map is not a set.
- Many of the maps may only involve certain of the elements in *Prog-Num*. The map therefore displays a partial nature while the values from *Prog-Num* that are mapped constitute the domain of the map. A similar argument extends to elements from *Prog-Name* and the range of the map.
- An element in the domain maps at most to one in the range but a member of the range may be associated with more than one member of the domain. Thus programmers *P*1 and *P*2 (say) might have the same name but the map regards them as different people.

21.9.1 'Relations' and special maps

A relation is normally regarded as a special kind of set, namely a set of ordered pairs representing a subset of the Cartesian product of two sets. However, if we regard a relation simply as a many-to-many mapping then a 'relation' can be modelled in VDM by making elements of the *to set* individual sets in their own right, e.g. the relation called *Assignment* (Part 3 again) that records the relationship between programmers and the projects they undertake can be modelled thus:

given the types
Prog-Num = {*P*1, *P*2, *P*3, ...} and
Proj-Code = {*J*1, *J*2, *J*3, ...}, then
Prog-Proj = *Prog-num* $\xrightarrow{m}$ *Proj-code*-set and
Assignment : *Prog-Proj*

The set constructor (-set) produces a type from *Proj-Code* having values each of which is a set:

Proj-Code-set = {{ }, {*J*1}, {*J*2}, {*J*3}, {*J*1, *J*2}, {*J*1, *J*3}, {*J*2, *J*3}, {*J*1, *J*2, *J*3}, ...}

the type *Prog-Proj* then has values corresponding to all possible maps that can be constructed from subsets of the types *Prog-num* and *Proj-code*-set. The type therefore reflects the fact that a programmer can be associated with a number of different projects at any one time, while each project may employ a number of different programmers. Figure 21.1 illustrates one possible map value within this type (contrast this with the description of the relation in typed set theory and Z).

SAQ 21.2 By inspection of the map you can easily list the projects associated with each of the programmers. How would you use map application and the operators of set theory to determine the programmers associated with a given project?

Because of the similarity with the partial function it comes as no surprise to find that VDM supports map types that can be regarded as analogues of certain of the special functions of typed set theory and in particular we consider the injective map. In Part 3

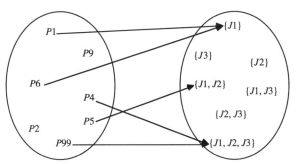

Figure 21.1   One possible condition for the variable *Prog-Proj.*

we showed how each of the special functions could be described in terms of the basic partial function by applying a suitable predicate. In VDM the corresponding process involves applying an invariant to the general map type. Invariants can be added to most compound type definitions and represent a mechanism by which the specification can be enriched beyond the predefined types supplied by VDM. In the particular case of maps, probably the most useful of these special types is the injective map type denoted by the type constructor $D \xrightarrow{m} R$ which evolves from the general map type predicated with an invariant:

$$D \xrightarrow{m} R = D \xrightarrow{m} R \text{ inv } M \underline{\Delta} \forall m_1, m_2 \in \text{dom } M \bullet (M(m_1) = M(m_2) \Rightarrow (m_1 = m_2))$$

Notice that the invariant embodies precisely the same restriction as the predicate of the partial injective function of typed set theory and Z.

SAQ 21.3   In VDM the injective map type is predefined. Write a corresponding invariant definition to describe a surjective map. (*Hint: Surjective-map-type* $= D \xleftrightarrow{m} R \text{ inv } M \underline{\Delta} \dots$) How can maps be made 'total'?

21.9.2 The map operators

The notion of change is an important characteristic of the map and just like relations and functions in typed set theory a rich set of operators exists to reveal and alter map states. Indeed, the behaviour of the map operators closely parallels that of Z although there are naturally differences in notation given their differing philosophy and evolution. The major map operators are given here.

The element (r) of the range of a map (M) that corresponds to a particular element of its domain (d) is accessed by *map application*, i.e. $M(d) = r$. Thus, given some map M where:

$$M = \{200 \mapsto Huw, 100 \mapsto Wyn, 150 \mapsto Deri, 130 \mapsto Marilyn, 300 \mapsto Huw\}$$

we have the following applications:

$$M(200) = Huw$$
$$M(100) = Wyn$$
$$M(150) = Deri$$
$$M(130) = Marilyn$$
$$M(300) = Huw$$

In general, map application can be expressed as $M(E)$ where E is an expression that evaluates to an element in the domain of M. Notice that, unlike a function, we provide no 'rule' for this evaluation.

Equality ($=$) and *inequality* ($\neq$) of maps are available. $M_1 = M_2$ is true if each map has the same domain and range and each element of the domain is mapped to the same element in M_2 as it is in M_1 otherwise it is false. $M_1 \neq M_2$ is false if $M_1 = M_2$ is true and vice versa.

dom M returns the set of elements that currently comprise the domain of the map M, while rng M returns those elements that comprise the range. Thus, assuming we are again given:

$M = \{200 \mapsto Huw, 100 \mapsto Wyn, 150 \mapsto Deri, 130 \mapsto Marilyn, 300 \mapsto Huw\}$ then
dom $M = \{200, 100, 150, 130, 300\}$ and
rng $M = \{Huw, Wyn, Deri, Marilyn\}$

Notice that each operator returns a set and therefore in this example rng M returns only one occurrence of *Huw*.

There are four map *restriction operators* that correspond to the restriction and subtraction operators of typed set theory. Each of these operators accepts a map M and a set S and returns a submap of M with domain or range restricted either by including only those elements that are also elements of S or by excluding those elements that are elements of S. All four possibilities are catered for:

- $S \lhd M$ returns a map with *domain* restricted to elements of S.
- $S \mathbin{⩤} M$ returns a map with *domain* restricted by excluding elements of S.
- $M \rhd S$ returns a map with *range* restricted to elements of S.
- $M \mathbin{⩥} S$ returns a map with *range* restricted by excluding elements of S.

In each case the symbols act as a mnemonic device; the domain operand is on the left and the range operand on the right, both pointed to by the symbol. The inner 'minus' sign or 'bar' denotes exclusion or subtraction. The behaviour of the operators is analogous to those of typed set theory.

Map *union* takes the general form; $M_1 \cup M_2$ where M_1 and M_2 are *compatible maps*. The term 'compatible' assumes that any common element of dom M_1 and dom M_2 is mapped to the same value by both maps. This assumption prevents the possibility of an indiscriminate union destroying the property of the resultant map. In this sense the term 'union' is unfortunate for, unlike set union, map union cannot be applied to any two arbitrary maps. This further emphasizes the fact that maps are *not* simply sets. The union:

$$\{a \mapsto 1, c \mapsto 3, d \mapsto 1\} \cup \{b \mapsto 4, c \mapsto 5\}$$

is therefore illegal for the maps are not compatible. If union were permitted it would produce:

$$\{a \mapsto 1, b \mapsto 4, c \mapsto 3, c \mapsto 5, d \mapsto 1\}$$

which is clearly not a map because c is mapped to both 3 and 5.

Map *merge* is simply a distributed union across a set of compatible maps. If S represents a set of compatible maps then merge is expressed as merge S.

with these observations again reflecting map-like origins. All sequence operators in VDM can be written in terms of len and/or (map) application. The following operators largely correspond to those of typed set theory and Z, but in most cases the definitions are considerably simpler and more readable. This is particularly so in the case of concatenation ($\frown$). Notice also that in VDM each of the operators *head* (hd), *tail* (tl), *front* (ft), and *last* (lt) are defined for non-empty sequences only.

$$\_ \frown \_ (s_1 : X^*, s_2 : X^*)rs : X^*$$
pre *true*
$$\text{post len } rs = \text{len } s_1 + \text{len } s_2 \wedge$$
$$\forall i \in \text{dom } s_1 \bullet rs(i) = s_1(i) \wedge$$
$$\forall i \in \text{dom } s_2 \bullet rs(i + \text{len } s_1) = s_2(i)$$

$$\text{hd}\_ (s : X^*) r : X$$
pre $s \neq [\,]$
post $r = s(1)$

$$\text{tl}\_ (s : X^*) rs : X^*$$
pre $s \neq [\,]$
post $s = [\text{hd } s] \frown rs$

$$\text{lt}\_ (s : X^*) r : X$$
pre $s \neq [\,]$
post $r = s(\text{len } s)$

$$\text{ft}\_ (s : X^*) r : X^*$$
pre $s \neq [\,]$
post $s = r \frown [\text{lt } s]$

The remaining operators are *sequence modification, subsequence* (written $(i, \ldots, j)$), inds, elems, *rev* and *squash*. Sequence modification largely corresponds to map override (†) and parallels function override (⊕) in typed set theory and Z. The subsequence operator extracts a subsequence from a given sequence. Thus:

$$\text{if } s = [a, b, c, d, f, f]$$
$$\text{then } s (2, \ldots, 4) = [b, c, d]$$

The VDM definition of this operator is quite simply $s(i, \ldots, j) \underline{\Delta} [s(k) \mid k \in \{i, \ldots, j\}]$

The operator inds provides the set of integers that can be used as valid indices for the sequence. Thus, assuming:

$$s = [a, b, c, d, f, f]$$

then:

$$\text{inds } s = \{1, \ldots, 6\}$$

The definition of the operator is inds $s \underline{\Delta} \{1, \ldots, \text{len } s\}$.

elems returns the set of elements that make up the sequence. Assuming once again that:

$$s = [a, b, c, d, f, f]$$

then:

$$\texttt{elems}\ s = \{a, b, c, d, f\}$$

Notice now that duplicates are naturally eliminated from the resultant set. The definition is:

$$\texttt{elems}\ s \triangleq \{s(i) \mid 1 \leq i \wedge i \leq \texttt{len}\ s\}$$

Both *squash* and *rev* parallel the definition of the operators of typed set theory and Z. Their direct definitions are as follows:

$$rev : X^* \rightarrow X^*$$
$$rev(s) \triangleq \texttt{if}\ s = [\ ]$$
$$\qquad\qquad \texttt{then}\ [\ ]$$
$$\qquad\qquad \texttt{else}\ [\texttt{lt}\ s] \curvearrowright rev\ (\texttt{ft}\ s)$$
$$squash : (\mathbb{N} \xrightarrow{\ m\ } X) \rightarrow X^*$$
$$squash(m) \triangleq \texttt{if}\ m = \{\ \}$$
$$\qquad\qquad \texttt{then}\ [\ ]$$
$$\qquad\qquad \texttt{else}\ \texttt{let}\ i \in min(\texttt{dom}\ m)\ \texttt{in}$$
$$\qquad\qquad [m(i)] \curvearrowright squash\ (\{i\} \triangleleft m)$$

The signature for *rev* shows that it accepts a sequence and returns a sequence. If the sequence received is empty then an empty sequence results. In the case of *squash* the function accepts a map from the natural numbers to some arbitrary type X and returns a sequence (another map) from the segment $1, \ldots, n$ to X the actual sequence values.

SAQ 21.4 The equality operator ($=$) returns *true* if two sequences have the same elements in the same order. Provide a formal definition of equality for sequences s_1 and s_2 and as a result define the inequality operator ($\neq$).

21.11 BAGS (OR MULTISETS) IN VDM-SL

Unlike Z, bags are not supported as a separate type in VDM and therefore there is no specific type constructor or generator. However, a bag is easily modelled as a map from each possible element to the number of times it appears. In particular, a bag of items of some type X is defined:

$$Bag(X) = X \xrightarrow{\ m\ } \mathbb{N}_1$$

with the empty bag denoted by $b_0 = \{\mapsto\}$. The map therefore associates each element of the bag with its (non-zero) multiplicity ($\mathbb{N}_1$). This of course is very similar to the corresponding description in typed set theory and Z (bag $X == X \nrightarrow \mathbb{N}_1$) and the relationship between the map and the partial function has been discussed previously.

The description of the fundamental bag operators in VDM is usually achieved by the direct definition of auxilliary functions using the operators of maps. Thus:

$in : X \times Bag(X) \to \mathbb{B}$
$in\ (e,b) \underline{\Delta} e \in \mathrm{dom}\ b$

$count : X \times Bag(X) \to \mathbb{N}$
$count(e,b) \underline{\Delta}\ \text{if}\ e \in \mathrm{dom}\ b\ \text{then}\ b(e)\ \text{else}\ 0$

$Bag\text{-}union : Bag\ (X) \times Bag\ (X) \to Bag\ (X)$
$Bag\text{-}union(a,b) \underline{\Delta} \{p \mapsto count(p,a) + count(p,b) \mid p \in (\mathrm{dom}\ a \cup \mathrm{dom}\ b)\}$

$items : X^* \to Bag\ (X)$
$items\ (s) \underline{\Delta} \{x \mapsto \mathrm{card}\ \{\forall i : \mathrm{dom}\ s \mid s(i) = x\} \mid x \in \mathrm{rng}\ (s)\}$

The definitions of *in* and *count* are quite straightforward (and somewhat simpler than with typed set theory). *Bag-union* and *items* are expressed in terms of **VDM** map comprehension while *count* embodies map application. *Bag-union* is again defined in terms of the addition of multiplicities, whilst *items* defines the bag in which each element x appears exactly as often as x appears in s.

By using this basic set the specifier is free to extend the notation for bags and describe more complex operators as and when needed. For example, *inc-bag* and *dec-bag* make use of the *count* function. These operations perform a unit increase and decrease (respectively) on the number of occurrences of a specific element within a bag. If the element is not in the bag then *inc-bag* inserts it with multiplicity of 1, while for *dec-bag* we have a precondition such that the element e must be a member of the bag for the function to be defined.

$inc\text{-}bag : X \times Bag(X) \to Bag(X)$
$inc\text{-}bag\ (e,b) \underline{\Delta}\ b \dagger \{e \mapsto count(e,b) + 1\}$

$dec\text{-}bag : X \times Bag(X) \to Bag(X)$
$dec\text{-}bag\ (e,b) \underline{\Delta}\ \text{if}\ b(e) > 1\ \text{then}\ b = b \dagger \{e \mapsto count(e,b) - 1\}$
$\qquad\qquad\qquad\qquad\qquad \text{else}\ b = \{e\} \triangleleft b$

$\text{pre}\ e \in \mathrm{dom}\ b$

Similarly we can define bag subset as a truth-valued function in terms of *count* and a suitable predicate:

$Bag\text{-}subset : Bag(X) \times Bag(X) \to \mathbb{B}$
$Bag\text{-}subset(b_1,b_2) \underline{\Delta} \forall x : X \bullet count(x,b_1) \leq count(x,b_2)$

Each operator is described in terms of explicit function definitions with particular types X. A very useful further extension to the notation would be to describe the operators generically. In this respect we parallel the generic constructs of Z and in particular the role of the generic definition of *bag subset* in the drinks dispenser case study in Part 5.

Recall from Chapter 20 that generic definitions of explicit functions in VDM are called polymorphic definitions. The signature of a polymorphic function definition takes the general form:

Function-name $[@\mathrm{Id}_1, @\mathrm{Id}_2, @\mathrm{Id}_3, \ldots, @\mathrm{Id}_n] : T_1 \times T_2 \times T_3 \times \cdots T_n \to T$

The *type variable list* is enclosed in [ ] and its identifiers represent the formal generic parameters. In order to get a particular function from a definition these have to be replaced by actual parameters through a function instantiation. As a first illustration consider the generic definition of the *count* operator:

$$count \; [@elem] : @elem \times (@elem \xrightarrow{\text{m}} \mathbb{N}_1) \to \mathbb{N}$$
$$count(e,b) \; \underline{\Delta} \; \text{if} \; e \in \text{dom} \; b \; \text{then} \; b(e) \; \text{else} \; 0$$

@elem is a type variable which can be used to introduce any type. The function *count* is then defined as accepting an element of this type together with a bag of elements of that type and returning a natural number representing the number of times that element occurs in the bag. To create a particular instance of this function we provide an actual generic parameter to replace *@elem*. Referring to the drinks dispenser case study in Part 5, assuming we have defined types:

> types
> *British-coin* = {*one-penny, two-pence, ..., one-pound*}   and
> *Coin-bag* = *British-coin* $\xrightarrow{\text{m}}$ $\mathbb{N}_1$

together with some declaration:

$$Takings : Coin\text{-}bag$$

a useful instantiation would proceed as follows:

$$count \; [British\text{-}coin] \; (one\text{-}penny, \; Takings)$$

In this instantiation the *count* function determines how many one penny coins are in the current takings; *British-coin* is the actual parameter used to effect instantiation, *one-penny* is a *British-coin* while *Takings* is a bag of *British-coin*.

Just as *count* was used earlier to create definitions of *inc-bag* and *bag-union*, polymorphic definitions of *count* can also be used in polymorphic definitions of the operators, for example:

$$inc\text{-}bag \; [@elem] : @elem \times (@elem \xrightarrow{\text{m}} \mathbb{N}_1) \to (@elem \xrightarrow{\text{m}} \mathbb{N}_1)$$
$$inc\text{-}bag(e,b) \; \underline{\Delta} \; b \dagger \{e \mapsto count \; [@elem](e,b) + 1\}$$

and:

$$Bag\text{-}union[@elem] : (@elem \xrightarrow{\text{m}} \mathbb{N}_1) \times (@elem \xrightarrow{\text{m}} \mathbb{N}_1) \to (@elem \xrightarrow{\text{m}} \mathbb{N}_1)$$
$$Bag\text{-}union(a,b) \; \underline{\Delta} \; \{p \mapsto count \; [@elem](p,a)$$
$$+ \; count \; [@elem](p,b) \mid p \in (\text{dom} \; a \cup \text{dom} \; b)\}$$

Some of these polymorphics will be used in the VDM case studies later.

21.12 COMPOSITE VALUES OR RECORDS

When writing specifications it is often necessary to support objects that can be thought of in two ways; either as a single complete entity or as an object with component parts. Probably the most familiar example of this is a date, which is normally thought of as a discrete unit but often has to be 'disassembled' into individual days, months and years. In VDM such support is provided by the *composite value type* or *record*. A composite type is a discrete collection of component values often called *fields*. These fields may have identifiers by means of which they can be referenced. A *composite type expression* takes one of two general forms:

```
compose Id of      or      compose Id of
    Id₁: T₁                      T₁
    Id₂: T₂                      T₂
      ⋮                          ⋮
    Idₙ: Tₙ                      Tₙ
  end                        end
```

In the first form each Id_i acts as an identifier for a field of type T_i—provided by a type expression. In this form the composite type expression denotes Id as the type identifier for records with fields Id_i and types T_i, respectively. The order in which fields are declared is entirely arbitrary. In the second form the fields are anonymous and cannot be referenced individually. This is a less useful form. The first form, however, is very reminiscent of the record structure of a programming language and continues the close relationship that VDM has with the programming environment.

The record type identifier Id is the *tag* of the type; it cannot itself be used in declarations such as *var* : Id because the tag does not represent a set of such records but merely a collection of field values of particular types. However, we can build a type (Id') corresponding to the set of all possible records of type Id in the definitions block of a specification by statements such as:

```
types
Id′ = compose Id of
        Id₁: T₁
        Id₂: T₂
          ⋮
        Idₙ: Tₙ
      end
```

where the Id' identifier is the name of the type and can now be used to distribute the type throughout the specification by means of definitions such as:

$$Map = X \xrightarrow{m} Id'$$
$$Record\text{-}Sequence = Id'^* \text{ or}$$
$$Record\text{-}set = Id'\text{-set}$$

These definitions correspond to: a map type from a set of elements of type X to a set of records of type Id; a sequence of records of type Id; and a type whose individual elements are themselves sets of records of type Id. Straightforward declarations such as *var* : Id' declare *var* to be at any one time a particular record of type Id (not Id'). It is therefore the name of the type rather than its tag that is used for all references to the type; the role of the tag is simply to allow different composite types to be defined within the specification with exactly the same fields.

This discussion is a little confusing because the tag Id and the identifier Id' are not the same name, but as we have seen in other areas it is common practice in VDM to give a name to a set which is the same as the type of its elements, e.g. in the set *Student* introduced earlier, the type of each element is taken as *Student*. In such circumstances the following shorthand notation can be used:

$$\text{Id} :: \text{Id}_1 : \text{T}_1$$
$$\text{Id}_2 : \text{T}_2$$
$$\vdots$$
$$\text{Id}_n : \text{T}_n$$

which corresponds exactly to the definition:

$$\text{Id} = \text{compose Id of}$$
$$\text{Id}_1 : \text{T}_1$$
$$\text{Id}_2 : \text{T}_2$$
$$\vdots$$
$$\text{Id}_n : \text{T}_n$$
$$\text{end}$$

where the type identifier is now the same as the tag. This is less confusing and this convenient form will be used frequently in the case studies.

With such useful objects available in VDM we clearly have to address important aspects of their behaviour: how can we *create* them, *modify* them and determine their *contents*?

Specific instances of records of a particular type are created using *record construction* which has the general form:

$$mk - \text{Id} \ (\text{E}_1, \text{E}_2, \text{E}_3, \ldots, \text{E}_n)$$

where Id is the composite type identifier (tag) and the various E_is are expressions yielding values appropriate to each of the various field types (E_i corresponding to the ith field in the definition). In 'classical' VDM $mk - \text{Id} \ (\ )$ is frequently referred to as a *make function* and its role is to create some compound object instance from its component parts; there will be further variations on the make function in the next chapter.

Once an object instance has been created and given a value we can reference its contents by a *field selection* which has a form familiar from the programming environment, $R.\text{Id}_f$. Here R is a particular record value and Id_f is the identifier of a field within R's record type. Field selection provides the value of the field with field name Id_f in the record value R. Such selectors are really masquerading as functions which can be written in familiar form. This point will be examined with an actual example shortly.

The value(s) in a record can be changed using the *record modification* operator μ (mu). A record modification takes the general form:

$$\mu \ (R, \ \text{Id}_1 \mapsto \text{E}_1, \ \text{Id}_2 \mapsto \text{E}_2, \ldots, \ \text{Id}_n \mapsto \text{E}_n)$$

where R is a record value, the various Ids are the distinct field identifiers and the Es are expressions yielding values of the appropriate types. It denotes a record value which is the same as R except that the fields with identifiers Id_i now contain the E_i values, i.e. the contents of these specific fields are changed. Record modification needs to refer only to those fields it wishes to change.

Finally, composite objects represent collections of values and in many cases certain combinations may not be meaningful. For example, referring once more to the *Date* example, a record formed with 32, *May* and 1992 would be illegal. In such circumstances the values that a record may take in combination can be (optionally) restricted by the application of an invariant included within the composite type definition. The definition of the type *Date* must therefore proceed:

types
    Day = {1, ...,31};
    Month = {*Jan, Feb, Mar, Apr, May, Jun, Jul, Aug, Sep, Oct, Nov, Dec*};
    Year = {1583, ..., 2599}:
Date :: *Dy* : *Day*
        Mnth : *Month*
        Yr : *Year*
        inv (*mk-Date*(d, m, y)) $\underline{\Delta}$
            ($m \in$ {*Jan, Mar, May, Jul, Aug, Oct, Dec*} $\wedge\, d \in$ {1, ..., 31}) $\vee$
            ($m \in$ {*Apr, Jun, Sep, Nov*} $\wedge\, d \in$ {1, ..., 30}) $\vee$
            ($m = Feb \wedge \neg\ is\text{-}leap\text{-}yr(y) \wedge d \in$ {1, ..., 28}) $\vee$
            ($m = Feb \wedge is\text{-}leap\text{-}yr(y) \wedge d \in$ {1, ..., 29});
functions
    is-leap-yr : *Year* $\to \mathbb{B}$
    is-leap-yr(y) $\underline{\Delta}$ (($y\ MOD\ 4 = 0) \wedge \neg(y\ MOD\ 100 = 0)) \vee (y\ MOD\ 400 = 0)$

where the auxiliary function *is-leap-yr*( ) is defined as in SAQ 21.1. The declaration of the invariant uses a combination of the keyword inv and a make function. The integration of these two terms is best thought of as a shorthand for the explicit definition of the truth-valued function:

inv -*Date* : *Date* $\to \mathbb{B}$
inv -*Date* (*mk-Date*(d, m, y)) $\underline{\Delta}$
            ($m \in$ {*Jan, Mar, May, Jul, Aug, Oct, Dec*} $\wedge\, d \in$ {1, ..., 31}) $\vee$
            ($m \in$ {*Apr, Jun, Sep, Nov*} $\wedge\, d \in$ {1, ..., 30}) $\vee$
            ($m = Feb \wedge \neg is\text{-}leap\text{-}yr(y) \wedge d \in$ {1, ..., 28}) $\vee$
            ($m = Feb \wedge is\text{-}leap\text{-}yr(y) \wedge d \in$ {1, ..., 29})

which simply accepts an instance of a *Date* record (created using the make function) and determines whether it is legal or not. Record selection is available for records of type *Date* such that *Date.Dy*, *Date.Mnth* and *Date.Yr* decompose a *Date* into its constituent parts. Indeed, each of these selectors can be regarded as an explicit function which can be written in familiar form, e.g. *Date.Dy* is really a language convenience which is shorthand for:

                Day-of-the-Date : *Date* $\to$ *Day*
                Day-of-the-Date(*make-Date*(d, m, y)) $\underline{\Delta}\ d$

which accepts a *Date* (made from *d*, *m* and *y* by the make function) and returns the day that was used to make it.

To make all these points more meaningful, we can look at some specific examples of the use of records in specifications. Consider once again the *Project–Programmer* scenario used in Part 3 and the chapters on Z. Recall that the variable *Programmer* was a partial function from a set of programmer numbers to a set of programmer names. We showed in earlier parts of this chapter that we can represent this relationship as a map. However, by using appropriate composite types we can include more details about the programmer than simply a name. The types required are as follows:

```
types
    Prog-Num = ... ;
    Prog-Name = ... ;
    Address = char⁺;
    Telephone-no = ℕ⁺;
    Day = {1, ..., 31};
    Month = {Jan, Feb, Mar, Apr, May, Jun, Jul, Aug, Sep, Oct, Nov, Dec};
    Year = {1583, ..., 2599};
    Date :: Dy : Day
            Mnth : Month
            Yr : Year
            inv (mk-Date(d, m, y)) △
            (m ∈ {Jan, Mar, May, Jul, Aug, Oct, Dec} ∧ d ∈ {1, ..., 31}) ∨
            (m ∈ {Apr, Jun, Sep, Nov} ∧ d ∈ {1, ..., 30}) ∨
            (m = Feb ∧ ¬ is-leap-yr(y) ∧ d ∈ {1, ..., 28}) ∨
            (m = Feb ∧ is-leap-yr(y) ∧ d ∈ {1, ..., 29});
    Entry :: Name : Prog-Name
            Addr : Address
            Date-of-birth : Date
            Telephone-Number : Telephone-no ;
        Prog = Prog-Num ──ᵐ→ Entry;
functions
    is-leap-yr : Year → 𝔹
    is-leap-yr(y) △ ((y MOD 4 = 0) ∧ ¬ (y MOD 100 = 0)) ∨ (y MOD 400 = 0)
```

Prog-Num and *Prog-Name* are two sets whose members are not fully defined. Each item in these sets will eventually have to have some agreed format but such detail is unimportant at this point in the specification and, as such, the use of ... for these types corresponds to the given sets of Z. An address is a non-empty sequence of characters, while telephone numbers are modelled as a non-empty sequence of strictly positive natural numbers. Dates are represented as composite objects subject to the familiar invariant, while the programmer's details (*Entry*) are similarly represented as records with *Name, Address, Date* and *Telephone number* fields. Entries for individual programmers are uniquely referenced by *Prog-Num* values through the map type *Prog*. It is possible that an injective map type might be more appropriate but this is a consideration that can be left until later. The declaration:

Programmer : Prog

somewhere in the specification introduces an appropriate map. Specific instances of programmer entries can be created using *record construction* with statements such as:

mk-Entry(Huw Sheppard, Bell House, mk-Date(23, Jun, 1975), 0446235876)
mk-Entry(Wyn Sheppard, Bell House, mk-Date(18, Nov, 1980), 0446235876)
mk-Entry(Mike Read, Caeffermaen, mk-Date(17, Aug, 1943), 0272467459)

where the sequence notation has been omitted for brevity. Because these entries can participate in the map, we can add to the programmer details using map override and a suitable identifier *id* (where *id* ∈ *Prog-Num*), for example:

$$Programmer \dagger \{id \mapsto mk\text{-}Entry(Huw\ Sheppard,\ Bell\ House,$$
$$mk\text{-}Date(23,\ Jun,\ 1975),\ 0446235876),\dots\}$$

This mechanism can be used to add new programmer details or (if *id* ∈ dom *Programmer*) to replace ones that already exist.

Using *range subtraction* (▷) programmer entries can be removed. For example, assuming now that *id* ∈ dom *Programmer* then:

$$Programmer \rhd \{Programmer\ (id)\}$$

while amending the entry for the customer can be be achieved by *record modification*:

$$\mu(Programmer\ (id),\ Date\text{-}of\text{-}birth \mapsto mk\text{-}Date(d,m,y))$$

which uses map application to recover the record value subject to the modification. In this example only the *Date-of-birth* field is modified.

Simple enquiries are achieved by recovering entries with map application followed by *field selection*. For example:

$$: = Programmer\ (id).Name$$
$$: = Programmer\ (id).Addr$$

and because the definition of an *Entry* has a nested composite object, if we wanted to determine the year of birth for a particular programmer we would write:

$$: = Programmer(id).Date\text{-}of\text{-}birth.Yr$$

where once again we assume *id* ∈ dom *Programmer*. This is an example of function composition in VDM; the result of the first selector matching the argument of the second.

Recovery of a record instance for use in field selection or record modification depends of course on the compound type in which it participates. In these examples we use map application which extends also to bags but records could be used to form sequences where sequence application would be more appropriate.

21.13 SUMMARY

The mathematics of VDM draws many parallels with that of Z; a similar set of objects is supported which are employed in much the same ways. As was suggested in Chapter 20, however, there is a pronounced difference in notation between the two with VDM being much closer to the structure of a programming language than Z. Even so, VDM-SL is entirely abstract so that we can reason about aspects of its specifications in much the same way as in Z, by generating and discharging proof obligations. Those we have met so far, however, address only the well-formedness of functions.

The relationship with a programming language is a deliberate design choice and manifests itself first in the 'finiteness' of the objects in VDM. Sets, maps, etc., have

326 AN INTRODUCTION TO FORMAL SPECIFICATION WITH Z AND VDM

countable numbers of members and therefore assume a quality characteristic of all the data structures in a target language. Whereas most of the objects are familiar from Z (there is really little difference between the descriptions of sets, sequences and bags) the map and the composite value are specific to VDM. The map, however, is really only a manifestation of the function type in Z; a manifestation deliberately biased towards a familiar object—the table—which we know can be represented on a machine in a variety of ways. The migration of a VDM specification to a final implementation is therefore assisted by such structures, yet the map is sufficiently abstract to permit us to reason about its role in a specification in much the same fashion as with functions in Z. Indeed all the operators of maps parallel those of relations and functions in Z. The composite type is clearly a formal analogue of the 'record' in programming languages and again provides the specification with a structure that translates directly to most programming environments.

Finally, the first impression we may form on looking at the mathematics of Z and VDM is one which tends to emphasize the differences between the two. After all they *look* quite different. However, this is really a superficial difference only, the major difference being not of notation but rather of philosophy. Whereas Z may have an advantage in terms of its schema calculus, VDM counters with its role almost as a loosely specified programming language. In the next chapter this theme is continued and extended by considering abstract states and operations upon them.

22

ABSTRACT STATES AND OPERATIONS IN VDM-SL

CHECKLIST OF OBJECTIVES

After reading this chapter you should be able to:

- Understand the abstract state definition in VDM-SL.
- Understand the structure of implicit and explicit operation definitions.
- Build total operation definitions by using the error definition block.
- Discharge proof obligations for initial states, implementability and specification properties.

22.1 INTRODUCTION

Like Z, VDM uses the notion of an *operation* to specify the intended behaviour of a program or part thereof. To be true to the nature of specification it is important that the operation describes the obligations of the program and the environment in which these must be discharged, thereby only conveying *what* the program has to achieve. The programmer remains free to consider *how* that should be realized. Aspects of both data and processing efficiency may well suggest a whole host of possible implementations corresponding to a given VDM operation. The relationship between the former and latter is therefore many to one and it is this characteristic that causes the activity of programming to be complex.

The separation of the what from the how means that operations in VDM are largely described in implicit fashion. Implicit definition was introduced for the function, but the application of a function is quite distinct from the execution of a program. A function always returns the same result given the same argument(s), a program need not. A program often has its results influenced by events that have preceded its execution, e.g. if my bank executes a program that accepts my account number and returns my current balance it will give quite a different answer at the end of a month compared to the beginning! The difference is due to the various transactions that have occurred against my account during this period. The effect of these transactions is recorded through the state of my account and this influences the result the program returns at the end of the month. States therefore correspond to stored data that reflect a history of events. Programs are characterized by observing that their execution can be

327

affected by, and in turn affects, this underlying persistent state. The program may have access to all or part of the state and may read from it and/or write to it. The program may also have input(s) that it uses to alter the state and output(s) that are influenced by it. In VDM, operations and states are used to model the behaviour of the program and its environment; the notation used must therefore be extended beyond that used for functions to capture the difference. Readers should now be aware, however, that whatever the notation, operations in VDM like those of Z describe programs in terms of abstract state data, state data invariants, initial states and operations with inputs and outputs.

It should also be mentioned that in VDM certain operations can be defined in explicit fashion, which largely parallels the explicit definition used for functions. This permits an operation to be specified at a rather low level without the use of pre- and postconditions but for obvious reasons excessive use of such descriptions should be avoided. However, some reference to explicit definitions will be made for the sake of completion; whichever way they are defined, operations in VDM-SL cannot be polymorphic. As a final point, the discussion that follows makes reference to the case studies in Part 3 to illustrate various features of VDM and the reader is free to compare this with the approach taken by Z in Part 4.

22.2 THE ABSTRACT STATE DEFINITION IN VDM-SL

As with Z, a state definition must precede the definition of any operation. A state definition in VDM largely corresponds to the abstract state schema of Z and represents the mechanism by which a VDM module retains a knowledge of the history of operation calls. In Z the schema introduces the mathematical objects that compose the persistent state together with the invariant (if any) that restricts their values in combination. The schema is included in every Z operation thereby distributing the invariant throughout the specification. In Z we describe an initial state by a separate initial state schema. In VDM the abstract state definition is made once and implicitly assumed by each operation, while the initial state can (optionally) be described as part of the state definition. The general form of this statement is as follows:

$$
\begin{aligned}
&\texttt{state } \textit{VDM-State } \texttt{of}\\
&\quad \texttt{id}_1 \texttt{: } T_1\\
&\quad \texttt{id}_2 \texttt{: } T_2\\
&\qquad \vdots\\
&\quad \texttt{id}_n \texttt{: } T_n\\
&\quad \texttt{inv } \textit{mk-VDM-state } (a,b,\ldots,n) \ \underline{\Delta} \ \ldots\\
&\quad \texttt{init } \textit{mk-VDM-state } (a,b,\ldots,n) \ \underline{\Delta} \ \ldots\\
&\texttt{end}
\end{aligned}
$$

The state definition declares the state identifier (in this case *VDM-State*) and the field identifiers ($\texttt{id}_1$ to $\texttt{id}_n$) with global scope. The fields are called *state variables* and may be thought of as composing a single instance of a record type containing those fields. The state identifier is used to refer to the state in a module document and in the invariant and initialization definitions but is otherwise purely for annotation. The fields can be referenced only within the body of an operation and each field is of corresponding type T_i. The invariant condition and the initial state are introduced by the keywords inv and init, respectively. In each case the state instance used in the definition is made using a make function and this parallels the composite types discussed in Chapter 21; the *a*s, *b*s, etc., refer to state variables. The invariant declared here is implicitly assumed to apply in all subsequent operation definitions without further reference. We can make much more sense of all this if we build the state definition statement for a state with which we are familiar. We therefore return to the classroom *Homework* problem used in Parts 3 and 4. The VDM state definition for this problem is as follows:

```
types
Student = ...
Studset = Student-set
state Homework of
Class        : Studset
Handed-in    : Studset
Not-handed-in : Studset
    inv mk-Homework (Class, Handed-in, Not-handed-in) ≙
        Handed-in ∪ Not-handed-in = Class ∧
        Handed-in ∩ Not-handed-in = { }
    init mk-Homework (Class, Handed-in, Not-handed-in) ≙
        Not-handed-in = Class ∧
        Handed-in = { }
end
```

The types definition block introduces the sorts of data that interest us. *Student* represents a collection of values that distinguish individual students. Each element in this collection is therefore of the same type, *Student*. The notation (...) shows that this type is not yet fully defined because such detail is unimportant at this stage of a specification and would only add unnecessary complexity to the description. The important point to note is that each element in this set is uniquely identifiable and the whole set corresponds to a finite universe of concern, i.e. all students we are ever likely to be interested in. This corresponds to our use of given sets in the earlier Z description.

Studset is a compound type formed by applying the VDM set constructor (-set) to *Student*. Each individual value of the type *Studset* is therefore a set of students in its own right and the use of -set here parallels the use of power set ($\mathbb{P}$) in Z.

The keywords state ... of introduce the abstract state space for the *Homework* problem. The state space is composed from the persistent objects *Class*, *Handed-in* and *Not-handed-in*. Each of these state variables is declared to be of type *Studset* and therefore at any time each represents one of many possible sets of students.

The abstract state is a useful starting point for the description of the *Homework* problem but the raw state again permits combinations of student that are unrealistic, e.g. the same student may appear in all three sets without restriction, corresponding to a student who is a member of the class and who has handed in and not handed in homework at the same time! The state data must therefore be restricted so that it can only ever contain combinations of sets of students that are meaningful within the context of the problem. In addition, it is important that state variable types are preserved by operations. VDM achieves all this by the inclusion of an explicit state data invariant through the combined use of the keyword inv and a make function. The integration of these two terms in the specification is best thought of as a shorthand for the definition of the following truth-valued function:

$$inv\text{-}Homework : Homework \rightarrow \mathbb{B}$$
$$inv\text{-}Homework \ (mk\text{-}Homework \ (Class, \ Handed\text{-}in, \ Not\text{-}handed\text{-}in)) \ \underline{\Delta}$$
$$Handed\text{-}in \ \cup \ Not\text{-}handed\text{-}in = Class \ \wedge$$
$$Handed\text{-}in \ \cap \ Not\text{-}handed\text{-}in = \{\ \}$$

inv-Homework is therefore a function that accepts an object of the type of the state *Homework* and returns a Boolean (*true, false*) indicating whether or not that state is valid. The requirement that the application of *inv-Homework* always returns *true* is therefore the mechanism by which the invariant to the state is applied.

The argument for *inv-Homework* is an instance of the *Homework* state and this instance is created using a make function for which there is no real counterpart in Z. As usual the make function is written with the prefix *mk-* followed by the name of the state. The arguments to the function are the persistent objects that compose the state (taken in the order they appear in the field definition) and return an object that has the type of the state. Thus the application:

$$mk\text{-}Homework \ (Class, \ Handed\text{-}in, \ Not\text{-}handed\text{-}in)$$

produces a state instance that has components *Class, Handed-in* and *Not-handed-in*. We of course know that these objects can assume a range of conditions but the body of the definition of the *inv-Homework* function implies that only those component combinations where the predicate is *true* can form a legal state. In fact the invariant can be regarded as identifying a set of legal states (the so-called state space) of type *Homework* in terms of the comprehension:

$$Homework = \{mk\text{-}Homework(Class, \ Handed\text{-}in, \ Not\text{-}handed\text{-}in) \mid$$
$$Class, \ Handed\text{-}in, \ Not\text{-}handed\text{-}in \in Stdset \ \wedge$$
$$inv\text{-}Homework \ (mk\text{-}Homework \ (Class, \ Handed\text{-}in, \ Not\text{-}handed\text{-}in))\}$$

Notice also that the state invariant of a VDM specification (unlike that in the delta notation of Z) makes no reference to after objects and before objects; the implication being that the invariant must be *true* in any state condition. We shall see later how we use the invariant when a distinction needs to be made between the two situations.

The final part of the definition describes an (optional) initial condition for the state; this is introduced by the keyword init. The meaning of this paragraph develops naturally from the previous one: the initial value of the state is constructed using the *mk-Homework* function with arguments that correspond to an empty 'handed in' group and a 'not handed in' group that equals the whole class (whatever that may be). In other words the initial state corresponds to the case where no one has yet submitted homework. Once again the integration of the keyword init and the make function are really shorthand for the definition of the following truth-valued function:

init-Homework : *Homework* → $\mathbb{B}$
init-Homework (*mk-Homework* (*Class, Handed-in, Not-handed-in*)) $\underline{\Delta}$
   Not-handed-in = *Class* ∧
Handed-in = { }

Initial states, like any other, must satisfy the state invariant and the constraints on the state variable types. The presence of `init` in a state definition therefore generates a proof obligation which can be expressed by demanding that `if` the initial state is *true* `then` the invariant must also hold. The obligation can be expressed as a theorem in terms of an implication using the two truth-valued functions.

22.2.1 Proof obligation

   ∀*Class, Handed-in, Not-handed-in* ∈ *Stdset* •
   init-Homework (*mk-Homework* (*Class, Handed-in, Not-handed-in*)) ⇒
   inv-Homework (*mk-Homework* (*Class, Handed-in, Not-handed-in*))

Proof

`from` *Class, Handed-in, Not-handed-in* ∈ *Stdset*		
1	`from` *Handed-in* = { } ∧ *Not-handed-in* = *Class*	
2	*Handed-in* = { }	h,h1
3	{ } ∩ *Not-handed-in* = { }	h, ∩
4	*Handed-in* ∩ *Not-handed-in* = { }	= t-subs(3,2)
5	*Not-handed-in* = *Class*	h, h1
6	{ } ∪ *Class* = *Class*	h, ∪
7	{ } ∪ *Not-handed-in* = *Class*	= t-subs(6,5)
8	*Handed-in* ∪ *Not-handed-in* = *Class*	= t-subs(7,2)

   `infer` *Handed-in* ∩ *Not-handed-in* = { } ∧ *Handed-in* ∪ *Not-handed-in* = *Class*
   `infer` *inv-Homework* (*mk-Homework* (*Class, Handed-in, Not-handed-in*))
   `infer` *init-Homework* (*mk-Homework* (*Class, Handed-in, Not-handed-in*)) ⇒
      inv-Homework (*mk-Homework* (*Class, Handed-in, Not-handed-in*))

Here line 1 represents the body of the *init-Homework* function which of course we assume to be *true* because there would be little point in conducting the proof if this were not so! (See precondition calculations in Z.) Because the left-hand side of the implication is *true* the implication as a whole is proven if we can show that the right-hand side is *true* under these conditions. This we achieve largely by using substitution and the properties of sets.

In VDM-SL the `init` clause expresses a property of the state. However, the clause is optional and when it is omitted we have to consider bringing about an initial state by some alternative means, namely by a separate operation. This operation parallels the initial state schema in Z. The proof obligation, however, is slightly different and this is considered in more detail after examining VDM operations in the next section. Whichever way the initial state is created, however, an initial state theorem must be constructed and proven as in the case of Z.

22.3 IMPLICIT OPERATION DEFINITIONS IN VDM-SL

Implicit operation definitions in VDM-SL have a general form which consists of a signature, an external variables clause, a pre- and postcondition and an error definition block. This format can be regarded as an extension of the implicit definition of a function to accommodate the existence of the persistent state and the possibility of error conditions (neither of which are characteristics of functions):

$$
\begin{aligned}
&\texttt{Op-name}\ (p_1 : T_1, p_2 : T_2, \ldots, p_n : T_n)\ r : T_r \\
&\texttt{ext}\ Md_1\ Nm_{11}, Nm_{12}, \ldots : T_1 \\
&\qquad Md_2\ Nm_{21}, Nm_{22}, \ldots : T_2 \\
&\qquad \vdots \\
&\qquad Md_n\ Nm_{n1}, Nm_{n2}, \ldots : T_n \\
&\texttt{pre}\ \mathbf{B} \\
&\texttt{post}\ \mathbf{B'} \\
&\texttt{errs}\ \textit{err-id}_1 : \mathbf{B}_1 \rightarrow \mathbf{B}_1{}' \\
&\qquad \textit{err-id}_2 : \mathbf{B}_2 \rightarrow \mathbf{B}_2{}' \\
&\qquad \vdots \\
&\qquad \textit{err-id}_n : \mathbf{B}_n \rightarrow \mathbf{B}_n{}'
\end{aligned}
$$

The first line constitutes the signature where $\texttt{Op-name}$ is the identifier to be associated with the operation throughout the specification; $\texttt{Op-name}$ is therefore declared with global scope. The term in parentheses represents the operation parameters and their types (the inputs) while the final term names the result and its type (the output(s)). The effect of returning several results can be achieved by making T_r a tuple or product type. The scope of the parameters is the body of the operation (the precondition, post-condition and error definition block), while the scope of the result is the postcondition and the error postconditions ($\mathbf{B}_i'$) of the error definition block. Some examples will shortly be examined which make these points more tangible. Because of the signature VDM has no need to distinguish inputs and outputs by special decoration (compare with Z), while an operation does not have to accept parameters or return a result; it is perfectly possible for it to manipulate state variables only and this is another feature distinguishing an operation from a function.

Operations, like functions, have their own *operation types*. The type of an operation can be deduced from the signature, while the operation type expression itself takes the form:

$$
T_1 \times T_2 \times \ldots \times T_n \xrightarrow{\ o\ } T_r
$$

where the symbolism $\xrightarrow{\ o\ }$ differentiates an operation type from a function type. If there are no parameters and/or results the notation ( ) replaces the appropriate types list. Operation type expressions (rather than signatures) are used in explicit operation definitions, while the exports section of the interface part of a module always refers to the types of the operations it exports using operation type expressions, regardless of whether the actual definitions are implicit or explicit. These points will be made clear later; the notion of a type expression can be ignored for now.

Those state variables which can be accessed by the operation are listed immediately after the signature in the *external variables clause* which begins with the keyword $\texttt{ext}$.

In VDM, because the state definition is made just once and its existence is implicitly assumed throughout the specification, each operation simply has to declare which state variable(s) it has an interest in through its external variables clause. State variables not mentioned in the clause cannot be accessed by the operation, while those which are declared can be accessed in either 'read only' or 'write/read' mode depending upon whether the mode identifier (Md_i) preceding the list of state variable names (Nm_{ij}) is r d or wr respectively. State variables declared with r d access cannot be changed by the operation; indeed the use of r d is equivalent to adding a predicate to the postcondition that says nothing changes (cf. Z). Those declared with wr access can. All this means that the effect an operation has on the state can easily be deduced from the use of r d or wr in its external variables clause which parallels the delta and xi notation in Z.

The preconditions and postconditions fulfil the usual role expected of them in an implicit definition; postconditions are of course mandatory but trivial preconditions are often omitted. The precondition (when present) is a Boolean expression (**B**) involving possibly inputs and initial state variable values, while the postcondition (**B′**) is a Boolean expression which can include references to the initial state variable values, the final state variable values, the inputs and the result. Because of this, whenever a state variable declared with mode wr appears in the postcondition, the postcondition needs to refer to the condition of the object before and after the operation has occurred in order to explain the effect of the write. In this respect the *hook* symbol[1] (*id* ⁀) denotes an 'old name', i.e. the condition of a state object *before* the operation, while the after condition is left undecorated. For operations, this distinction is really needed only in a postcondition and not in a precondition. In a precondition the state referenced is (by definition) the state just before the operation is executed and confusion should not arise. Similarly, in an init statement or a initialization operation the state referred to is always that *after* the initialization has occurred. However, in a statement such as:

$$\text{post } \textit{Not-handed-in} = \textit{Not-handed-in}^{\frown} - \{std\}$$

the hook is needed to distinguish between two references to the condition of the *Not-handed-in* component. It is clear that after the operation has executed, a student will have been removed from the *Not-handed-in* group. In this respect VDM parallels the decorations of Z but Z decorates after objects (with ′) rather than before objects. It should also be pointed out that any state variable declared with mode r d normally occurs in the postcondition as an undecorated identifier (indicating the same value before and after the operation).

This decoration convention is perfectly adequate for describing operations but when the pre- and postconditions are used in theorems we often find it helpful to decorate all 'before' variables so that they can be unambiguously distinguished for the proof. Some theorems will be constructed shortly to show how the decorations are applied in context.

The final part of the definition is the *error definition block* which extends the definition of the operation to combinations of input parameters and state variables for which the precondition fails to hold. The appearance of the error definition block converts a partial operation to a total one in precisely the same manner as in Z, except

---

[1] In earlier versions of VDM the hook extends across the whole identifier, e.g. $\overline{\textit{Not-handed-in}}$. This is difficult to typeset and frankly unnecessary. This text conforms to the VDM-SL convention as in Dawes (1991).

the absence of any calculus forces us to describe the total operation all in one rather than through a combination of separate concerns. This style can make the final description somewhat overwhelming. In the error definition block:

$$\texttt{errs } err\text{-}id_1 : \mathbf{B}_1 \rightarrow \mathbf{B}_1'$$
$$err\text{-}id_2 : \mathbf{B}_2 \rightarrow \mathbf{B}_2'$$
$$\vdots$$
$$err\text{-}id_n : \mathbf{B}_n \rightarrow \mathbf{B}_n'$$

each $err\text{-}id_i$ is an identifier denoting an *error condition*; its purpose is purely annotatory. Each $\mathbf{B}_i$ is an *error precondition* being deduced by the negation of the pre-condition as in Z. Similarly each $\mathbf{B}_j'$ is an *error postcondition*. The general idea is that we extend the normal pre- and postconditions such that if an error precondition is *true* the effect of the operation is described by the corresponding error postcondition which effectively describes what should happen when an error occurs. Of course the normal precondition and the error preconditions are mutually exclusive, while if more than one error precondition is *true* then any of the corresponding error postconditions hold. In this sense a VDM total operation is non-deterministic as in Z. All this means that if some operation is declared as:

$$\texttt{pre } \mathbf{B}$$
$$\texttt{post } \mathbf{B}'$$
$$\texttt{errs } err\text{-}id_1 : \mathbf{B}_1 \rightarrow \mathbf{B}_1'$$
$$err\text{-}id_2 : \mathbf{B}_2 \rightarrow \mathbf{B}_2'$$
$$\vdots$$
$$err\text{-}id_n : \mathbf{B}_n \rightarrow \mathbf{B}_n'$$

we could equally well write:

$$\texttt{pre } \mathbf{B} \vee \mathbf{B}_1 \vee \mathbf{B}_2 \vee \ldots \vee \mathbf{B}_n$$
$$\texttt{post } (\mathbf{B} \wedge \mathbf{B}') \vee (\mathbf{B}_1 \wedge \mathbf{B}_1') \vee \ldots \vee (\mathbf{B}_n \wedge \mathbf{B}_n')$$

but placing the error pre/postconditions into an separate error definition block makes the whole operation rather more readable. This is especially true if the error condition identi-fiers are chosen in meaningful ways such that the condition name equals the name of the exception. In this way they signal error messages with no predisposition as to how they are returned. In this respect they serve the same purpose as the set *Message* in typed set theory and Z. Readers may also notice the parallels to be drawn between this form of the VDM operation and certain total operations written without the use of schema disjunction in Z.

As a final point it should be mentioned that, like functions, implicit operation defi-nitions such as:

$$\text{Op-name } (p_1 : T_1, p_2 : T_2, \ldots, p_n : T_n)\, r : T_r$$

simultaneously define two truth-valued functions *pre*-Op-name and *post*-Op-name which correspond to the operations' precondition and postcondition functions respect-ively. These are used in proof obligations for operations in exactly the same way as the pre- and postcondition functions were used to determine implementability for implicit functions. The identifiers *pre*-Op-name and *post*-Op-name are declared with global scope and they effectively correspond to the explicit definitions:

pre-Op-name $: T_1 \times T_2 \times \ldots \times T_k \times T_1' \times T_2' \times \ldots \times T_m' \to \mathbb{B}$
pre-Op-name $(p_1, p_2, \ldots, p_k, id_1, id_2, \ldots, id_m) \underline{\Delta} \ \mathbf{B}$
$post$-Op-name $: T_1 \times T_2 \times \ldots \times T_k \times T_1' \times T_2' \times \ldots \times T_m' \times T_1'' \times T_2'' \times \ldots$
$\qquad \qquad \times T_n'' \times T_r \to \mathbb{B}$
$post$-Op-name $(p_1, p_2, \ldots, p_k, id_1, id_2, \ldots, id_m, id_1', id_2', \ldots, id_m', r) \underline{\Delta} \ \mathbf{B}'$
pre $\mathbf{B}$

In these definitions, $\mathbf{B}$ and $\mathbf{B}'$ are the precondition and postcondition respectively of the operation Op-name. If the precondition is trivial $\mathbf{B}$ is taken as *true*. The p_is are the input parameters, the id_is are *all* the state variable parameters (of type T_i') mentioned in the operations' external variables clause, the id_i's are those with mode wr (and types T_i''), while r is the result (of type T_r). In certain circumstances (e.g. when used in theorems) the various id_is appearing in the functions may be hooked to make it perfectly clear that they relate to before states. We shall see examples of how to construct and use these functions later.

22.3.1 Some examples of implicit operation definitions in VDM-SL

This discussion has become rather technical and needs an actual example to make the points clear. We therefore return again to the *Homework* problem and rework our typed set theory and Z solutions through the medium of VDM. Recall that we informally described a number of operations that the system should support:

- *Enrol*   Adds a new student to the class.
- *Enquire*   Enquires whether a particular student has submitted homework.
- *Submit*   Records the fact that a student has now submitted homework.
- *Remove*   Removes a student from the class.

We shall assume that each operation performs as described in typed set theory and Z and that the abstract state for the system is as defined in Parts 3 and 4 . The operations are as follows:

Enrol $(std : Student)$
ext wr *Not-handed-in* : *Stdset*
$\qquad$ wr *Class* $\qquad$: *Stdset*
pre $\neg (std \in Class)$
post *Not-handed-in* $=$ *Not-handed-in*$\overleftarrow{} \cup \{std\} \wedge Class = Class\overleftarrow{} \cup \{std\}$
errs *PRESENT* : $\quad (std \in Class) \to$
$\qquad\qquad\qquad\qquad$ *Not-handed-in* $=$ *Not-handed-in*$\overleftarrow{} \wedge$
$\qquad\qquad\qquad\qquad \ Class = Class\overleftarrow{}$

Enquire $(std : Student)$ $enq : \mathbb{B}$
ext rd *Handed-in* : *Stdset*
$\qquad$ rd *Class* $\qquad$: *Stdset*
pre $std \in Class$
post $enq = (std \in Handed\text{-}in)$
errs *NOT-IN-CLASS* : $\neg (std \in Class) \to enq = false$

Submit (*std* : *Student*)
ext wr *Not-handed-in* : *Stdset*
    wr *Handed-in*   : *Stdset*
    rd *Class*   : *Stdset*
pre *std* $\in$ *Class* $\wedge$ *std* $\in$ *Not-handed-in*
post *Not-handed-in* = *Not-handed-in*$^{\leftarrow}$ − {*std*} $\wedge$ *Handed-in* = *Handed-in*$^{\leftarrow}$ $\cup$ {*std*}
errs *SUBMIT-ERR* : $\neg$ (*std* $\in$ *Class*) $\vee$ $\neg$ (*std* $\in$ *Not-handed-in*) $\rightarrow$
                    Not-handed-in = *Not-handed-in*$^{\leftarrow}$ $\wedge$
                    Handed-in = *Handed-in*$^{\leftarrow}$

Remove (*std* : *Student*)
ext wr *Not-handed-in* : *Stdset*
    wr *Handed-in*   : *Stdset*
    wr *Class*   : *Stdset*
pre *std* $\in$ *Class*
post *Not-handed-in* = *Not-handed-in*$^{\leftarrow}$ − {*std*} $\wedge$
    Handed-in   − *Handed-in*$^{\leftarrow}$ − {*std*} $\wedge$
    Class   = *Class*$^{\leftarrow}$ − {*std*}
errs *NOT-IN-CLASS* : $\neg$ (*std* $\in$ *Class*) $\rightarrow$
                    Not-handed-in = *Not-handed-in*$^{\leftarrow}$ $\wedge$
                    Handed-in = *Handed-in*$^{\leftarrow}$ $\wedge$
                    Class = *Class*$^{\leftarrow}$

The signature for *Enrol* shows that it accepts a student as input. The operation does not return a result but it does change the condition of the state components *Not-handed-in* and *Class* because of the mode identifier wr preceding these state variable names in the external variables clause. We deduce that *Handed-in* is unchanged by the operation for it has no access to this component. The precondition requires that the student is not a current member of the class, while the postcondition describes the nature of the state change caused by *ENROL*: the new student becomes a member of the class and the group that has not handed in. The error condition for this operation is that the input student is already a member of the class. If the error precondition holds the state variables remain unchanged.

The signature for *Enquire* shows that it accepts a student as input and returns a result, *enq*; a Boolean variable indicating whether or not the student has submitted. The ext clause shows that the operation has read (rd) access only to the state variables and therefore it cannot bring about a state change. The precondition shows that the student we enquire upon must be a member of the class, while the result of the operation is determined by the truth of *std* $\in$ *Handed-in*. The error condition for this operation is that the input student is not a member of the class. If the error precondition holds the result returned is *false*.

The signature for *Submit* shows that it accepts a student as input. The operation does not return a result but its execution brings about a state change. We deduce this from the appearance of the keyword wr preceding the state variables *Handed-in* and *Not-handed-in* in the external variables clause. The student submitting homework must be a member of the class and the group that has not handed in. Of course the invariant will demand that if the student belongs to the not-handed-in group that student also belongs to the class, but as we discovered in Z it is often sensible to make implicit preconditions explicit for the sake of clarity. The student is then removed from the not-handed-in group and added to the handed-in group. The operation has only read (rd) access to *Class* and so we deduce that *Class* remains the same. There are two error conditions for this operation; that the student does not belong to the class (nor to the not-handed-in group) *or* the student belongs to the class but not to the not-handed-in group. These are obtained in the usual way (cf. Z) by negating the normal precondition using de Morgan:

$$\neg\,(std \in Class \land std \in \textit{Not-handed-in}) \Leftrightarrow \neg\,(std \in Class\,) \lor \neg\,(std \in \textit{Not-handed-in})$$

If either of these error preconditions for the operation holds then the state variables remain unchanged. In the operation we have therefore combined the two conditions in a single error precondition. This is purely a matter of style and readers are free to rewrite the operation using individual error condition identifiers and error pre-conditions.

The signature for *Remove* shows that it also accepts a student as input. The operation does not return a result but it brings about a comprehensive state change affecting each one of the state variables. We again deduce this from the ext clause where the preceding wr shows that all three components are written to by the operation. The student to be removed must be a current member of the class, while the removal itself is achieved using set difference. Notice that if *std* is not a member of (say) *Handed-in* the difference leaves the set unchanged in content, but writing the same set back to a state variable is still regarded as bringing about a state change. The error condition for this operation is that the student does not belong to the class; if the error precondition holds the state variables remain unchanged.

22.3.2 Alternative styles of exception reporting

The style used to present these first VDM operations permits the error condition iden-tifiers to assume the role of 'error messages' by *signalling* an exception. No indication is given as to how such messages could be conveyed, however, this being regarded as an implementation issue to be addressed later in the development process. For our operations this is quite an acceptable approach, especially when we realize that three of them do not return anything at all. However we might like those operations that do return results to issue messages explicitly. Therefore in the case of *Enquire*, if we introduce the quote type:

UNKNOWN-STUDENT

we could modify the result type using the *type union* operator as follows:

Enquire (*std* : *Student*) *enq* : $\mathbb{B}$ | UNKNOWN-STUDENT
ext rd *Handed-in* : *Stdset*
    rd *Class*   : *Stdset*
pre *std* $\in$ *Class*
post *enq* = (*std* $\in$ *Handed-in*)
errs *NOT-IN-CLASS*: $\neg\,(std \in Class) \to enq =$ UNKNOWN-STUDENT

In the earlier style the result *false* could indicate that the student has either not submitted or is not a member of the class. A fine distinction possibly, because in both cases the student could not have submitted anyway. In the second style, however, we distinguish these cases; *false* is returned only when the student is known but has not submitted, UNKNOWN-STUDENT being returned otherwise. This approach might make the intention of the operation clearer, but it does have drawbacks in that the typing is weakened for the result while the operation appears to return *either* a result *or* a message. As far as subsequent reification is concerned, this is a problem which can be resolved only with some difficulty in strongly typed programming languages.

An alternative approach might mirror that taken by Z where we assume that if an operation can report an exception we should, for the sake of consistency, report success as well. Therefore assuming the union type *Message*:

$$\textit{Message} = \text{OK} \mid \text{PRESENT} \mid \text{NOT-IN-CLASS} \mid \text{SUBMIT-ERROR}$$

we can reformulate the specifications in the following fashion:

Enrol (std : Student) Report : Message
ext wr *Not-handed-in : Stdset*
    wr *Class*   : *Stdset*
pre $\neg(std \in Class)$
post *Not-handed-in* $= \textit{Not-handed-in}^{\leftarrow} \cup \{std\} \wedge$
    Class $= \textit{Class}^{\leftarrow} \cup \{std\} \wedge$
    Report $= \text{OK}$
errs *PRESENT* : $(std \in Class) \rightarrow$
                    Not-handed-in $= \textit{Not-handed-in}^{\leftarrow} \wedge$
                    Class $= \textit{Class}^{\leftarrow} \wedge$
                    Report $= \text{PRESENT}$

Enquire (std : Student) enq : ($\mathbb{B}$* × Message)*
ext rd *Handed-in : Stdset*
    rd *Class*   : *Stdset*
pre *std* $\in$ *Class*
post *enq* $= mk\text{-}((std \in Handed\text{-}in), \text{OK})$
errs *NOT-IN-CLASS* : $(std \in Class) \rightarrow enq = mk\text{-}(\textit{false}, \text{NOT-IN-CLASS})$

Submit (std : Student) Report : Message
ext wr *Not-handed-in : Stdset*
    wr *Handed-in*   : *Stdset*
    rd *Class*   : *Stdset*
pre *std* $\in$ *Class* $\wedge$ *std* $\in$ *Not-handed-in*
post *Not-handed-in* $= \textit{Not-handed-in}^{\leftarrow} - \{std\} \wedge$
    Handed-in $= \textit{Handed-in}^{\leftarrow} \cup \{std\} \wedge$
    Report $= \text{OK}$
errs *SUBMIT-ERR* : $\neg(std \in Class) \vee \neg(std \in Not\text{-}handed\text{-}in)$
                    Not-handed-in $= \textit{Not-handed-in}^{\leftarrow} \wedge$
                    Handed-in $= \textit{Handed-in}^{\leftarrow} \wedge$
                    Report $= \text{SUBMIT-ERROR}$

Remove (*std* : *Student*) *Report* : *Message*
ext wr *Not-handed-in* : *Stdset*
     wr *Handed-in*   : *Stdset*
     wr *Class*   : *Stdset*
pre *std* ∈ *Class*
post *Not-handed-in* $= Not\text{-}handed\text{-}in^{\leftarrow} - \{std\} \wedge$
     Handed-in $= Handed\text{-}in^{\leftarrow} - \{std\} \wedge$
     Class $= Class^{\leftarrow} - \{std\} \wedge$
     Report $= \text{OK}$
errs *NOT-IN-CLASS* : $\neg (std \in Class) \rightarrow$
                           $Not\text{-}handed\text{-}in = Not\text{-}handed\text{-}in^{\leftarrow} \wedge$
                           $Handed\text{-}in = Handed\text{-}in^{\leftarrow} \wedge$
                           $Class = Class^{\leftarrow} \wedge$
                           $Report = \text{NOT-IN-CLASS}$

The majority of the alterations in this new style are (hopefully) quite obvious especially in the light of the specifications in Z. The modifications to the *Enquire* operation, however, need some explanation. Here we have taken the opportunity to use a tuple type for the result which permits 'more than one result' to be returned. The appropriate tuple is built using tuple construction (i.e. *mk*-(...)) in the postconditions. This mechanism again differentiates the two cases where *false* could be returned and is an improvement on the use of type union which delivered only a result *or* a message. The treatment, however, is rather strict, in most VDM specifications the construction of the tuple is taken as implicit and the operation is often written as follows which is rather more in keeping with Z:

Enquire (*std* : *Student*) *Enq* : 𝔹, *Report* : *Message*
ext rd *Handed-in* : *Stdset*
    rd *Class*   : *Stdset*
pre *std* ∈ *Class*
post $Enq = (std \in Handed\text{-}in) \wedge Report = \text{OK}$
errs *NOT-IN-CLASS* : $\neg (std \in Class) \rightarrow Enq = false \wedge Report = \text{NOT-IN-CLASS}$

The operation type implied here is *Student* $\xrightarrow{\text{o}}$ 𝔹 × *Message*

As a final point it should be mentioned that whichever of these various styles is adopted is really only a matter of personal preference.

22.4 IMPLEMENTABILITY PROOF OBLIGATIONS IN VDM-SL: COMPARISON WITH Z

In VDM an operation is specified by quoting its preconditions and postconditions. Operations of course perform transitions upon some abstract state and VDM regards describing the transition in two parts as good practice. The primary reasons for this are that:

- It differentiates between the assumptions that an implementor is allowed to make (the precondition) and the obligation(s) that must be met (the postcondition) thereby separating and simplifying the two concerns, and
- It leads to some pleasing formulations of the obligations themselves (Jones, 1986).

It may also appear that we have a third and possibly even greater benefit; we do not have to perform a precondition calculation as we have done in Z. Unfortunately this is an illusion. Preconditions and postconditions cannot be simply quoted without some evidence that they describe an operation that is implementable in practice. In Z we dealt with the implementability problem by assuming the truth of the postcondition and then trying to calculate the precondition schema *preOP*. This calculation is usually performed on the 'raw' state first and then modified if necessary to take account of the invariant. If a precondition is found on this basis, we have evidence that the operation can be implemented. If a precondition cannot be found for the postcondition, the operation can never be realized in practice and some redesign will be necessary. The *implementability obligation* of VDM amounts to exactly the same thing as the precondition calculation of Z. However, in VDM we start with a suggested precondition so that the proofs sometimes involve less effort. Research is continuing in Z circles to see if explicit pre- and postconditions will benefit the technique.

Informally, the notion of implementability in VDM demands that there should be an 'output' satisfying the postcondition of the specification for every 'input' over which it is defined, i.e. every 'input' satisfying the precondition. For functions we showed that this obligation can be formalized as:

$$\forall d \in D \bullet \textit{pre-f}(d) \Rightarrow \exists r \in R \bullet \textit{post-f}(d,r)$$

where D is the domain space of the function and R the range space. The implementability obligation for operations carries over in a natural way from that of functions except now of course we have to consider state variables as well within the domain and range spaces together with a possible state invariant. Consequently the informal terms 'input' and 'output' must reflect these additional considerations.

Before we construct an actual proof obligation we would do well to consider the case for some general operation Op (say). Let us assume that an abstract state (with state identifier *State* and some invariant) has been defined that encompasses the domain and range spaces. The 'inputs' and 'outputs' for the operation are $s^{\leftarrow}$ and s, respectively, and where we demand $s^{\leftarrow}, s \in \textit{State}$. The term 'input' covers the normal input parameters for the operation together with the initial state variable values. The term 'output' refers to the result together with the initial and final state variable values. We decorate the 'input' simply to differentiate it in the theorem. Extending the argument for functions, we can write the general implementability proof obligations as:

$$\forall s^{\leftarrow} \in \textit{State} \bullet \textit{pre-Op}(s^{\leftarrow}) \Rightarrow \exists s \in \textit{State} \bullet \textit{post-Op}(s^{\leftarrow}, s)$$

Unfortunately, because we demand $s^{\leftarrow}, s \in \textit{State}$, this general proof obligation is made more difficult because it also includes the state invariant. In this respect the expression we have written implicitly assumes that the invariant is conjoined to the predicates in the bodies of the pre- and postcondition functions. The proof would therefore have to be conducted bearing this in mind at all times. However, we can recognize *State* through the definition:

$$\textit{State} = \{s \in \textit{State}' \mid \textit{inv}(s)\}$$

where *State'* of course is the state *without* the invariant. We could therefore consider the proof in two stages. First, it can be shown that the specification can be implemented on the general state:

$$\forall s^{\leftarrow} \in State' \bullet pre\text{-}\mathrm{Op}(s^{\leftarrow}) \Rightarrow \exists s \in State' \bullet post\text{-}\mathrm{Op}(s^{\leftarrow}, s)$$

and then that the operation preserves the invariant when the invariant is conjoined:

$$\forall s^{\leftarrow}, s \in State' \bullet pre\text{-}\mathrm{Op}(s^{\leftarrow}) \wedge inv(s^{\leftarrow}) \wedge post\text{-}\mathrm{Op}(s^{\leftarrow}, s) \Rightarrow inv(s)$$

In this second form the invariant is made explicit and in fairly straightforward cases we may well attempt this proof all in one go. Whatever we do, discharging proof obligations in VDM will be every bit as difficult and tedious as precondition calculations in Z.

SAQ 22.1 Write these two obligations in natural language.

In order to see how to construct these obligations in practice we now consider an exemplary VDM operation that contains all the ingredients of the general case:

$$\mathrm{Op\text{-}name}\,(p_1 : T_1, p_2 : T_2, \ldots)\, r : T_r$$
$$\mathrm{ext\ rd}\ e_1 : T_1'$$
$$\mathrm{wr}\ e_2 : T_2'$$
$$\mathrm{pre} \ldots p_1 \ldots p_2 \ldots e_1 \ldots e_2 \ldots$$
$$\mathrm{post} \ldots p_1 \ldots p_2 \ldots e_1 \ldots e_2 \ldots e_2{}^{\leftarrow} \ldots r \ldots$$

where we assume the existence of some state (Op-state) defined in terms of state variables:

$$e_1 : T_1', e_2 : T_2', \ldots, e_n : T_n'$$

The operation accepts input parameters (p_i), returns some result (r), has read access (rd) to one state variable (e_1) and write access (wr) to another (e_2). The precondition involves the input parameters and all the state variables mentioned in the externals clause (variables not mentioned in this clause cannot be affected by the operation and therefore need not be considered in an obligation of implementability). The values of the state variables referenced here are those which exist before the operation. The postcondition involves the input parameters, the new values of the state variables in the externals, the old values of those state variables declared with wr access, and the result.

For this operation we can construct pre- and postcondition functions *pre*-Op-name and *post*- Op-name, respectively. The body of these functions for our example operation is as follows:

$$pre\text{-}\mathrm{Op\text{-}name}(p_1, p_2, e_1{}^{\leftarrow}, e_2{}^{\leftarrow}) \triangleq \mathbf{B}$$
$$post\text{-}\mathrm{Op\text{-}name}(p_1, p_2, e_2, e_1{}^{\leftarrow}, e_2{}^{\leftarrow}, r) \triangleq \mathbf{B'}$$

Here, **B** and **B'** represent the explicit definition of the pre- and postconditions while, anticipating the proof, all the 'before' state variables have been decorated to avoid ambiguity. The proof obligation for this particular operation—ignoring any state invariant—can then be formalized as:

$$\forall p_1 \in T_1, p_2 \in T_2, e_1{}^{\leftarrow} \in T_1', e_2{}^{\leftarrow} \in T_2' \bullet pre\text{-}\mathrm{Op\text{-}name}(p_1, p_2, e_1{}^{\leftarrow}, e_2{}^{\leftarrow}) \Rightarrow$$
$$\exists r \in T_r, e_2 \in T_2' \bullet post\text{-}\mathrm{Op\text{-}name}(p_1, p_2, e_2, e_1{}^{\leftarrow}, e_2{}^{\leftarrow}, r)$$

The universal quantification extends across the whole implication and it introduces the input parameters together with all the initial state variables in the externals clause. The existential quantification applies to the postcondition function only and introduces the result and those new variables (undecorated) from the externals clause that were declared with wr access.

Because they are bound by the universal quantification, the $p_1, p_2, e_1{}^{\leftarrow}$ and $e_2{}^{\leftarrow}$ that appear in *post-* Op-name are the clearly same ones that appear in *pre-* Op-name. If the state variables are constrained by an invariant $inv(mk\text{-Op-state}(e_1, e_2, \ldots, e_n))$, the second stage proof becomes:

$$\forall p_1 \in T_1, p_2 \in T_2, e_1{}^{\leftarrow}, e_1 \in T_1', e_2{}^{\leftarrow}, e_2 \in T_2', \ldots, e_n{}^{\leftarrow}, e_n \in T_n', r \in T_r, \bullet$$
$$pre\text{-}\ \text{Op-name}(p_1, p_2, e_1{}^{\leftarrow}, e_2{}^{\leftarrow}) \wedge$$
$$inv(mk\text{-Op-state}(e_1{}^{\leftarrow}, e_2{}^{\leftarrow}, \ldots e_n) \wedge$$
$$post\text{-}\ \text{Op-name}(p_1, p_2, e_2, e_1{}^{\leftarrow}, e_2{}^{\leftarrow}, r) \Rightarrow$$
$$inv(mk\text{-Op-state}(e_1, e_2, \ldots, e_n))$$

Discharging the first proof obligation makes this one much simpler—because the pre- and postconditions can be taken as *true*—alternatively this obligation alone may be discharged in one attempt. As an actual example of the proof obligation consider the *Submit* operation for the classroom homework problem, the Z precondition calculation for which was conducted in Part 4. For the *Submit* operation to be capable of implementation on the 'raw' state we are required to prove the theorem:

$$\forall Std \in Student, Not\text{-}handed\text{-}in^{\leftarrow}, Handed\text{-}in^{\leftarrow}, Class^{\leftarrow} \in Stdset \bullet$$
$$pre\text{-}Submit(std, Not\text{-}handed\text{-}in^{\leftarrow}, Class^{\leftarrow}) \Rightarrow$$
$$\exists Report \in Message, Not\text{-}handed\text{-}in, Handed\text{-}in \in Stdset \bullet$$
$$post\text{-}Submit(std, Not\text{-}handed\text{-}in, Handed\text{-}in, Not\text{-}handed\text{-}in^{\leftarrow}, Handed\text{-}in^{\leftarrow}, Report)$$

This proof can be conducted in the usual way by assuming the truth of the postcondition function on the right-hand side and then using its predicates to prove the left-hand side of the implication. If the antecedent and consequent are both *true*, then the theorem as a whole is proven. Substituting for the bodies of these functions provides the actual theorem:

$$\forall Std \in Student, Not\text{-}handed\text{-}in^{\leftarrow}, Handed\text{-}in^{\leftarrow}, Class^{\leftarrow} \in Stdset \bullet$$
$$std \in Class^{\leftarrow} \wedge std \in Not\text{-}handed\text{-}in^{\leftarrow} \Rightarrow$$
$$\exists Report \in Message, Not\text{-}handed\text{-}in, Handed\text{-}in \in Stdset \bullet$$
$$Not\text{-}handed\text{-}in = Not\text{-}handed\text{-}in^{\leftarrow} - \{std\} \wedge$$
$$Handed\text{-}in = Handed\text{-}in^{\leftarrow} \cup \{std\} \wedge$$
$$Report = \text{OK}$$

Unfortunately, in this particular case there is not enough information to establish the theorem and this often happens in VDM when trying to prove implementability. In such circumstances the postcondition is often strengthened by conjoining the invariant on the after state then trying to establish implementability again. This of course now assumes the truth of the invariant and is quite similar to expanding the state schema for the after state in the precondition calculation for Z. In this form the theorem is really only equivalent to the second form of the proof obligation above, i.e. we try to prove:

$$\forall Std \in Student, Not\text{-}handed\text{-}in^{\leftarrow}, Not\text{-}handed\text{-}in, Handed\text{-}in^{\leftarrow}, Handed\text{-}in,$$
$$Class^{\leftarrow}, Class \in Stdset, Report \in Message \bullet$$

pre-Submit(std, Not-handed-in$^\leftarrow$, Class$^\leftarrow$) $\wedge$
inv-Homework (mk-Homework (Class$^\leftarrow$, Handed-in$^\leftarrow$, Not-handed-in$^\leftarrow$)) $\wedge$
post-Submit(std, Not-handed-in, Handed-in, Not-handed-in$^\leftarrow$, Handed-in$^\leftarrow$, Report)
$\Rightarrow$ *inv-Homework (mk-Homework (Class, Handed-in, Not-handed-in))*

If we substitute the bodies of the various functions and omit the universal quantification for a moment (it is not really needed for any purpose other than showing that the variables are of the correct types) we get:

$$std \in Class^\leftarrow \wedge std \in Not\text{-}handed\text{-}in^\leftarrow \wedge$$
$$Handed\text{-}in^\leftarrow \cup Not\text{-}handed\text{-}in^\leftarrow = Class^\leftarrow \wedge$$
$$Handed\text{-}in^\leftarrow \cap Not\text{-}handed\text{-}in^\leftarrow = \{\ \} \wedge$$
$$Not\text{-}handed\text{-}in = Not\text{-}handed\text{-}in^\leftarrow - \{std\} \wedge$$
$$Handed\text{-}in = Handed\text{-}in^\leftarrow \cup \{std\} \wedge$$
$$Report = \mathrm{OK}$$
$$\Rightarrow Handed\text{-}in \cup Not\text{-}handed\text{-}in = Class \wedge$$
$$Handed\text{-}in \cap Not\text{-}handed\text{-}in = \{\ \}$$

where now both the postcondition and the invariant on the after state can be taken as *true*. The proof of this theorem can be conducted in natural deduction style as with the proof of the initial state. However, an informal proof is equally valid and usually much more readable. An informal proof is now presented.

Because the *Submit* operation has only read access to the state variable *Class* we can infer *Class = Class$^\leftarrow$* is also *true*. As in the Z precondition calculation the only way that *Class* can remain unchanged by this operation is by *std* being a member of either the *Not-handed-in$^\leftarrow$* or *Handed-in$^\leftarrow$* groups. Thus *std $\in$ Class$^\leftarrow$ $\wedge$ std $\in$ Not-handed-in$^\leftarrow$* is certainly an acceptable precondition and can be assumed *true* with confidence. All that now remains is to show that the operation preserves the invariant on the initial state:

$$Handed\text{-}in^\leftarrow \cup Not\text{-}handed\text{-}in^\leftarrow = Class^\leftarrow \wedge$$
$$Handed\text{-}in^\leftarrow \cap Not\text{-}handed\text{-}in^\leftarrow = \{\ \} \wedge$$

Using the fact that *Class = Class$^\leftarrow$* we can substitute into the invariant on the after state to give:

$$Handed\text{-}in \cup Not\text{-}handed\text{-}in = Class^\leftarrow \wedge$$
$$Handed\text{-}in \cap Not\text{-}handed\text{-}in = \{\ \}$$

which of course is still *true*. Using the postcondition definitions for *Handed-in* and *Not-handed-in* we can substitute further giving:

$$(Handed\text{-}in^\leftarrow \cup \{std\}) \cup Not\text{-}handed\text{-}in^\leftarrow - \{std\} = Class^\leftarrow \wedge$$
$$(Handed\text{-}in^\leftarrow \cup \{std\}) \cap Not\text{-}handed\text{-}in^\leftarrow - \{std\} = \{\ \}$$

These expressions can be simplified in exactly the same fashion as for the Z precondition calculation (Chapter 16) to establish finally that:

$$Handed\text{-}in^\leftarrow \cup Not\text{-}handed\text{-}in^\leftarrow = Class^\leftarrow \wedge$$
$$Handed\text{-}in^\leftarrow \cap Not\text{-}handed\text{-}in^\leftarrow = \{\ \} \wedge$$

is *true*, which completes the theorem proof.

It is clear that constructing and discharging proof obligations in VDM is every bit as difficult and laborious as precondition calculations are in Z and that there is a remarkable degree of similarity between the two. In most cases, however, our obligations are discharged by intuition and experience rather than by the laborious exercises performed in this chapter. Whenever simple implementability is difficult to establish, strengthen the postcondition by adding the invariant. This gives extra predicates which can be assumed *true* and which can be used to establish the preconditions and the before state invariants. If implementability still cannot be achieved some redesign of the operation specification will be necessary.

22.5 PROPERTIES OF VDM SPECIFICATION

In the Z case studies and examples theorems were frequently constructed to establish:

- The correctness of initial states (the initial state theorem)
- The preconditions for an operation (really an implementability theorem) and
- Various properties of the specification

In VDM the counterparts to these activities are reflected in the initial state and implementability proof obligations, while theorems can also be readily constructed to show that specifications enjoy particular properties.

Recall that in Z, schema composition (;) was heavily used to prove that the sequential application of two operations would ensure some desired result. Section 16.6.8 on schema composition showed that the operation *Rem_prog_ona_proj* followed immediately by *Add_prog_proj* with the same programmer had the effect of moving a programmer from one project to another. We could equally have showed that *Add_prog_proj* followed by *Rem_prog_ona_proj* would leave the system state unchanged. In VDM we have no operation operators or calculus but we can still construct theorems to claim the same effects as in Z. As an example consider the application of the *Enrol* operation followed immediately by *Remove*—where both operations involve the same student. The claim we make about this situation of course is that the sequential application represents the *identity* operation in that the content of the *Class* remains unchanged, i.e. $Class = Class^{\leftarrow}$. The general strategy we would employ to construct the theorem in VDM proceeds: given some initial state $s^{\leftarrow}$ that satisfies the precondition for *Enrol*, there exists an output state s^{+} that satisfies the postcondition for *Enrol*. If s^{+} also satisfies the precondition for *Remove* then there must exist some final state that satisfies the postcondition for *Remove*. If *Enrol* followed by *Remove* is the identity operation then $Class = Class^{\leftarrow}$.

All of which really amounts to our being able to prove that:

$$\exists s^{+} \in State \bullet pre\text{-}Enrol(s^{\leftarrow}) \wedge post\text{-}Enrol(s^{+}) \wedge$$
$$pre\text{-}Remove(s^{+}) \wedge post\text{-}Remove(s) \Rightarrow$$
$$Class^{\leftarrow} = Class \wedge \dots \text{there may be other consequences.}$$

where the State now involves inputs, outputs and state variables as appropriate. The phrase `there may be other consequences` refers to the fact that we may well be able to prove other properties but we have no interest in these. The mechanism for all this may be quite different in **VDM** but it is clear that what we are describing is really the sequential composition of two operations as in Z. Assuming that *pre-Enrol* is satisfied, substituting to guarantee a suitable final state for *Enrol* and for the various definitions of the pre- and postconditions we get:

$$\exists Not\text{-}handed\text{-}in^{+}, Class^{+} \in Stdset, Report \in Message \bullet$$
$$\neg (std \in Class) \wedge$$
$$Not\text{-}handed\text{-}in^{+} = Not\text{-}handed\text{-}in^{\leftarrow} \cup \{std\} \wedge$$
$$Class^{+} = Class^{\leftarrow} \cup \{std\} \wedge$$
$$Report = \text{OK} \wedge$$
$$Not\text{-}handed\text{-}in = Not\text{-}handed\text{-}in^{+} - \{std\} \wedge$$
$$Handed\text{-}in = Handed\text{-}in^{+} - \{std\} \wedge$$
$$Class = Class^{+} - \{std\} \rightarrow$$
$$Class = Class^{\leftarrow} \dots \texttt{there may be other consequences.}$$

In this substitution we have assumed that *pre-Submit* is satisfied with the input parameter $std \in Student$ and that this same parameter is used in *Remove*. Because the final state s^{+} for *Enrol* satisfies *pre-Remove* (i.e. $Class^{+} = Class^{\leftarrow} \cup \{std\}$ hence $std \in Class^{+}$), the precondition can be replaced by *true* and omitted because it is redundant.

An informal proof can proceed by the same substitution mechanism used in the examples in Z that eliminated the variables decorated with $^{+}$. Thus, with $Class^{+} = Class^{\leftarrow} \cup \{std\}$ we can replace the reference to $Class^{+}$ in $Class = Class^{+} - \{std\}$ giving:

$$Class = Class^{\leftarrow} \cup \{std\} - \{std\}$$

or simply:

$$Class = Class^{\leftarrow}$$

because the same student *std* is involved in the two operations.

SAQ 22.2 Construct and prove a theorem showing that if a student submits homework the *Enquire* operation returns *true*.

22.6 EXPLICIT OPERATION DEFINITIONS IN VDM-SL

An explicit operation in VDM is defined in terms of an operation type expression, a body definition and (optionally) a precondition:

$$\texttt{Exp-Op-Name} : T_1 \times T_2 \times \dots \times T_n \xrightarrow{o} T_r$$
$$\texttt{Exp-Op-Name}(p_1, p_2, \dots, p_n) \texttt{ ext} \dots \underline{\Delta} \texttt{ St}$$
$$\texttt{pre } B$$

Notice that this format is very similar to an explicit function definition but the operation is distinguished by the use of the $\xrightarrow{o}$ convention and the (optional) presence of the `ext` clause. In the definition `Exp-Op-Name` is the name to be associated with the operation, the T_is are the types of the parameters, T_r is the type of the result and

St is an explicit *statement*[2] defining the effect of the operation. T_r may be a product type allowing the effect of 'several' results, while either or both of $T_1 \times T_2 \times \ldots \times T_n$ and T_r may be replaced by ( ) showing that there are no parameters accepted or results returned. The precondition assumes its usual role.

In addition to the parameters, the statement and the precondition may refer to state variables—those introduced in the ext clause. In the precondition the values referenced are those prior to the operation while the statement can update state variables by means of assignments (:=) as in ordinary structured programming languages (the hook not being required). This analogy extends to the use of the semicolon as a separator in a compound statement, while all the expressions used previously in explicit function definitions (*if ... then ... else, cases, let ... in, etc.*) can also be used within statements in explicit operation definitions.

As an example of the use of an explicit operation consider the redefinition of *Remove* operation which dismisses a student from the class. In the following definition the result type is defined as a union type, while the keyword return is used to terminate the operation and identify the returned value:

$$Remove : Student \xrightarrow{\text{o}} \text{SUBMITTED} \mid \text{NOT-SUBMITTED}$$

$Remove(std)$
  ext wr *Not-handed-in*
      wr *Handed-in*
      wr *Class* Δ
      if $std \in$ *Not-handed-in* then
          (*Not-handed-in* := *Not-handed-in* $- \{std\}$;
          Class := *Class* $- \{std\}$;
          return NOT-SUBMITTED)
      else (*Handed-in* := *Handed-in* $- \{std\}$;
          Class := *Class* $- \{std\}$;
          return SUBMITTED)
  pre $std \in$ *Class*

Explicit operation definitions are algorithmic and should be used sparingly within a specification. They are most useful in straightforward situations where the final implementation to be used suggests itself quite naturally. Such definitions direct the developer towards a specific rather than an individual implementation. More information on these definitions can be found in Dawes (1991).

22.7 SUMMARY

The introduction to this chapter suggested that specifications in VDM were conducted in terms of abstract state data, data invariants, initial states and operations with inputs and outputs. Indeed all the ingredients that constitute a specification in Z! The similarities extend further in that the theorems constructed in Z to establish the correctness

---

[2]*Statements* in VDM are rather like programming language statements involving for example 'for ... to', 'while ... do', local declarations or assignments. This text is not terribly strict in its reference to statements; see Dawes (1991) for a more complete description.

of initial states, to determine preconditions for operations and to prove properties of the specification emerge as proof obligations in VDM addressing exactly the same concerns. The expression of these theorems and their subsequent proofs may be constructed and discharged in different ways but there is no fundamental difference between the two techniques in this respect.

VDM imposes its own individuality, however, in a number of ways. Abstract state data is declared just once and implicitly assumed by each operation in the specification. Unlike Z, the description is not physically included (either explicitly or through shorthand notation) in every operation definition. Initial states can be brought about by separate operations or included as part of the abstract state data definition. This latter feature is not supported in Z. Input and output decorations in VDM are unnecessary because each operation has a distinctive signature that distinguishes these two components, while the externals clause establishes the visibility of the abstract state as seen from a particular operation. This device partitions a (possibly) complex state and makes a VDM specification less 'fussy' than a corresponding Z operation when its delta or xi notation is expanded.

Pre- and postconditions in VDM are stated directly. As we have seen, this does not absolve us of the responsibility of demonstrating implementability, but it does provide a clearer structure to the specification that differentiates between that which we can assume and that which we must deliver. From a methodological point of view, it also leads to a more precise formulation of the proof obligations themselves which tends to eliminate some of the inspirational guesswork—followed by proof—that we indulged in with Z. Ultimately, of course, specification must be transformed to implementation and there is now quite formidable experience in the development of programming language code from pre- and post-assertions. Several researchers have therefore suggested that Z also follows this approach with separate assertions rather than with a single predicate.

VDM of course has no operation constructors or operators corresponding to the schema calculus of Z and this is probably most noticeable when building the definition of a total operation. In Z, we can individually specify schemas describing the normal case and each exception, combining these later with schema conjunction and disjunction. This is essentially a divide-and-conquer approach that greatly simplifies the specification of a complex operation. In VDM, we are compelled to describe the operation in one complete unit, our only mechanism for simplification being the error definition block and/or describing appropriate parts of the specification in terms of auxiliary functions. This approach can make certain specifications somewhat overwhelming. In the chapters which follow, we rework the case studies of Part 5 through the medium of VDM so that the reader can compare the two techniques in more detail.

PART SEVEN

VDM-SL Case Studies

An idea does not pass from one language to another without change.
Miguel de Unamuno y Jugo (1864–1936), Spanish writer

INTRODUCTION

The case studies in this chapter closely follow the Z specifications presented in Part 6. In this way the behaviour of the objects being specified can be assumed, leaving the reader free to concentrate on the structure and techniques of the two approaches. There is, however, an equally important reason for this approach in that the implementability obligations expressed through the various initial state and precondition theorems can be largely taken as discharged. (As we shall see, the mathematical objects used by VDM in the case studies vary somewhat from those in Z. However, the pre- and postconditions are so similar that it is reasonable to use them without recourse to formal proofs of implementability.) Consequently, the pre- and postconditions associated with the Z specifications can be used safely in the corresponding VDM descriptions. In certain cases, however, the proof obligations are phrased thereby inviting the reader to undertake their proof as an exercise.

Large-scale specifications in VDM should also be accompanied by input, output, pre- and postcondition summaries together with indexes that help readers find their way around the formal aspects of the text. For the sake of brevity these will not be reproduced; it suffices to say that they would only be variations on the theme already used for the case studies in Z.

23

GENERIC STACKS AND QUEUES

23.1 INTRODUCTION AND BASIC SPECIFICATIONS

We begin by presenting the VDM specifications for stacks and queues as basic *Modules*, the general form of which was discussed in Chapter 20. For each module the structure is modelled as a sequence and initialized using the `init` clause from within the state definitions rather than a separate initialization operation. Incomplete definitions are used for both X (the elements of the stack or queue) and the values *StackMax* and *QueueMax*, allowing us to defer a decision on both these issues until later in the development process. The type *Message* serves the same purpose as the simple data type in Z and is constructed as a union type from individual quote values. In the light of Chapter 22 most of the specifications should be straightforward. Notice, however, that *Stack-Empty* and *Queue-Empty* have no preconditions and will always succeed, while for the *Top* and *Front* operations no constraint is placed on the result in cases where an error occurs. The same point was made for the corresponding Z specifications, e.g. *Total_Top* [X]. The specifications assume the existence of the orders $<$ and $\leq$ over the natural numbers.

```
Module Stack-Module
  definitions
    types
      X is not yet defined;
      Message = OK | THE STACK IS EMPTY | THE STACK IS FULL |
                THE QUEUE IS EMPTY | THE QUEUE IS FULL;
    values
      StackMax : ℕ is not yet defined;
    state Stack-Module of
      Stack : X*
    inv mk-Stack-Module(Stack ) ≜ 0 ≤ len Stack ∧ len Stack ≤ StackMax
    init mk-Stack-Module(Stack ) ≜ Stack = [ ]
    end
    operations
    Push (i : X ) Report : Message
    ext wr Stack : X*
    pre len Stack < StackMax
    post Stack = [i] ⌢ Stack⁻ ∧
         Report = OK
```

errs *STACK-FULL* : (len *Stack* = *StackMax*) →
$\qquad\qquad$ *Stack* = *Stack*$^{←}$ ∧
$\qquad\qquad$ *Report* = THE STACK IS FULL
Pop ( ) *Report* : *Message*
ext wr *Stack* : *X**
pre $\quad$ 0 < len *Stack*
post $\quad$ *Stack* = tl *Stack*$^{←}$ ∧
$\qquad$ *Report* = OK
errs *STACK-EMPTY* : (len *Stack* = 0) →
$\qquad\qquad$ *Stack* = *Stack*$^{←}$ ∧
$\qquad\qquad$ *Report* = THE STACK IS EMPTY
Top ( ) *i* : *X*, *Report* : *Message*
ext rd *Stack* : *X**
pre 0 < len *Stack*
post *i* = hd *Stack* ∧ *Report* = OK
errs *STACK-EMPTY* : (len *Stack* = 0) →
$\qquad\qquad$ *Report* = THE STACK IS EMPTY
Stack-Empty ( ) *i* : 𝔹, *Report* : *Message*
ext rd *Stack* : *X**
post *i* = (len *Stack* = 0) ∧ *Report* = OK
end *Stack-Module*

SAQ 23.1 Write the operation type expressions for each of the operations of the stack.

The extension of the previous specification to the queue is quite obvious and is presented without comment:

Module *Queue-Module*
$\quad$ definitions
$\qquad$ types
$\qquad\quad$ *X* is not yet defined;
$\qquad\quad$ *Message* = OK | THE STACK IS EMPTY | THE STACK IS FULL |
$\qquad\qquad\qquad$ THE QUEUE IS EMPTY | THE QUEUE IS FULL;
$\qquad$ values
$\qquad\quad$ *QueueMax* : ℕ is not yet defined;
$\qquad$ state *Queue-Module* of
$\qquad\quad$ *Queue* : *X**
$\qquad$ inv *mk-Queue-Module*(*Queue*) △ 0 ≤ len *Queue* ∧ len *Queue* ≤ QueueMax
$\qquad$ init *mk-Queue-Module*(*Queue*) △ *Queue* = [ ]
$\qquad$ end
$\qquad$ operations
$\qquad\quad$ *Addtoqueue*(*i* : *X*) *Report* : *Message*
$\qquad\quad$ ext wr *Queue* : *X**
$\qquad\quad$ pre len *Queue* < *QueueMax*
$\qquad\quad$ post *Queue* = *Queue*$^{←}$ ⁀ [*i*] ∧
$\qquad\qquad$ *Report* = OK

errs *QUEUE-FULL* : (len *Queue* = *QueueMax*) →
     Queue = *Queue*$^{\leftarrow}$ ∧
     Report = THE QUEUE IS FULL
Deletefromqueue ( ) *Report* : *Message*
ext wr *Queue* : X^*
pre 0 < len *Queue*
post *Queue* = tl *Queue*$^{\leftarrow}$ ∧
  Report = OK
errs *QUEUE-EMPTY* : (len *Queue* = 0) →
     Queue = *Queue*$^{\leftarrow}$ ∧
     Report = THE QUEUE IS EMPTY
Front ( ) *i* : *X*, *Report* : *Message*
ext rd *Queue* : X^*
pre 0 < len *Queue*
post *i* = hd *Queue* ∧ *Report* = OK
errs *QUEUE-EMPTY* : (len *Queue* = 0) →
     Report = THE QUEUE IS EMPTY
Queue-Empty ( ) *i* : $\mathbb{B}$, *Report* : *Message*
ext rd *Queue* : X^*
post *i* = (len *Queue* = 0) ∧ *Result* = OK
end *Queue-Module*

SAQ 23.2 Write the operation type expressions for the operations of the queue.

23.2 PROOF OBLIGATIONS

Certain proof obligations for the stack are phrased below and readers are invited to discharge them formally or informally as exercises. If you are unsure how to conduct the proofs follow the methods provided and refer to the examples in Chapter 22.

Initial state

   ∀*Stack* ∈ X^* • *init-Stack-Module*(*mk-Stack-Module* (*Stack*))
   ⇒ *inv-Stack-Module*(*mk-Stack-Module* (*Stack*))

Assume that the left-hand side of the implication is *true* and prove the theorem by showing that the right-hand side is also *true* (by substitution).

Implementability

As a typical example, the implementability proof obligation for *Push* is as follows:

    ∀*i* ∈ *X*, *Stack*$^{\leftarrow}$, *Stack* ∈ X^*, *Report* ∈ *Message* •
   pre-Push(*i*, *Stack*$^{\leftarrow}$) ∧
    inv-Stack-Module(*mk-Stack-Module*(*Stack*$^{\leftarrow}$)) ∧
    post-Stack-Module(*i*, *Stack*$^{\leftarrow}$, *Stack*, *Report*) ⇒
    inv-Stack-Module(*mk-Stack-Module*(*Stack*))

First, substitute for the various pre- and postcondition functions and the invariant truth-valued functions. Separate the implication into subgoals if necessary. Assume the truth of the postcondition and conjoined invariant and remove it from the implication but make use of its predicates in substitutions.

Properties of the specifications

The identity operation would be represented by *Push* followed immediately by *Pop*. In general, if we use *State* to refer to the collection of inputs, outputs and state variables for this problem we need to prove that:

$$\exists s^+ \in State, Report \in Message \bullet \; pre\text{-}Push(s^{\leftharpoonup}) \wedge Post\text{-}Push(s^+) \wedge$$
$$pre\text{-}Pop(s^+) \wedge Post\text{-}Pop(s) \Rightarrow$$
$$Stack^{\leftharpoonup} = Stack \wedge \ldots$$
$$\texttt{there may be other consequences.}$$

To prove this theorem first substitute for the various definitions of the pre- and postcondition functions. Assume that the input parameter satisfies *pre-Push*; because the final state s^+ for *Push* satisfies *pre-Pop*, the precondition can be removed and used to eliminate decorated variables ($^+$).

SAQ 23.3   Write the corresponding proof obligations for the queue.

23.3 IMPORTS AND EXPORTS

VDM-SL provides a mechanism by means of which entities defined in the basic modules can be used by other modules. In this respect the basic module definition can be enriched by adding an *interface* which permits defined entities to be *exported* to other parts of the specification and correspondingly for entities defined elsewhere to be *imported* for use here. The imports section of the module interface takes the general form:

$$\texttt{imports from Id}_1 \; Ms_1$$
$$\texttt{from Id}_2 \; Ms_2$$
$$\vdots$$
$$\texttt{from Id}_n \; Ms_n$$

where each $\texttt{Id}_i$ represents the name of a module within the specification and each Ms_i represents a *module signature*—sequences of descriptions of types, values, functions and operations as appropriate (each description called a 'signature block'). The module referred to by the identifier $\texttt{Id}_i$ must previously have made the entities mentioned in the module signature available through a corresponding exports section in its definition.

The exports section takes the general form $\texttt{exports}\ Ms$ where Ms is a module signature containing descriptions of entities defined in the current module or imported into this module from some other. The purpose of the exports declaration is therefore to identify entities which can be imported into other modules. In the case of types, the whole type definition may be exported or simply the name; the actual definition appearing in a definition block in the current module or elsewhere if the type has itself been imported. The exports list is the only place a type definition can occur in a module signature. In this respect it is possible that a module has no definition part at all if all that it exports are explicit types. Normally, however, an exports section is accompanied by at least one corresponding definition block. 'Cyclic' imports, i.e. where two modules import from each other, are not allowed so that all imports must be 'acyclic'.

If we were to embed *Stack-Module* or *Queue-Module* within a larger specification they must be able to export their operations and the types and values needed to call them. At the same time we could define a module called *Types-Module* that contained the definition of the type *Message* and permit this type to be exported to any module that required it. In this way, both *Stack-Module* and *Queue-Module* could import type *Message* but use only those messages that were applicable thus 'hiding' the fact that the type contains other (irrelevant) messages. The following modules illustrate the mechanism for the stack specification:

```
Module Types-Module
  exports
    types Message;
  definitions
    types Message = OK | THE STACK IS EMPTY | THE STACK IS FULL |
                    THE QUEUE IS EMPTY | THE QUEUE IS FULL;
end Types-Module
```

```
Module Interface-Stack-Module
  imports from Types-Module
    types Message;
  exports
    types
      X;
      Types-Module ` Message;
    values
      StackMax : ℕ;
    operations
      Push : X ⟶ᵒ Message
      Pop : ( ) ⟶ᵒ Message
      Top : ( ) ⟶ᵒ X × Message
      Stack-Empty : ( ) ⟶ᵒ 𝔹 × Message
  definitions
    types
      X is not yet defined;
    values
      StackMax : ℕ is not yet defined;
    state Interface-Stack-Module of
      Stack : X*
    inv mk-Interface-Stack-Module(Stack) △ 0 ≤ len Stack ∧ len Stack ≤ StackMax
    init mk-Interface-Stack-Module(Stack) △ Stack = [ ]
    end
    operations
    ... all operation definitions as for Stack-Module
end Interface-Stack-Module
```

Notice that `Module` *Types-Module* is an example of a situation where we need have no definition block at all because the type definition could have been included directly in the exports block:

```
exports
  types Message = OK | THE STACK IS EMPTY | THE STACK IS FULL |
                  THE QUEUE IS EMPTY | THE QUEUE IS FULL;
```

In the second module we import the type *Message* and export the types, values and operations mentioned in the various signature blocks and defined in the corresponding definition blocks. *Message*, however, is also exported and the use of the *grave* accent (`` ` ``) in the reference *Types-Module* `` ` `` *Message* indicates that the definition of this type appears elsewhere, in `Module` *Types-Module*. Both X and *StackMax* must be defined before this module can be properly used, while the operation signature block always uses operation type expressions ($\xrightarrow{o}$) regardless of whether the operations are defined implicitly or explicitly in the corresponding operation definitions block. The type expression of course is independent of the definition style and that is why it is used.

23.4 GENERIC (PARAMETRIZED) MODULES

The basic import/export mechanism in VDM distributes definitions throughout a specification and in a (very!) loose fashion parallels certain aspects of schema inclusion in Z. However, the stacks and queues described in such modules contain elements of specific types (i.e. X—whatever that may ultimately be) and have populations fixed by the values of *StackMax* and *QueueMax*. If we ever have a situation where a specification required stacks or queues containing elements of different types and different populations, separate modules would have to be written in each case and their operations individually imported into the target specification. Clearly there is a need for modules to be written in generic fashion and instantiated using appropriate type parameters such that specifications can be reused and 'customized' to particular environments. In Z this problem was solved by means of generic schema definitions; in VDM-SL the direct counterpart is the *parametrized module*.

The problem is addressed in two stages: first, modules such as stacks and queues are described in generic fashion making their various entities available through suitable exports, and then these entities are instantiated and imported from another module by providing particular definitions for the various type parameters involved. To illustrate the mechanism, assume we wish to write a specification for a system that requires both a *character stack* and a *numeric stack*, stacks whose individual elements are non-empty sequences of characters ($char^+$) and natural numbers ($\mathbb{N}$), respectively. Begin by writing the previous *Interface-Stack-Module* in generic form:

```
Module Generic-Stack
  parameters
    types entry;
    values StackMax;
  import from Types-Module
    Message;
```

```
exports
  types
    Types-Module ` Message;
    GenStack;
  operations
    Push : entry ─ᵒ→ Message
    Pop : ( ) ─ᵒ→ Message
    Top : ( ) ─ᵒ→ entry × Message
    Stack-Empty : ( ) ─ᵒ→ 𝔹 × Message
definitions
  types GenStack = entry*;
  state Generic-Stack of
    Stack : GenStack
  inv mk-Generic-Stack(Stack) Δ 0 ≤ len Stack ∧ len Stack ≤ StackMax
  init mk-Generic-Stack(Stack) Δ Stack = [ ]
  end
  operations
    Push(i : entry) Report : Message
    ext wr Stack : GenStack
    pre len Stack < StackMax
    post Stack = [i] ⌢ Stack⁻ ∧
         Report = OK
    errs STACK-FULL : (len Stack = StackMax) →
                       Stack = Stack⁻ ∧
                       Report = THE STACK IS FULL
    Pop ( ) Report : Message
    ext wr Stack : GenStack
    pre 0 < len Stack
    post Stack = tl Stack⁻ ∧
         Report = OK
    errs STACK-EMPTY : (len Stack = 0)
                       Stack = Stack⁻ ∧
                       Report = THE STACK IS EMPTY
    Top ( ) i : entry, Report : Message
    ext rd Stack : GenStack
    pre 0 < len Stack
    post i = hd Stack ∧ Report = OK
    errs STACK-EMPTY : (len Stack = 0) →
                       Report = THE STACK IS EMPTY
    Stack-Empty ( ) i : 𝔹, Report : Message
    ext rd Stack : GenStack
    post i = (len Stack = 0) ∧ Report = OK
end Generic-Stack
```

Much of the specification remains unchanged but the inclusion of the module parameter section converts this module into a parametrized module. The module parameter section takes the general form parameters *Ms* where the module signature (*Ms*) contains sequences of descriptions of types, values or functions that act as formal generic parameters, allowing the module to be written in a general form and later instantiated with particular values. In our example, the type *entry* and the value *StackMax* are the formal generic parameters. The references to these within the specification are later replaced by actual parameters provided by *definitions* within the importing module. The example is rather contrived, however, because the value passed must be a positive number otherwise the instantiation will fail; the types *integer* or *natural number* can achieve this giving us at least some choice of type parameter. Notice also that it perfectly legal for a parametrized module to import from a non-parametrized module (i.e. *Message* from *Types-Module*) and to export non-parametrized entities (*Types-Module`Message*) along with its parametrized entities (*GenStack* and all the operations). Hopefully, the use of the formal generic parameters within the various definition blocks follows directly from the earlier specifications.

In order to produce actual instances of stacks with particular population limits, the importing module makes use of a *module instantiation section* which takes the general form:

instantiation
Id_1 as Id_1' ($\text{Id}_{1,1} \rightarrow \text{Nm}_{1,1}$, $\text{Id}_{1,2} \rightarrow \text{Nm}_{1,2}, \ldots$) Ms_1
Id_2 as Id_2' ($\text{Id}_{2,1} \rightarrow \text{Nm}_{2,1}$, $\text{Id}_{2,2} \rightarrow \text{Nm}_{2,2}, \ldots$) Ms_2
$\vdots$
Id_n as Id_n' ($\text{Id}_{n,1} \rightarrow \text{Nm}_{n,1}$, $\text{Id}_{n,2} \rightarrow \text{Nm}_{n,2}, \ldots$) Ms_n

It defines instances of parametrized modules for use within this module by supplying the actual parameters, and simultaneously imports entities from the instantiated module's export section. In the instantiation section, the first identifier Id_i, provides a name for the newly created module instance. The second identifier Id_i' is the name of the parametrized module that has just been instantiated. The list in parentheses is the *substitution list* and it gives the *actual parameter* ($\text{Nm}_{i,j}$) to be substituted for each module parameter ($\text{Id}_{i,j}$) in the parametrized module, while the module signature (Ms_i) acts as an import definition list importing entities from the instantiated module's export section.

Once again, such definitions are much more meaningful if applied to some actual example. The following partially completed module *Actual-Stack* shows that we could use the parametrized module *Generic-Stack* to generate instances of both character and numeric stacks for use within the specification. For the sake of brevity, however, those parts of the specification that actually use the imported entities are omitted. Concentrating largely on the instantiation mechanism:

Module *Actual-Stack*
  instantiation
  CharStack as *Generic-Stack* (*entry* → *string*, *StackMax* → *CharStackPopulation*)
  types
    Types-Module`Message ;
    GenStack ;

```
operations
```
   Push : entry $\xrightarrow{\text{o}}$ Message
   Pop : ( ) $\xrightarrow{\text{o}}$ Message
   Top : ( ) $\xrightarrow{\text{o}}$ entry $\times$ Message
   Stack-Empty : ( ) $\xrightarrow{\text{o}}$ $\mathbb{B}$ $\times$ Message
```
instantiation
```
NumStack as Generic-Stack (entry $\rightarrow$ number, StackMax $\rightarrow$ NumStackPopulation)
```
types
```
Types-Module `Message ;
GenStack ;
```
operations
```
   Push : entry $\xrightarrow{\text{o}}$ Message
   Pop : ( ) $\xrightarrow{\text{o}}$ Message
   Top : ( ) $\xrightarrow{\text{o}}$ entry $\times$ Message
   Stack-Empty : ( ) $\xrightarrow{\text{o}}$ $\mathbb{B}$ $\times$ Message
```
exports
```
   ⋮
```
definitions
types string = char$^+$;
```
        number = $\mathbb{N}$;
```
values CharStackPopulation : $\mathbb{N}$ = 50;
```
        NumStackPopulation : $\mathbb{N}$ = 100;
```
state Actual-Stack of
```
   s_1 : CharStack `GenStack
   s_2 : NumStack `GenStack
      ⋮
```
inv mk-Actual-Stack$(s_1, s_2, \ldots)$ $\underline{\Delta}$ $0 \leq$ len $s_1$ $\leq$ len $s_1$ $\leq$ CharStackPopulation $\wedge$
                                    $0 \leq$ len $s_2$ $\wedge$ len $s_2$ $\leq$ NumStackPopulation $\ldots$
init mk-Actual-Stack(Actual-Stack) $\underline{\Delta}$ $s_1 = [\ ] \wedge s_2 = [\ ] \wedge \ldots$
```
end
operations
   ⋮
end Actual-Stack
```

The module contains two instantiation sections; the first creates an instance of a module called *CharStack* the second creates an instance of a module called *NumStack*. The substitution list for *CharStack* renames *entry* to *string* and *StackMax* to *CharStackPopulation*. The definitions block of the module *Actual-Stack* shows that these are provided with types char$^+$ (a non-empty sequence of characters) and value 50 respectively. The instantiation therefore refers to a stack whose individual elements are character strings and whose maximum population is 50. The instantiation for *NumStack* follows a similar pattern and refers to a stack whose individual elements are natural numbers with a maximum stack population of 100.

The module signatures of the two instantiation sections describe what they import from the newly instantiated modules. From *CharStack* we import the types *Message* (the definition appears in *Types-Module*) and *GenStack* together with all the
```

operations. Remember that the substitution list for this instantiation replaced *entry* with *string*, therefore the operations are now defined to deal with characters while the type *GenStack* is defined as *string**. *NumStack* imports the same entities but the parametrized ones now deal with numbers. To differentiate between the two references to *GenStack* and the parametrized operations we use the terminology:

$CharStack`GenStack, NumStack`GenStack, CharStack`Push, CharStack`Pop, ...,$
$NumStack`Push, NumStack`Pop, ...$

and this terminology is used in the (incomplete) state definition for *Actual-Stack* which consists (in part) of two state variables, one of which models the stack as a sequence of characters, the other as a sequence of numbers. References to the imported operations would appear in the operations definition block, e.g. we might define an explicit operation that simultaneously adds items to both stacks:

```
definitions
```
$ADD : String \times Number \xrightarrow{o} (\ )$
$ADD(s, n) \triangleq CharStack`Push(s)$ using $s1;$
$\qquad NumStack`Push(n)$ using $s2$
```
pre len
```
$s1 < CharStackPopulation$ and `len` $s2 < NumStackPopulation$
```
end
```
Actual-Stack

Here the keyword `using` followed by the *state designator* directs the operations to use particular state variables. State designators are used when calling an operation from a module other than the one it is declared in and in this respect the state variables subject to the 'push' are those in *Actual-Stack* and not those in the instantiated modules from which the operations were exported. Of course, the state designator must refer to the same sort of state as before (i.e. a sequence) and is subject to the same kind of invariant. Interested readers are now referred to Dawes (1991)where more detail can be found together with some substantial examples.

23.5 SUMMARY OF THE STACK SPECIFICATION

The general structure of this VDM specification shows that it has much in common with Z but notable differences appear in the handling of exceptions and in writing generic modules. Projecting our ideas forward to much larger specifications suggests that the specification of total operations in VDM may become somewhat unwieldy, while the definition and manipulation of the generics require very careful management because of the complexity of the approach which require the instantiation of parametrized modules followed by selective imports from them. However, the fact that these aspects are similar to mechanisms found in certain programming languages (such as Ada), may make the process rather more familiar to some. Readers are now free to tackle the alternative stack specification that was presented in the case study for Z.

$$24$$

THE SYMBOL TABLE

24.1 INTRODUCTION AND OVERALL SPECIFICATION

This second case study reworks the alternative symbol table specification presented in Chapter 18. It is assumed that the reader is familiar with the various ideas used there; if not, it would be sensible to review the Z specification before tackling the VDM version. This chapter also takes advantage of the earlier Z precondition calculations which are adapted for use here. This of course removes us from the obligation of implementability which would otherwise have to be discharged. The VDM specification also assumes the existence of the total order $\geq$ over the natural numbers, while the specification itself is presented as a simple monolithic module. The specification of the simple symbol table is left as an exercise.

As far as possible those mathematical objects of VDM that correspond most closely to the earlier Z specification are used. In this respect the table is again modelled as a sequence of entries while the partial function used for the frequency table in Z is replaced by its VDM equivalent, the map. Wherever possible, the names used in the Z specification have been retained. The full specification is as follows:

```
Module Symbol-Table
  definitions
    types
      SYM = ...;
      VAL = ...;
      Entries :: symbol : SYM
                 value  : VAL;
      Access = SYM ─m→ ℕ;
      Message = OK | THE SYMBOL IS NOT IN THE TABLE |
                SYMBOL ALREADY PRESENT;
    state Symbol-Table of
      Freq-Tab : Access
      Table : Entries*
    inv mk-Symbol-Table(Freq-Tab, Table) △
      dom Freq-Tab = {Table(i).symbol | i ∈ inds Table} ∧
      ∀i,j ∈ inds Table • (
      i ≠ j ⇒ Table (i).symbol ≠ Table (j).symbol ∧
      i < j ⇒ Freq-Tab(Table (i).symbol) ≥ Freq-Tab (Table (j).symbol))
    init mk-Symbol-Table(Freq-Tab, Table) △ Freq-Tab = {↦} ∧ Table = [ ]
```

```
end
functions
```

  Sort-Table(*in* : *Entries**, *A* : *Access*)*out* : *Entries**

  pre {*in*(*i*).*symbol* | *i* ∈ inds *in*} ⊆ dom *A*

  post ∀*i,j* : inds *out* • (*i* < *j* ⇒ *A*(*out* (*i*).*symbol*) ≥ *A*(*out* (*j*).*symbol*)) ∧
          items(*in*) = *items*(*out*)

```
operations
```

  Delete(*s* : *SYM*) *Report* : *Message*

  ext wr *Freq-Tab* : *Access*
       wr *Table* : *Entries**

  pre *s* ∈ {*Table*(*i*).*symbol* | *i* ∈ inds *Table*} ∧ *s* ∈ dom *Freq-Tab*

  post ∃*i* ∈ inds *Table*⁻ • (*Table*⁻(*i*).*symbol* = *s* ∧
          ∃*j* ∈ {0} ∪ inds *Table* • *Table* (1,...,*j*) ⌢ [*Table*⁻(*i*)] ⌢
          Table ((*j*+1), ..., len *Table*) = *Table*⁻) ∧
          Freq-Tab = {*s*} ◁ *Freq-Tab*⁻ ∧
          Report = OK

  errs *DEL-ERR* : *s* ∉ {*Table*(*i*).*symbol* | *i* ∈ inds *Table*} ∨
                   s ∉ dom *Freq-Tab* →
                   Freq-Tab = *Freq-Tab*⁻ ∧
                   Table = *Table*⁻ ∧
                   Report = THE SYMBOL IS NOT IN THE TABLE

  Insert(*s* : *SYM*, *v* : *VAL*) *Report* : *Message*

  ext wr *Freq-Tab* : *Access*
       wr *Table* : *Entries**

  pre *s* ∉ {*Table*(*i*).*symbol* | *i* ∈ inds *Table*} ∧ *s* ∉ dom *Freq-Tab*

  post *Table* = *Table*⁻ ⌢ [*mk-Entries*(*s,v*)] ∧
          Freq-Tab = *Freq-Tab*⁻ † {*s* ↦ 0} ∧
          Report = OK

  errs *PRESENT* : *s* ∈ {*Table*(*i*).*symbol* | *i* ∈ inds *Table*} ∨
                   s ∈ dom *Freq-Tab* →
                   Freq-Tab = *Freq-Tab*⁻ ∧
                   Table = *Table*⁻ ∧
                   Report = SYMBOL ALREADY PRESENT

  Find(*s* : *SYM*) *v* : *VAL*, *Report* : *Message*

  ext wr *Freq-Tab* : *Access*
       wr *Table* : *Entries**

  pre *s* ∈ {*Table*(*i*).*symbol* | *i* ∈ inds *Table*} ∧ *s* ∈ dom *Freq-Tab*

  post *Freq-Tab* = *Freq-Tab*⁻ † {*s* ↦ *Freq-Tab*⁻(*s*)+1} ∧
          Table = *Sort-SymT* (*Table*⁻, *Freq-Tab*) ∧
          ∃*i* ∈ inds *Table* • (*Table*(*i*).*symbol* = *s* ∧ *v* = *Table*(*i*).*value*) ∧
          Report = OK

  errs *FIND-ERR* : *s* ∉ {*Table*(*i*).*symbol* | *i* ∈ inds *Table*} ∨
                    s ∉ dom *Freq-Tab* →
                    Table = *Table*⁻ ∧
                    Report = THE SYMBOL IS NOT IN THE TABLE

end *Symbol Table*

24.2 THE TYPES REQUIRED

The incomplete definitions for *SYM* and *VAL* correspond to the given sets in the Z specification. Ultimately, definitions of both types will have to be provided but at this point such detail is a distraction. *Access* is a type describing all possible maps that can be constructed from subsets of symbols and natural numbers. This type parallels the partial function used to guarantee the association of a symbol with a single frequency count. The type *Message* serves the same purpose as the simple data type in Z and as usual is constructed as a union type from individual quote values. The type *Entries* is a composite type or record and the two fields of a particular record replace the (*symbol, value*) ordered pairs used in the Z specification. A more direct comparison with the Z specification could have been achieved if we had chosen to model type *Entries* as a set of pairs or even as a product type, for example:

$$Entries = \{(s,v) \mid s \in SYM, v \in VAL\} \qquad \text{or} \qquad Entries = SYM \times VAL$$

However, sets of pairs in VDM do not have the same characteristics as sets of pairs in Z while no operators are available to decompose tuples into their component parts. (It would have been possible to define auxiliary functions for 'first' and 'second' as in typed set theory but these are really unnecessary when we have the 'record' available.) With the symbol table ultimately represented as a sequence of such entries, sequence application would yield either a pair or a tuple, which makes recovery of individual symbols or values difficult. With records, however, this problem is simply overcome by the use of *field selection* (.).

24.3 THE ABSTRACT STATE

The abstract state consists of two state variables, *Freq-Tab* and *Table*. *Freq-Tab* is a map from symbols to natural numbers and records the number of times a symbol has been looked up. A symbol of course is associated with no more than one frequency count in this structure. *Table* represents the symbol table proper and is simply a sequence of entries. As with the Z specification the state invariants demand that:

- There is an entry in the frequency table for every unique symbol in the symbol table.
- No two entries in the table have the same symbol.
- The table is ordered according to the number of times the symbol in an entry has been accessed.

These predicates are phrased largely as for the Z specification but with adjustments made to reflect the use of records rather than ordered pairs as the sequence elements. In the first predicate, the set of symbols currently in the symbol table is defined by (VDM) set comprehension:

$$\{Table(i).symbol \mid i \in \texttt{inds } Table\}$$

This set is formed by application of the sequence (*Table(i)*) with every valid sequence index value *i* (where $i \in \texttt{inds } Table$). Each application returns a record from which the symbol is recovered by field selection (*Table(i).symbol*). This set must equal the set

of symbols currently in the domain of the *Freq-Tab* map for there to be proper correspondence between the two structures. The next two predicates again use sequence
application and field selection in much the same way, while the initial state corresponds
to an empty symbol table and an empty frequency table.

SAQ 24.1   Compose the theorem that represents the initial state proof obligation.

24.4 THE FUNCTIONS

In the Z specification *Sort_Table* was defined as a global constant in terms of an axiomatic
description. This represents a fixed mapping between pairs (seq *Entries* × *Access*) and seq
Entries. In VDM we use functions to achieve such mappings. The *Sort-Table* function is
defined implicitly rather than explicitly because this permits us to describe the properties of
a sorted symbol table without indicating how the sort is brought about. The signature
shows that the function accepts a symbol table (*in*) and a frequency table (*A*) and returns a
symbol table (*out*). The precondition is simply that there must be an entry in the frequency
table for every unique symbol in the symbol table. The postcondition demands that
symbols present in the output symbol table are in descending order of frequency access
(i.e. $i < j \Rightarrow A(out\ (i).symbol) \geq A(out\ (j).symbol)$) and that the output table contains all
the same symbols as the input table (*items*(*in*) = *items*(*out*)).

24.5 THE OPERATIONS

The operations have been deliberately written to reflect the Z specification as closely as
possible. The pre- and postconditions have been borrowed *en masse* and in this respect
we regard the earlier precondition calculations as largely discharging the VDM implementability proof obligations—even though we have used a slightly different set of
objects. The similarity really makes the process unnecessary. Each operation is made
total by the presence of the error definition block, and the error conditions themselves
are deduced by negation of the preconditions.

   Delete accepts a symbol as input and returns a message reflecting the success, or
otherwise, of the operation. The operation has write/read access to both state variables
and therefore brings about a state change. The precondition again requires that the
target symbol be present in both the symbol table and the frequency table. The postcondition determines the index value associated with the target symbol ($\exists i \in$ inds
Table • (*Table*(*i*).*symbol* = *s*)) and uses it in the remaining predicate in precisely the
same way as before: if we concatenate the first *j* entries of the after table with the
sequence formed from the record we have just deleted and then concatenate this with
the remaining entries of the after table, we recreate the original table. The final parts of
the predicate remove the symbol from the frequency table and report OK. The error
condition(s) for the operation are that the symbol is absent from the symbol table, or
the frequency table, or both. In such circumstances the status quo is maintained and an
appropriate message returned.

   Insert accepts a symbol and a value as input and returns a message reflecting the success, or otherwise, of the operation. The operation has write/read access to both state variables and therefore brings about a state change. The precondition demands that the symbol is absent from both the symbol and frequency tables. The effect of the operation under normal circumstances is described by the postcondition which adds the symbol value pair to the logical end of the table by concatenating the symbol table sequence with the sequence formed using the new record entry. Notice the use of the make function in the record construction. The new symbol (associated with a frequency count of 0) is subsequently added to the frequency table using map override and the OK message issued. The error definition block shows that an exception occurs if the symbol is present in either the symbol table or the frequency table (or both). In such circumstances the status quo is maintained and an appropriate message returned.

Find accepts a symbol as input and, under normal conditions, returns the value associated with it in the symbol table. The operation has write/read access to both state variables and therefore brings about a state change. The precondition demands that the symbol is present in both the symbol and frequency tables. The postcondition shows that the frequency count for the symbol in the new frequency table is one more than the value in the old table, the symbol table is sorted according to the new frequency and, using the new table, the value associated with the symbol is returned together with OK. Exceptions occur when the symbol is absent from the symbol table or the frequency table or both. Under such circumstances, the value associated with the symbol is undefined, the status quo is maintained and a suitable report is issued.

24.6 SUMMARY

The typing system of VDM does not permit us to use its mathematical objects in precisely the same way as in Z. Even so, we have achieved a remarkable degree of commonality between the two specifications. The construction of the VDM specification however was driven more by an academic comparison of the two languages rather than by a search for the best VDM solution. Indeed, in general, the best solution to a specification in one particular language cannot be achieved by a direct conversion from the best solution in another, for that does not always make use of the most appropriate features of the language—a point which led us to use records in the VDM specification rather than sets or tuples. In this particular case we might find that the record is rather more difficult to manipulate than the ordered pairs of Z, yet some readers might be aware of advantages offered by the record, in that the frequency count could easily be incorporated directly into the symbol table entry thereby eliminating the need for the separate frequency table altogether. The same approach is possible in Z of course, but a much 'fussier' specification would result with a relatively complex structure for the type *Entries*.

Although this has been a useful exercise in language comparison, there will always be advantages and disadvantages associated with individual specification languages so that specifications are best constructed without keeping an eye on what can or cannot be achieved in other systems.

25

A DRINKS DISPENSING MACHINE

25.1 INTRODUCTION AND OVERALL SPECIFICATION

This final case study re-examines the specification of the drinks dispenser; the front panel for which is shown in Fig. 19.1. Readers should ideally familiarize themselves with the earlier Z specification because much of the functionality revealed there is assumed here.

So far, both our VDM case studies have stuck closely to the approach taken by Z. By using similar mathematical objects we are able to reveal common aspects of the two methods and to benefit from the Z precondition calculations which established valid pre- and postconditions for the various operations. However, the symbol table example suggests that it is not always possible, or indeed desirable, to conduct the building of one specification in strict correspondence with another. Consequently, this last example takes an unashamedly VDM approach and presents the specification using those features of the language which are most appropriate rather than those which parallel Z. To some extent this final effort represents a 'celebration' of VDM and introduces further techniques which have not appeared so far in the book. To make the specification more manageable it is constructed as a simple monolithic module; the various proof obligations are neither phrased nor discharged. Both these aspects are left as exercises, although some hints regarding modularization of the specification are suggested. The complete specification follows and the discussion analyses each of the definition blocks in turn. The discussion again assumes that commercial chocolate powder contains both whitener and sweetener.

Module *Drinks-Dispenser*
  definitions
  types
    Coin = *One-Penny* | *Two-Pence* | *Five-Pence* | *Ten-Pence* | *Twenty-Pence* |
          Fifty-Pence | *One-Pound* | *Unacceptable-coin*;
    British-Coin = {c | c : *Coin* • $c \neq$ *Unacceptable-coin*};
    Ingredient = *Milk-powder* | *Chocolate-powder* | *Tea-bag* | *Coffee-granules* |
          Sugar | *Water*;
    Onoff = *on* | *off*;
    Message = *this drink is unavailable* | *try another coin* | *not in use* | *insert coin*
          insert more money and select drink again |
          correct change unavailable | *no cups in machine*;
    TEA-or-COFFEE :: *FLAVOUR* : *TEA* | *COFFEE*
                    SWEET : $\mathbb{B}$
                    WHITE : $\mathbb{B}$;

$Drink = TEA\text{-}or\text{-}COFFEE \mid CHOCOLATE$;
$Costs = Drink \xrightarrow{m} \mathbb{N}$
           inv $cost \underline{\Delta} \forall d : Drink \bullet d \in \mathrm{dom}\ cost$;
   $Bag(Ingredient) = Ingredient \xrightarrow{m} \mathbb{N}_1$;
   $Bag(British\text{-}Coin) = British\text{-}Coin \xrightarrow{m} \mathbb{N}_1$;
values
           $Recipe : Drink \xrightarrow{m} Ingredient\text{-}\mathtt{set}\ \underline{\Delta}$
                       $\{CHOCOLATE \mapsto \{Chocolate\text{-}powder,\ Water\}\} \cup$
                       $\{d \mapsto \{Water\} \cup$
                       (if $d.FLAVOUR = TEA$ then$\{Tea\text{-}bag\}$
                       else $\{Coffee\text{-}granules\}) \cup$
                       (if $d.WHITE$ then$\{Milk\text{-}powder\}$
                       else $\{\ \}) \cup$
                       (if $d.SWEET$ then$\{Sugar\}$
                       else $\{\ \}) \mid d : TEA\text{-}or\text{-}COFFEE\}$;
           $Worth : British\text{-}Coin \xrightarrow{m} \mathbb{N}_1\ \underline{\Delta}$
                       $\{One\_Penny \mapsto 1,\ Two\_Pence \mapsto 2,$
                       $Five\_Pence \mapsto 5,\ Ten\_Pence \mapsto 10,$
                       $Twenty\_Pence \mapsto 20,\ Fifty\_Pence \mapsto 50,$
                       $One\_Pound \mapsto 100\}$;
           $HopperMax : British\text{-}Coin \xrightarrow{m} \mathbb{N}_1$ is not yet defined;
           $StockMax : Ingredient \xrightarrow{m} \mathbb{N}_1$ is not yet defined;
           $CupMax : \mathbb{N}_1$ is not yet defined;
   state $Drinks\text{-}Dispenser$ of
           $Balance : Bag(British\text{-}Coin)$
           $Takings : Bag(British\text{-}Coin)$
           $Stock : Bag(Ingredient)$
           $Cups : \mathbb{N}$
           $Prices : Costs$
           $Service\text{-}light : Onoff$
           $Coin\text{-}display : \mathbb{N}$
           $Report\text{-}display : Message$
   inv $mk\text{-}Drinks\text{-}Dispenser(B,T,S,C,P,Sl,Cd,R)\ \underline{\Delta}$
           $\forall c : \mathrm{dom}\ T \bullet 0 \le count\ [British\text{-}Coin](c,T) \le HopperMax\ (c) \wedge$
           $\forall i : \mathrm{dom}\ S \bullet 0 \le count\ [Ingredient](i,S) \le StockMax\ (i) \wedge$
           $0 \le Cups \le CupMax$
   init $mk\text{-}Drinks\text{-}Dispenser(B,T,S,C,P,Sl,Cd,R)\ \underline{\Delta}$
           $B = \{\mapsto\} \wedge$
           $T = \{\mapsto\} \wedge$
           $S = \{\mapsto\} \wedge$
           $C = 0 \wedge$
           $P = \{d \mapsto 0 \mid d : Drink\} \wedge$
           $Sl = on \wedge$
           $Cd = Value(B) \wedge$
           $Rd = not\ in\ use$
   end
   functions

$count\ [@elem] : @elem \times (@elem \xrightarrow{m} \mathbb{N}_1) \rightarrow \mathbb{N}$
$count(e,b)\ \underline{\Delta}$
if $e \in$ dom b then $b(e)$ else 0
$Bag\text{-}union\ [@elem] : (@elem \xrightarrow{m} \mathbb{N}_1) \times (@elem \xrightarrow{m} \mathbb{N}_1) \rightarrow (@elem \xrightarrow{m} \mathbb{N}_1)$
$Bag\text{-}union(a,b)\ \underline{\Delta}$
$\{p \mapsto count\ [@elem]\ (p,a) + count\ [@elem]\ (p,b) \mid p \in (\text{dom}\ a \cup \text{dom}\ b)\}$
$Bag\text{-}subset\ [@elem] : (@elem \xrightarrow{m} \mathbb{N}_1) \times (@elem \xrightarrow{m} \mathbb{N}_1) \rightarrow \mathbb{B}$
$Bag\text{-}subset(b_1, b_2)\ \underline{\Delta}$
$\forall x \in (\text{dom}\ b_1 \cup \text{dom}\ b_2) \bullet count\ [@elem]\ (x, b_1) \leq count\ [@elem]\ (x, b_2)$
-- *count, Bag-union and Bag-subset are polymorphic definitions*
$Sum : \mathbb{N}_1\text{-set} \rightarrow \mathbb{N}$
$Sum(s)\ \underline{\Delta}$
if $s = \{\}$ then 0 else let $m \in s$ in
$m + Sum(s - \{m\})$
-- *This function sums the elements in a set of strictly positive natural numbers.*
$Value : Bag(British\_Coin) \rightarrow \mathbb{N}$
$Value(b)\ \underline{\Delta}\ Sum\ (\{Worth(c) * b\ (c) \bullet c \in \text{dom}\ b\})$
-- *This function returns the value (in pence) of a bag of British coins.*

operations

$Service\text{-}Machine\ (new\text{-}stocks : Bag(Ingredient),\ new\text{-}cups : \mathbb{N},$
$\qquad\qquad new\text{-}takings : Bag(British\text{-}Coin),\ new\text{-}prices : Drink \xrightarrow{m} \mathbb{N})$
ext rd $Balance : Bag(British\text{-}Coin)$
$\quad$ wr $Takings : Bag(British\text{-}Coin)$
$\quad$ wr $Stock : Bag(Ingredient)$
$\quad$ wr $Cups : \mathbb{N}$
$\quad$ wr $Prices : Costs$
$\quad$ wr $Service\text{-}light : Onoff$
$\quad$ wr $Coin\text{-}display : \mathbb{N}$
$\quad$ wr $Report\text{-}display : Message$
post $Stocks = Bag\text{-}union[Bag(Ingredient)](Stocks^{\leftarrow}, new\text{-}stocks) \wedge$
$\qquad Takings = Bag\text{-}union[Bag(British\text{-}Coin)](Takings^{\leftarrow}, new\text{-}takings) \wedge$
$\qquad Prices = Prices^{\leftarrow} \dagger new\text{-}prices \wedge$
$\qquad Cups = Cups^{\leftarrow} + new\text{-}cups \wedge$
$\qquad Coin\text{-}display = Value\ (Balance) \wedge$
$\qquad Service\text{-}light = off \wedge$
$\qquad Report\text{-}display = insert\ coin$

$Insert\text{-}Coin(co : Coin)\ Reject\text{-}coin : Coin$
ext wr $Balance : Bag(British\text{-}Coin)$
$\quad$ wr $Takings : Bag(British\text{-}Coin)$
$\quad$ wr $Coin\text{-}display : \mathbb{N}$
$\quad$ wr $Report\text{-}display : Message$
pre $\quad co \neq Unacceptable\text{-}coin \wedge$
$\qquad count[British\text{-}Coin](co, Takings) < HopperMax(co)$

post $Balance = Bag\text{-}union[Bag(British\text{-}Coin)](Balance^{\leftarrow}, \{co \mapsto 1\}) \land$
  $Takings = Bag\text{-}union[Bag(British\text{-}Coin)](Takings^{\leftarrow}, \{co \mapsto 1\}) \land$
  $Report\text{-}display = insert\ coin \land$
  $Coin\text{-}display = Value\ (Balance)$
errs $REJECT : co = Unacceptable\text{-}coin \lor$
  $count[British\text{-}Coin](co, Takings) = HopperMax(co) \rightarrow$
  $Balance = Balance^{\leftarrow} \land$
  $Takings = Takings^{\leftarrow} \land$
  $Report\text{-}display = try\ another\ coin \land$
  $Coin\text{-}display = Value\ (Balance) \land$
  $Reject\text{-}coin = co$

Get-Drink (Choice : Drink) Change : Bag(British-Coin), Goods : Drink
ext wr *Balance : Bag(British-Coin)*
 wr *Takings : Bag(British-Coin)*
 wr *Stock : Bag(Ingredient)*
 wr *Cups :* $\mathbb{N}$
 rd *Prices : Costs*
 wr *Service-light : Onoff*
 wr *Coin-display :* $\mathbb{N}$
 wr *Report-display : Message*
pre $(Value(Balance) \geq Prices(Choice) \land$
  $\exists b{:}Bag(British\text{-}Coin) \bullet (Bag\text{-}subset[Bag(British\text{-}Coin)](b, Takings) \land$
  $Value(Balance) = Value(b) + Prices(Choice))) \land$
  $\forall i \in Recipe(Choice) \bullet count[Bag(Ingredient)](i, Stock) > 0 \land$
  $Cups > 0$
post $Balance = \{\mapsto\} \land$
  $Bag\text{-}union[Bag(Ingredient)](Stock, \{i \mapsto 1 \mid i \in Recipe(Choice)\}) = Stock^{\leftarrow} \land$
  $Cups = Cups^{\leftarrow} - 1 \land$
  $Bag\text{-}subset[Bag(British\text{-}Coin)](Change, Takings^{\leftarrow}) \land$
  $Value(Balance^{\leftarrow}) = Value(Change) + Prices(Choice) \land$
  $Bag\text{-}union[Bag(British\text{-}Coin)](Takings, Change) = Takings^{\leftarrow} \land$
  $Coin\text{-}display = Value(Balance) \land$
  $Service\text{-}light = Service\text{-}light^{\leftarrow} \land$
  $Report\text{-}display = insert\ coin \land$
  $Goods = Choice$

errs $MONEY : Value(Balance) < Prices(Choice) \rightarrow$
  $Takings = Takings^{\leftarrow} \land$
  $Balance = Balance^{\leftarrow} \land$
  $Stocks = Stocks^{\leftarrow} \land$
  $Cups = Cups^{\leftarrow} \land$
  $Service\text{-}light = Service\text{-}light^{\leftarrow} \land$
  $Coin\text{-}display = Value(Balance) \land$
  $Report\text{-}display = insert\ more\ money\ and\ select\ drink\ again$

  $STOCKS : \exists i \in Recipe(Choice) \bullet count[Bag(Ingredient)](i, Stock) = 0 \rightarrow$
  $Takings = Takings^{\leftarrow} \land$

$$Balance = Balance^{\leftarrow} \land$$
$$Stocks = Stocks^{\leftarrow} \land$$
$$Cups = Cups^{\leftarrow} \land$$
$$Service\text{-}light = on \land$$
$$Coin\text{-}display = Value(Balance) \land$$
$$Report\text{-}display = this\ drink\ is\ unavailable$$

$CUPS : Cups = 0 \rightarrow$
$$Takings = Takings^{\leftarrow} \land$$
$$Balance = Balance^{\leftarrow} \land$$
$$Stocks = Stocks^{\leftarrow} \land$$
$$Cups = Cups^{\leftarrow} \land$$
$$Service\text{-}light = on \land$$
$$Coin\text{-}display = Value(Balance) \land$$
$$Report\text{-}display = no\ cups\ in\ machine$$

$CHANGE : Value(Balance) \geq Prices(Choice) \land$
$$\neg \exists b : Bag(British\text{-}Coin\ ) \bullet ($$
$$Value(Balance) = Value(b) + Prices(Choice)) \rightarrow$$
$$Takings = Takings^{\leftarrow} \land$$
$$Balance = Balance^{\leftarrow} \land$$
$$Stocks = Stocks^{\leftarrow} \land$$
$$Cups = Cups^{\leftarrow} \land$$
$$Service\text{-}light = Service\text{-}light^{\leftarrow} \land$$
$$Coin\text{-}display = Value(Balance) \land$$
$$Report\text{-}display = correct\ change\ unavailable$$

Take-Profit( ) Profit : Bag(British-Coin)
ext wr *Balance : Bag(British-Coin)*
    wr *Takings : Bag(British-Coin)*
    wr *Coin-display : Bag(British-Coin)*
    wr *Report-display : Message*
post *Bag-union[British-Coin](Takings, Profit) = Takings$^{\leftarrow}$ $\land$*
    Balance = $\{\mapsto\}$ $\land$
    Coin-display = Value(Balance) $\land$
    Report-display = insert coin

Refund( ) Refund : Bag(British-Coin)
ext wr *Balance : Bag(British-Coin)*
    wr *Takings : Bag(British-Coin)*
    wr *Coin-display : Bag(British-Coin)*
    wr *Report-display : Message*
pre *Value(Balance) $\neq$ 0*
post *Refund = Balance$^{\leftarrow}$ $\land$*
    Bag-union[British-Coin](Takings, Refund) = Takings$^{\leftarrow}$ $\land$
    Balance = $\{\mapsto\}$ $\land$
    Coin-display = Value(Balance) $\land$
    Report-display = insert coin

errs *NO-REFUND* : *Value*(*Balance*) = 0 →
$\qquad$ *Balance* = *Balance*$^{\leftarrow}$ ∧
$\qquad$ *Takings* = *Takings*$^{\leftarrow}$ ∧
$\qquad$ *Coin-display* = *Value*(*Balance*) ∧
$\qquad$ *Report-display* = *Report-display*$^{\leftarrow}$

end *Drinks-Dispenser*

25.2 THE TYPES REQUIRED

Many of the types presented in the `types` definition block follow directly from the earlier Z specification with simple data types being replaced by a series of union types with corresponding quote values. The `sans serif` font used in all earlier VDM specification has been replaced by the softer italicized style. Unlike Z, VDM has no predefined bag type constructor and so the various bags are modelled as maps from the items to the set of strictly positive natural numbers. Auxiliary functions are defined in the `functions` definition block to provide functionality for these objects. The type *Costs* is also a map and is introduced to provide the equivalent of a total function which ensures that every drink has a price. Totality is achieved by the type invariant that demands that every drink is included in the domain of the map.

A major departure from the Z specification is made in terms of the definitions for the drinks available. In Z we used a *set* of *sets of* button presses to characterize the drink— this being quite natural as Z is based on a typed set theory. In VDM, however, the use of sets in this fashion is less natural so that the VDM specification sees a drink as either *TEA-or-COFFEE* or *CHOCOLATE*. Chocolate drinks are always served *WHITE* and *SWEET*, while a customer's choice for *TEA-or-COFFEE* is reflected in the condition of a record that permits choices to be made for the fields *FLAVOUR*, *WHITE* and *SWEET*. Not only is this a more natural approach for VDM but it also has the added advantage in that the types *Drink* and *TEA-or-COFFEE* capture the legal set of button presses to which the machine responds. When we offer some input of type *Drink* to a subsequent operation, the precondition that determines whether the drink required is valid is rendered trivial. Although this solution is less intuitive than the one used in Z, the ability to omit trivial preconditions leads to a simplification which must be applauded.

SAQ 25.1 Could the Z specification be modified to incorporate this simplification? At what expense?

One final point concerns the use of the type ℕ to reflect monetary value (in pence). In a revision of the specification it might be advantageous to define a module such as `Module` *Monies* where the type *Money* and its operators are defined and made available to other modules by export. In this way we 'hide' the fact that *Money* is simply a natural number thereby preventing abuse within the specification by, for example, trying to divide or multiply two monetary amounts.

SAQ 25.2 Write a module `Module` *Monies* exporting the type *Money* and the functions *add* and *subtract*.

25.3 THE VALUES

The definitions in the `values` definition block represent the VDM versions of the axiomatic descriptions used in Z. Such entries describe objects that are constant, often with their contents well known. *HopperMax* and *StockMax* are maps that represent the maximum contents of the various coin tubes and stock levels respectively. These definitions are currently incomplete but will be total in that all coins and stocks have maximum storage limits. The detail of these definitions will be supplied later in the development process but we again expect the water limits to be infinite. *Worth* is a map corresponding to the total injection used in the Z specification with exactly the same contents. *CupMax* is a simple constant that determines the maximum number of cups the machine can hold. The definition is again incomplete.

The major difference from the Z specification is reflected in the definition provided for *Recipe*; an object that associates particular drinks with the ingredients needed to make them. In Z we defined this as a total injection from *Drink* to *List_of_ingredients*, but VDM sees *Recipe* as a map from *Drink* to *Ingredients*−`set`. Notice that the map is formed from two other maps using the map union operator (∪):

$$\{CHOCOLATE \mapsto \{Chocolate\text{-}powder\ Water\}\} \cup \{d \mapsto \dots \mid d : TEA\text{-}or\text{-}COFFEE\}$$

i.e. the map relating a chocolate drink to its ingredients and the map describing the ingredients for *TEA, COFFEE, TEA-WHITE, COFFEE-WHITE, TEA-SWEET, COFFEE-SWEET, TEA-WHITE-SWEET* and *COFFEE-WHITE-SWEET*. This second map is defined by forming maplets for every condition of the variable *d*. The set to which each *d* maps is then composed using if...then...else constructs together with the set union operator (∪). In the definition the map union has been written as the smaller of the two symbols in an attempt to avoid confusion.

25.4 THE ABSTRACT STATE

The composition of the abstract state corresponds exactly to the earlier *Abs_State_Machine* schema but with corresponding VDM types in place of those of Z. The invariant refers to instantiations of the polymorphic definition for *count* (see `functions`), while the Z requirement:

$$Coin\text{-}display = Value\ (Balance)$$

has been removed from the invariant and made a postcondition for every operation instead. This is really only a question of style and clarity. Like Z, the invariant in VDM applies to all operations and its satisfaction is demanded as part of the proof of implementability. But in Z, all state variables and invariant predicates migrate to every operation definition through the inclusion of the schema Δ*Machine_State*. This is not the case in VDM; operations have to explicitly declare which state variables they act upon and what they do to them. Through this mechanism we deduce which variables can be changed by the operation and which cannot. Because every operation changes the condition of *Coin-display* (even if only to write back that which was already there) it is best to give each operation `wr` access to update the display so that no confusion arises when writing externals clauses.

Notice also that the make functions used to compose state instances for the invariant and the initial state use a shorthand for the state variable names. The first symbolic argument refers to the first variable in the state list, the second argument to the second variable, etc. Thus *B* for *Balance*, *T* for *Takings*, *S* for *Stock* make the definitions of these functions more manageable. This is common practice in larger specifications. Finally, the initial state corresponds exactly to that of Z with empty bags for *Balance*, *Takings* and *Stock* and with each drink zero priced through map comprehension.

25.5 THE FUNCTIONS

Because VDM has no separate type constructor for bags, we are forced to provide auxiliary function definitions for those bag operations used in the specification body. Polymorphic function definitions are made for *count* and *Bag-union* and these correspond exactly in form and in use to those discussed in Part 3. The polymorphic definition for *Bag-subset* parallels the generic definition used in Z and assumes the existence of the total order $\leq$. Because the specification deals with bags of different types, appropriate instantiations of polymorphic definitions represent a more economic approach than duplicating each operator for bags of specific types. An alternative approach would be to write all the bag operators in a parametrized module, instantiating and importing the operators as required. This is rather more complex a solution but something which the reader might like to undertake as an exercise. Notice also the appearance of explanatory comments within this part of the specification. In *VDM-SL* comments are introduced by '--' and run to the end of the line.

25.6 THE OPERATIONS

Each operation corresponds in name and functionality to those of the earlier Z specification. Most operations are made total by the inclusion of an error definition block and the error preconditions are largely deduced by negation of the normal precondition(s). As with Z, certain variables remain undefined when exceptions occur. *Service-Machine* and *Take-Profit* are the only operations without preconditions—other than the trivial case of type compatibility for inputs. These operations are therefore already total. The need for a separate output variable such as *Report : Message* is avoided by the use of the state variable *Report-display* and this again parallels Z. A brief discussion of the important features of each operation now follows.

Service-Machine

This operation can bring about a major state change potentially affecting all the state variables. As there is no precondition, servicing can occur at any time and will always be used to replenish the machine's contents. As with the Z specification nothing can be removed during a service because all operations are incremental—although it is possible to leave certain aspects unchanged. *Stocks* and *Takings* are updated (subject to the invariant) by bag union and separate instantiations of the polymorphics are used to deal with bags of different types. The *Prices* map is overridden with a new map (which may be empty if price changes are not required), while the input map need not be total, permitting alteration of selected prices only. This parallels the use of the partial function in the Z specification. The total number of cups can be increased subject to the invariant. The operation has read access only to the *Balance* and so cannot affect it. The coin display is set to the current balance, the report display invites the user to insert a coin while the service light is set *off*. It was mentioned earlier that it is possible to perform a service that leaves the machine contents unchanged, however such a service would be mischievous and is, in effect, discounted.

Insert-Coin

Like the corresponding Z operation, *Insert-Coin* describes the process of inserting a single coin into the machine. The process of building a balance is therefore seen as repeated application of the insert operation. The operation has no access to *Stock*, *Cups*, *Prices* or the *Service-light* and so these remain unchanged. The preconditions demand that the coin be a *British-Coin* and that the coin tube for the coin is not full. If the coin is acceptable, both *Balance* and *Takings* are incremented by bag union, the coin display shows the new balance and the report display prompts for another coin. Notice also that under normal circumstances the 'rejected coin' is undefined. The error condition for the operation is that either the coin is 'unacceptable' or the coin tube for the coin is full. Both cannot be simultaneously *true* because the machine has no tube for unacceptable coins. Under these circumstances the input coin is rejected, the takings and balance remain undisturbed, the coin display shows the balance and the customer is invited to try another coin.

Get-Drink

Drinks are chosen by pressing some combination of selection buttons on the front panel and this combination is 'trapped' in the condition of the input record *Choice*. This mechanism again ensures that the order in which the buttons are pressed is irrelevant, while the precondition that the combination corresponds to a known drink is made trivial by the typing mechanism.

The preconditions again demand that the balance is at least enough to pay for the drink and that a bag of coins exists within the machine's takings equal in value to any change that needs to be issued. Sufficient stock levels for each ingredient of the drink must also be available, together with a cup. The expression of these predicates parallels those of the Z specification exactly, except that we now use the various objects of VDM. Under normal circumstances the operation reduces the balance to an empty bag, decrements every stock ingredient by one unit and issues the chosen drink (in a cup!) together with the correct change which is removed directly from the takings. The coin display then shows the new balance and the report display invites the next customer to insert a coin. The service light remains unaffected. Once again the predicates reflect those of the Z specification very closely. The reduction in stock is described by demanding that if we form the bag union between the after stocks and a bag in which every ingredient for the chosen drink is mapped to one unit, we recreate the original stock levels. This means that the after stocks levels for these ingredients must have been reduced by one. The change is fixed by demanding that a bag of coins equal in value to the required amount is present in the original takings, while the effect of removing the change from the machine is reflected in the predicate that requires the bag union of the change and the after takings to equal the original takings. The specification defers a commitment to the composition of the change, while appropriate instantiations of the polymorphics are used in all the predicates.

The various error conditions follow largely from the negation of the preconditions. Thus, the value of the current balance is not enough to pay for the chosen drink (*MONEY*), there exists at least one ingredient which is out of stock (*STOCKS*), the machine has run out of cups (*CUPS*) or the balance may be sufficient to pay for the drink, but the machine cannot find a bag of coins in its takings equal in value to the required change (*CHANGE*). In each circumstance the report display prompts with a suitable message and because the operation is non-deterministic, it is possible that more than one message might appear. When stock levels or cups are exhausted the service light is illuminated indicating to the staff that the machine needs attention. Otherwise the *status quo* is largely retained. Finally, notice that when an error occurs, *Goods* and *Change* are undefined and this reflects the situation in Z.

Take-Profit

Taking profit has no preconditions and will always succeed—even if the profit is zero. Any remaining balance is taken but it is not possible to remove more money than is in the machine. Like Z, this constraint is effected through the definition of bag union which does not deal with negative occurrences. Once profit is taken, the report display prompts customers to insert another coin.

Refund

Refunds can be issued only if the balance is in credit. The refund is removed from the takings in the machine and the balance is reduced to an empty bag. If a refund is demanded when the balance is empty the status quo is retained.

25.7 SUMMARY

The importance of this specification lies in its use of the various techniques of VDM which permits a useful comparison with the approach taken in Z. In most respects there is little to choose between the mathematics of the two, but a major difference is reflected in the treatment of total operations which is far more clumsy in VDM because of the need to describe normal and exceptional behaviour all in one construct. This is of course caused by the absence of an operation calculus, such as the schema calculus of Z, which also prevents us from writing convenient definitions for 'press button D' and 'press button R'.

26

EPILOGUE

To specify formally and to formally develop software is to create insight into, and theories about, otherwise complex systems .... it is refreshingly relaxing to develop beautiful software embodying elegant theories formally ....

Dines Bjørner, original VDM collaborator at the IBM Vienna laboratories

26.1 FORMAL SPECIFICATION AND FORMAL METHODS

Part 1 of this book spent some time explaining the structure of contemporary software engineering and the ways in which its individual techniques were organized into large-scale methodologies that brought discipline, order and guidance to the software development process. The remaining parts of the book have dealt largely with ways in which software can be formally specified, and since we would naturally expect formal specification to form part of an overall formal method for software development the questions arise as to what exactly a 'formal method' is and how it relates to the methodologies of contemporary software engineering.

The primary purpose of a formal method is to produce high-quality reliable software in which we have well-founded confidence. Software developed formally has a potential advantage over that of traditional methodologies in that our confidence is increased because (usually critical) parts of the system have been largely proven correct with regard to the specification rather than tested correct. The notion of a proof really corresponds to our having a symbolic execution of the intended program with all possible test cases run simultaneously—a situation which would be impossible in conventional methodologies. Proof mechanisms form a vital part of formally developed software and proofs are constructed and discharged at various points within the development process. The practical limitations imposed on large-scale projects together with the inherent difficulty associated with mathematical proofs prevent proofs being conducted for every aspect, so that fully proven software will always be expensive and rare. Testing will therefore never be eliminated entirely but the level of testing on a formally developed project is likely to be less demanding than with conventional techniques.

A traditional large-scale methodology such as SSADM resolves itself into at least six activities, while a (very) coarse-grained view of a formal method sees it as being composed of two separate but dependent activities—specification and verification. The point was made earlier (see Part 2) that retrospective verification of existing software, i.e. showing that a written program satisfies its specification, is a very demanding

376

activity. Consequently most contemporary formal methods such as Z and VDM approach the task of verification by gradually developing code from the specification in stages. In this process the abstract descriptions of the data are first slowly replaced by more 'concrete' mathematical structures—structures that ultimately have a direct correspondence with those found in most modern structured programming languages. Thus sets become sequences and sequences eventually translate to arrays, for example. This process is *data reification*.[1] As the more concrete data types are introduced the operations are modified to operate on the new data types; once the data types have been sufficiently reified, the operations on the final concrete data types can be translated to algorithms written in some target programming language and this process is known as *operation decomposition*.

An example of what is meant by this process might be suggested by the Z case study for generic stacks and queues. Here the specification was written in terms of a set of time-stamped elements and also in terms of sequences. Of the two, the sequence is the more 'concrete' description because sequences have a close similarity with a very familiar programming language data structure—the array. Indeed, most readers familiar with at least one structured programming language would have little difficulty in translating that specification directly into code. The formal development of the stack could therefore involve specification in terms of a set of time-stamped items, rewriting the specification in terms of sequences and then undertaking appropriate operation decomposition, eventually programming this using arrays.

The original abstract specification of course will have been subject to a number of proofs. The initial state will have been shown to be satisfactory, and implementability proofs will have shown that each operation can be realized in practice, and other proofs will show that the software enjoys particular behavioural properties. As the specification is transformed to a more and more concrete description it is important that all these features are preserved in the new version. This is demonstrated by constructing and discharging three separate proof obligations[2] during each distinct stage in the reification process. First, we must establish *adequacy*, which shows that each value allowed in the new type corresponds to one in the abstract type and that every value in the abstract type can be represented by at least one value in the new type. If these conditions are not true then the new type would be too restrictive in that certain situations could not be modelled. Secondly, we must establish that the concrete operations essentially 'do the same thing' as the abstract operations and this is achieved by showing that the new concrete operations satisfy both the *domain rule* and the *result rule*.

---

[1]The term 'refinement' was originally proposed for this process and is still used within the formal methods community. However, Michael Jackson pointed out to Cliff Jones that the term is hardly appropriate for a process that converts a clean abstract description into a messy representation dictated by a particular machine architecture. *The Concise Oxford Dictionary* defines the word 'reify' as 'convert (person, abstract concept) into a thing; materialize'. In other words, to 'make real' some abstract idea.

[2]These obligations were originally developed for VDM and in our discussion we use VDM terminology exclusively. The Z community has until recently tended to concentrate on issues of specification. However, texts are now emerging that present the Z approach to 'refinement'. Needless to say this approach has been heavily influenced by developments in VDM.

26.1.1 Adequacy

Given any abstract data type TA and a corresponding concrete type TC—both simply a set of permitted values—then the general proof obligation for adequacy can be written:

$$\forall a \in TA \bullet \exists c \in TC \bullet retr\text{-}TA(c) = a$$

where $retr\text{-}TA$ is the 'retrieve' function. For a concrete type to be a true representation of the abstract type it must be possible to say which element of the abstract type corresponds to which particular element of the concrete type. In this respect, the specifier is required to define a *retrieve function* which, given an element of the concrete type, retrieves the corresponding element of the abstract type. This function must be total in that it is defined for every element in the concrete type that satisfies the data type invariant and surjective in that every element of the abstract type can be reached from an element in the concrete type. By demanding that this relationship is functional we also ensure that a single concrete value relates to a single abstract value. If we cannot find such a function the new data type cannot *adequately* represent all the values of the abstract type and is therefore an inappropriate reification. Viewed in this light the proof obligation for adequacy reads: for every element in the abstract type there exists at least one element in the concrete type that it is related to through the retrieve function. Figure 26.1 illustrates the correspondence between the two sets of values that must be established through a suitable retrieve function.

In the specific case of reifying the set (TA) as a sequence (TC), a suitable retrieve function might take the following form:

$$retr\text{-}TA : TC \to TA$$
$$retr\text{-}TA\ (s) \underline{\Delta}\ \texttt{elems}(s)$$

Here, the function is total because of the absence of any precondition, while given any member of the concrete type TC—a sequence—the function returns the corresponding

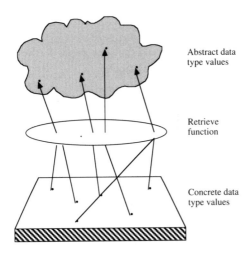

Abstract data
type values

Retrieve
function

Concrete data
type values

Figure 26.1 The retrieve function relating elements of the concrete type to those of the abstract type. Every element in the concrete type must be related to an element in the abstract type.

member of the abstract type *TA*—a set. A retrieve function along these lines would be required to prove adequacy between the set of time-stamped elements and the sequence in the case study on generic stacks and queues.

26.2.2 The domain and range rules

As the representation of a particular type is made more concrete, the operations on it have to be redefined in terms of the operators of the new type. In this respect we have to show that the operations on the concrete type are at least as generally applicable as the abstract operations and that they yield the correct results. These points establish that the new version 'does the same thing' as the abstract version and that questions of implementability and properties can be safely carried over to the concrete versions. These two requirements are captured in the domain and range rules, respectively. Assume as before that we have an abstract type *TA* and a corresponding concrete type *TC* for which we have established adequacy through some retrieve function *retr-TA*. If the concrete operation *OPC* corresponds to the abstract operation *OPA* then there must exist some relationship between the preconditions of these operations such that:

$$\forall c \in TC \bullet \texttt{let } a = \textit{retr-TA}(c) \texttt{ in } \textit{pre-OPA}(a) \Rightarrow \textit{pre-OPC}(c)$$

This obligation simply requires that for every value *c* in the concrete type, if the corresponding value *a* in the abstract type satisfies *pre-OPA(a)* then *pre-OPC(c)* must also be *true*, which ensures that the domain of the concrete operation contains at least every concrete element corresponding to an abstract element for which the *OPA* is defined. The domain rule must be satisfied for every single operation on a new data type and Figure 26.2 shows the relationship that must be achieved.

A concrete operation not only has to be defined over an appropriate range of concrete values but must also get the right answer! This condition is embodied in the result rule which basically demands that the value produced by a concrete operation must correspond to the value produced by the abstract operation through the retrieve

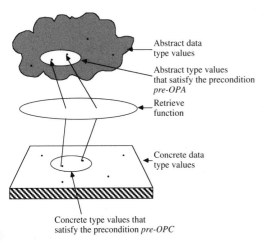

Abstract data type values

Abstract type values that satisfy the precondition *pre-OPA*

Retrieve function

Concrete data type values

Concrete type values that satisfy the precondition *pre-OPC*

Figure 26.2   The domain rule.

function. In the result rule we are dealing with the postcondition functions such that if $post\text{-}OPC(c^{\leftarrow}, c)$ is *true* and the concrete operation maps $c^{\leftarrow}$ to c then $post\text{-}OPA(a^{\leftarrow}, a)$ is *true* and the abstract operation maps $a^{\leftarrow}$ to a. If this were not so then it means that c is acceptable by the concrete postcondition but that the corresponding value a is not acceptable to the abstract postcondition, i.e. the concrete result is wrong. The domain rule with the retrieve function relating the various abstract and concrete values is as follows:

$$\forall c^{\leftarrow}, c \in TC \bullet \text{let } a^{\leftarrow} = retr\text{-}TA(c^{\leftarrow}), a = retr\text{-}TA(c) \text{ in}$$
$$pre\text{-}OPC(c^{\leftarrow}, c) \Rightarrow post\text{-}OPA(a^{\leftarrow}, a)$$

Figure 26.3 illustrates the relationship that must be achieved between the postconditions. The concrete operation OPC is shown converting concrete *before* values to concrete *after* values. OPA similarly converts the abstract values, while the two sets of values must be related through the *retrieve function*.

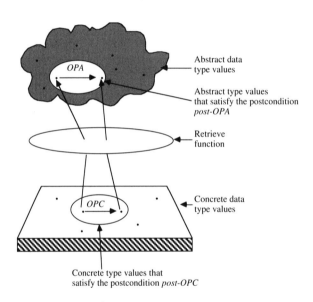

Figure 26.3 The range rule.

26.2 OPERATION DECOMPOSITION

Once the data type reification has been completed the process of building code can begin; this is referred to as *operation decomposition* and in most large-scale projects code is developed for relatively small segments which are then combined to produce the final product. Operation decomposition once again involves the construction and discharge of a series of proof obligations aimed at showing that the code written in the chosen programming language is correct with regard to the pre- and postconditions of the final concrete specification. The form and nature of these obligations differ somewhat from those we have become used to in specification and address questions of practicalities such as the programming constructs used by the language and whether or not the software terminates. Programming languages have a number of simple constructs, such as assignments and sequences, together with more complex structures which combine these simple constructs in different ways, e.g. loops or compound selection statements. In order to reason about such descriptions, correctness statements have to be derived for each type of structure involved in the language. In this respect we have already noted (Chapter 2) that most work has centred on Pascal-like languages which are exemplary in terms of the facilities offered by structured languages in general. It may well also be the case that only certain critical areas are subject to the full formal methodology involved in operation decomposition which once more reduces the overall effort.

Clearly all these rules and processes are difficult to comprehend for the non-mathematician, but what they mean is that every time we rewrite the specification to bring it closer to the kinds of data types available in some target programming language we have a formidable series of proof obligations to perform, and once the specification has reached a sufficiently stable concrete state further proof is necessary to establish that the program code properly corresponds to the concrete descriptions—even if only critical parts are examined. There is no doubt therefore that the most difficult part of developing software by a strictly formal regime lies not in its specification but in the effort expended in the reification and decomposition processes. This point has not been lost on the formal methods community, with the consequence that relationships between specifications and programming languages have been identified and often exploited largely to bypass the reification process altogether. This practice may not be desirable and to some extent offends the basic premise of formal methods, but it is a reflection of the practical difficulties involved in producing full or even partially formally verified software with today's techniques.

This book has concentrated on the various techniques of formal specification for reasons discussed shortly. There are, however, a growing number of books available which address (to a greater or lesser degree) the verification of software within Z and VDM and readers might like to look more closely at some of the issues introduced here in texts such as Spivey (1992), Woodman and Heal (1993), Andrews and Ince (1991), McDermid and Whysall (1992), Potter *et al.* (1991), Morgan (1990) and Woodcock (1993). Readers should also refer to Jones (1986, 1991) for a seminal text on these issues.

26.3 THE OVERALL STRUCTURE OF A FORMAL METHOD

The development process of a formal method from an original abstract specification (*SP*) through successive concrete representations ($C_1 \ldots Cn$) to an ultimate program (*PRG*) therefore proceeds:

$$\textbf{\textit{SP}} \rightarrow C_1 \rightarrow C_2 \rightarrow C_3 \rightarrow \ldots \rightarrow \text{Cn} \rightarrow \textbf{\textit{PRG}}$$

with various proof obligations generated and discharged at each stage. Such a development is associated with an overall proof of correctness because each step in the process has been proven to be a more concrete version of the previous step, which ultimately leaves **PRG** as a proven *real* version of **SP**. In this respect the organization of a formal method can be presented as:

Specification; *repeat*
             define given sets, global constants, functions, etc.,
             describe abstract state for the system,
             describe initial state,
             construct/discharge initial state theorem,
             build partial operations,
             build total operations,
             construct/discharge implementability obligations,
             construct/discharge property proofs,
             prototype
             until SP sufficiently stable
             complete the documentation of **SP**.
Verification; *begin with* **SP**.
             repeat
                data reification,
                construct/discharge adequacy, domain and range proof
                obligations
             until original SP sufficiently concrete
             operation decomposition for individual units,
             write program code for individual units,
             combine code,
             test.

which can be usefully compared to the general structure of (say) SSADM. Although this overall view does not show it, formal methods are also subject to project control and quality assurance. It is interesting to note that the prototype is often employed— especially important in view of the fact that the customer is very unlikely to understand the formal notation. Formal specification languages are of course are often based on predicate logic which in turn lends itself to animation through languages such as Prolog. Functional languages such as Miranda (Turner 1986) have also been employed and examples of the use of both Prolog and Miranda can be found in Diller (1990). Axiomatic specifications have been prototyped using languages such as OBJ which is well documented in (Gallimore *et al.* (1989). Prototypes using these languages correspond almost to executable specifications used to stabilsze customer/designer perceptions, although not everyone agrees that formal specifications should necessarily be executable (Hayes and Jones 1989).

26.4 FORMAL METHODS AND INDUSTRY

This chapter has so far tried to communicate the 'nuts and bolts' of formal methods. Bearing in mind the ultimate aim of producing proven correct software, it is really quite easy to become evangelical about the potential of the technique. Indeed, the use of formal methods has been much heralded as the next way forward and so an important consideration that must be addressed is the extent to which formal methods have been taken up by industry and in the way(s) in which they are used. The most recent and comprehensive survey of formal methods in (British) industry was undertaken by the National Physical Laboratory during the summer of 1992 (National Physical Laboratory 1992)—the conclusions from which are still likely to be valid. The survey polled some 3000 addresses taken from the areas of safety critical systems and security together with all the British universities and polytechnics. Over 800 requests for the questionnaire were received of which 444 were returned. The aims of the survey were to discover the views of people using (or considering the use of) formal methods in their software development. The researchers had already conducted a review of the claims made for formal methods in the literature (Austin and Parkin 1992). These claims were assessed in terms of 'rational argument and reported experimental evidence'. The conclusions drawn were that formal methods have not been widely accepted by industry and that the main reasons for the lack of uptake were the use of mathematics and perhaps the lack of suitable tools. It was therefore important to compare the results of the literature survey with an industrial survey.

The survey showed that the most widely used methods were Z and VDM with approximately equal market penetration.[3] Formal methods such as LOTOS (International Organization for Standardization 1989), CCS (Milner 1989), CSP (Hoare 1978, 1985), used to specify concurrent systems, were less widely used and the researchers regarded this as a natural consequence of the greater ratio of sequential to concurrent systems at the time. The survey also showed that formal methods have been used for all stages of the software development life cycle but that the main uses are for specification and its associated proofs. The fact that formal specification was used therefore did not always mean that it was used to develop the software formally.

Formal methods are being integrated into the software life cycle largely through structured methods (SSADM and Yourdon in particular) and much less through requirements analysis tools (such as CORE (Mullery 1979, Looney 1985)). Those who use formal methods do so largely because contracts demand it or because they work in areas of safety critical systems. Where contract work is involved the Ministry of Defence was one of the main organizations insisting on their use (through Defence Standard 00-55 (Ministry of Defence 1991). The other main influence was the security standard approved methodology for security evaluation (*Orange book*—for more information contact The Data Security Group, DITC, National Physical Laboratory, Queens Road, Teddington, Middlesex, UK, TD11 0LW).

The survey concluded that there are three main reasons why formal methods are not used more widely in industry:

- There is a lack of suitable *tool support*, especially in the commercial sector.
- It has not been shown conclusively that there is a *cost benefit* to be gained from their use.

---

[3]Author's comment: the equal standing that Z has achieved with VDM, however, might be significant in view of the undoubted maturity of the latter. This in turn might suggest an increased share of the market for Z in the future. The fact that no clear leader has yet emerged may also be an influence holding back commercial toolmakers reluctant to invest in a product that might lose its market share.

- Many of the barriers to the use of formal methods are symptoms of the process of *change*. People simply do not like moving from one technique to a completely different one ('the inertia of change'—see Pressman (1987)).

The lack of tools was confirmed by the literature survey but the other two conclusions were not—although the resistance to change might have been anticipated. Instead, the literature survey suggested that the mathematics might be a problem. The fact that this was not confirmed by the industry survey is pleasing but at the same time unexpected. A possible reason for this is that many industrial software engineers may have a traditional engineering/science background so that the mathematics presents few problems to them, or indeed it might be that the mathematics is not as difficult as some would have us think. On the lack of tools the researchers conclude that the small formal methods market might not allow developers to recover development costs or that potential developers are put off by the lack of universally accepted standards. Although LOTOS is standardized, the small concurrent market would seem to be responsible for its lack of tools, while for Z and VDM it is true that the standardization has not yet stabilized at a level which attracts the confidence of the commercial toolmakers.

The recommendation of the researchers is that a programme of education is necessary to spread the understanding of formal methods which in turn will help in the process of change. Case studies must be produced by practitioners which demonstrate the cost benefits to be gained from formal methods and these in turn must be associated with research on metrics to help in assessing the contribution of formal methods to the production of software. Finally, efforts must be made to get Z and VDM standardized as soon as possible.

26.5 FORMAL METHODS TODAY

To what extent is the software industry moving towards the recommendations of the NPL report? Education is being addressed in a number of ways. The reference section of this book presents a range of publications dedicated to Z or VDM or to discrete mathematics and the list is growing rapidly. A wide range of journals have appeared to support original research in formal aspects of computing, while industrial courses such as 'An introduction to Z and VDM' offered by the University of Oxford International Summer Engineering Programme spread the word through eminent practitioners such as Cliff Jones and Jim Woodcock. In-house training in formal methods is conducted by a large number of companies including IBM, Praxis and Logica, but probably the most effective long-term contribution will be made through the universities' (including the former polytechnics) incorporating formal aspects of computing into their undergraduate degree programmes. A report entitled *Undergraduate Curricula for Software Engineering* was prepared jointly by the British Computer Society and the Institution of Electrical Engineers and issued in 1989. This is still the major framework around which many universities have organized their software engineering degree structures. The need to introduce abstraction as a way of managing the complexity of software engineering is an implicit requirement of this framework. However, the report uses language such as 'student resistance and nervousness' (Topic S2, page 33) and 'it may be necessary to delay teaching this material... until the relevant (mathematical) foundation has been acquired' (5.12, page 37) which suggests that at the time, the authors anticipated mathematics forming a barrier to the teaching of formal methods. Whereas this might agree with the (subjective) interpretation of the literature survey conducted by the NPL, it does not agree with the results of their (more independent) industrial survey. Consequently we find the discrete mathematics being taught alongside formal methods rather than as a precursor. However it is approached, if the education of students to embrace formal methods is to be successful, the introduction of the mathematics must be carefully managed.

The case studies recommended by the NPL are of course a further aspect of education but one that the researchers suggest should be used to establish the benefits of formal methods among the software engineering community rather than the mechanics of a particular method. These studies should be based on successful industrial projects, but clearly we must accept that software developed under a fully formal regime will always be quite rare because of the large amount of intellectual effort that has to be expended. That such developments are often confined to safety critical areas such as in nuclear reactor control or aircraft design makes case studies in these areas not only rare but also unappealing to the general commercial community. Similarly, the use of formal methods in the defence industry is almost mandatory but the Official Secrets Act ensures that these projects will be less than fruitful candidates for case studies!

However, case studies can be used to illustrate the benefits of formal methods if they emphasize a further finding of the survey, namely that the majority of formal approaches to software development concentrate on the specification where the cost of 'getting it wrong' is at its highest and where the burden of proof is more manageable. Within the literature we have quite formidable evidence for the effectiveness of 're-engineering' using retrospective specification of existing products and for software engineering using formal specification coupled to ad hoc and object-oriented development together with the use of 'traditional' methodologies and databases. For example, once a stable specification has emerged it can be used to produce appropriate DFDs, E–R diagrams and ELHs which can then be used with traditional structured design techniques—these techniques now benefiting from the clarity that formal specification confers upon the various diagramming notations upon which they are based (Bryant 1989). Some research has also been undertaken on the opposite process, that of converting a traditional design document into a formal specification using Z (Polack *et al.* 1992). The experience of these researchers is that the conversion of (say) an SSADM database design to Z is largely mechanical and that the richness of the specification language in expressing constraints in a concise fashion forces 'awkward' questions to be asked about the design. It is subsequently argued that this is a useful quality audit exercise resulting in better information definition. Ad hoc approaches to refinement or reification rely largely upon the informal relationship that exists between the specification and the programming language used, together with the detailed understanding of the system behaviour that any exercise in formal specification provides. Take for example the following extract from David Brownbridge[4] (1989):

----

[4]At the time, of Praxis Systems plc, Bath. See also Hall (1990) which further relates the experiences of this company.

Experience on the ... project has shown that Z can be used to specify and implement a new system without formal refinement. It is sufficient to have an informal relationship between the specification and the software which implements it. By using an object oriented language, the gap between specification and implementation is narrower than with conventional languages.

Links made between object-oriented ideas (in particular the notion of class) and the abstract data types of formal specification languages have led to languages such as Modula-2, Ada and C++ being used to develop code directly in a number of successful projects. Indeed, methodologies for deriving object-oriented designs from functional specifications such as Z or VDM have been proposed, e.g. Alagar and Periyasamy (1992). Code is subsequently produced not by reification, but by mapping the design directly to the various constructs supported by the language. Formal methods' practitioners beware however; object-oriented languages often have performance penalties.

Formal specifications also have important informal relationships with the data models used in database design—especially relational databases developed directly from the mathematical theory of relations (Codd 1970). In the specific case of Oracle, the persistent objects in the abstract state space migrate readily to the logical views of tables, primary keys and foreign keys. Each of the relationships represented in the formal specification can be supported directly using these concepts together with appropriate integrity constraints reflecting the predicates involved in characterizing each of the mathematical structures. The state invariants are similarly supported by integrity constraints either at the database control system (DBCS) level or within each of the application programs. The formal specification of operations in both Z and VDM readily show which operations change the persistent (stored) data and which do not. This property is readily supported by the security and access privileges assigned with *GRANT* commands. Operations that change the state are permitted *SELECT*, *DELETE*, *INSERT*, *UPDATE*, etc., while those that do not are permitted *SELECT* (i.e. 'read') only. Creation of a valid initial state is frequently supported by data load utilities that have associated logic controlling the admission of records to the database. Multiple tables can be loaded in one operation and the invariants embodied in the state space can often be translated directly to the loader logic. The operation preconditions become additional integrity constraints at the *application level* (the state invariants are applied to all operations), while the negation of the preconditions highlight those exceptions that must be handled either by the DBCS or at the application level. In Oracle explicit mechanisms are available to handle exceptions once these have been identified.

Finally, the classic example of the use of formal specification to specify systems retrospectively, which have already been built and are 'live', is the IBM CICS (customer information and control system) (now some 20 years old) which has been the subject of re-engineering alongside on-going development—both using Z (Collins *et al.* 1987). CICS is used by IBM customers to develop interactive applications such as on-line reservation systems and automated financial transaction systems. It is a substantial software product consisting of over 500 000 lines of code and is in widespread use throughout the Western world. The most recent experience of the Hursley Park group with Z on the CICS project is that formal proof is often limited to establishing implementability, while refinement to program code is conducted informally with extensive use of the IBM convention of 'peer group review'. Approximately one-third of the product has now been treated formally, with the possibility that IBM may one day offer us a version of CICS which meets conventional engineering standards, i.e. it will be fault free. These examples show that there is already much published evidence upon which the case studies of the NPL recommendations could be built. This book takes a view that is fully consistent with the results of the industrial survey and suggests that formal specification is a valid activity in its own right because of the crucial part specification plays in the whole of the software development process. Poorly specified software ensures that developers are used unproductively thereby prolonging development times, increasing costs and adding to the burden of maintenance. The formal semantics associated with specification languages offers us the opportunity to 'get it right' at this critical stage—much more so than with the techniques of contemporary software engineering. 'Getting it right' means that there is well-founded confidence that initial states are satisfactory, that operations can be implemented, that exceptions are properly handled and that software built according to this model will exhibit certain behavioural characteristics which ultimately satisfy some customer. Such a degree of certainty is not achievable with traditional techniques.

The question of tool support identified by the NPL report is closely linked with the stabilization of standards. A Z base standard (version 1.0) has emerged from the Z Standards Change Group of the ZIP[5] project at the PRG in Oxford and books such as *Using Standard Z* (Woodcock 1993) have been written to promote understanding of the standard among users. ZIP was a unification initiative for Z standards, methods and tools and a tools catalogue has been available from the ZIP project for some time. Notice, however, that none of the tools as yet support code generation, while relatively few mainstream commercial companies are involved; those that are have well-known research/academic connections.

The BSI is actively addressing standards for VDM. This process, as with most language standardization efforts, seeks to reconcile the various dialects that have developed over the years and this is a particularly important activity for VDM in the light of its maturity. This standard embodies a formal, mathematically sound semantics for the language that designers of computer-based tools will need. The standardization has reached a stage where the main features of the language are stable and *The VDM-SL Reference Guide* (Dawes 1991) is based on the latest draft. Once again various tools are available, e.g. GENESIS which supports Z as well (IST, 1989). VDM tools, however, are not available to quite the same extent as Z and this again may say something about the sustainability of VDM in the long term. It is also worth noting that both Z and VDM still have on-going problems in their definitions. For Z there are difficulties with the semantics of the schema calculus, while for VDM the question of modularization of large specifications is still not fully resolved. These problems must be addressed if more commercial tool developers are to be attracted to the products.

---

[5]ZIP was a collaboration based on British Aerospace plc, British Petroleum, IBM UK Laboratories Ltd, Logica UK Ltd, Praxis Systems plc, Rutherford Appleton Laboratory and the Oxford University Computing Laboratory. The project finished in January 1994, however for more information contact the Secretary, ZIP Project, Oxford University PRG, 11 Keble Road, Oxford OX1 3QD.

No discussion of formal methods today, however, would be complete without some reference to the various myths—both favourable and unfavourable—that have arisen concerning this controversial subject (see also Chapter 1 where similar myths arose concerning traditional software development techniques). Seven of these myths have been gathered together and discussed extensively by Hall (1990). They are:

1. Formal methods guarantee perfect software.
2. They work by proving programs are correct.
3. Only safety critical systems can benefit from their use.
4. They involve complex mathematics.
5. They increase the cost of development.
6. Clients cannot understand them.
7. They simply are not used on real projects.

The first of these myths is particularly damaging because it leads to unrealistic expectations; in reality no such guarantee can be given. The main advantage of formal methods over traditional techniques lies in the role of the specification which can be subjected to much more rigorous examination by the construction of theorems aimed at establishing particular properties. However, only the most critical properties can be examined in this fashion and so a complete knowledge of the behaviour of the specification under all circumstances is still difficult to achieve, with obvious consequences concerning the subsequent software.

The second myth suggests that the method is useful only if we use it to derive the software formally. This book has suggested that such activities are intellectually very difficult and not yet supported by tools that make the process more manageable. However, the discipline imposed by the use of formal methods makes us think more deeply about the software we are about to build so that a great deal is achieved by the methods without conducting any formal proofs at all.

The third myth has arisen because critical systems demand the most thorough use of formal methods but almost any system can benefit from using at least some formal techniques, while the fourth myth is being dispelled by the experiences of many companies that teach the mathematics to their employees 'in house' and by the findings of the survey conducted by the National Physical Laboratory.

The fifth myth is one that concerns project managers in particular. Their budgets are largely for the development of software and not for its maintenance. The argument that the use of 'expensive' formal methods is worthwhile simply because of the reduced maintenance they achieve is therefore difficult to sell to hard-pressed managers. However Hall (1990) argues forcefully that in his company's experience at least, development costs are *reduced* by using formal methods. This view is supported by the CICS project which claimed a 9 per cent reduction in development costs (Collins *et al.* 1987) and by companies such as INMOS whose T800 transputer floating-point unit was brought to the market-place 12 months ahead of time (May 1990).

The sixth myth is quite understandable, but no sensible software engineer would ever expose customers to such descriptions. Indeed, because of the nature of the specification it becomes possible to write informal English descriptions of the intended software far more precisely than with conventional techniques. Also, the tendency of the software engineer to change the interpretation of the specification under pressure from a client becomes almost impossible with formal specifications so that perceptions are clarified at a much earlier stage in the engineering process.

Finally, myth seven is dispelled by the fact that formal methods are being used daily on many large-scale projects, some of which have been mentioned in this chapter. Familiar institutions such as Praxis, IBM, Rolls-Royce, Nuclear Electric, British Aerospace, British Petroleum, IBM, Logica and Plessey are all involved and the list is growing rapidly.

26.6 CONCLUSIONS

Formal methods present the software engineering community with an exciting new road to follow in search of a cure for the software crisis, but progress has been less rapid than some would have hoped. Broadly speaking there appear to be two major reasons for this: first, the failure of the software engineering community to embrace the potential of formal methods; and secondly, the methods themselves, which in their complete form *are* difficult to practise.

The first of these problems was identified by the NPL survey and is being addressed in a number of ways through undergraduate education, tool and case study support and the establishment of stable standards for the various formal methods on the market. It will take some time, however, for these measures to impact on both the software engineering community and those considering commercial exploitation through the provision of support tools. Any progress we make in this area has to be determined by a follow-up survey of the use of formal methods in industry—possibly in two or three years' time.

The second problem might be more fundamental and less disposed to a 'quick fix'. The well-being of formal methods clearly rests in part on the ease with which they can be applied. We must therefore demand additional tool support for the construction and discharge of proof obligations[6] throughout the formal development life cycle, while continued effort will be needed from those trying to bypass the burdensome reification and decomposition processes altogether. In the former respect it is interesting to note that the latest development of the ICL Z tool includes a product called 'proof power' which provides theorem-proving support, and that in addition to independent commercial arrangements, this product is being integrated in CADiZ to provide full refinement from Z specifications to SPARC Ada.[7] In the latter respect the harnessing of traditional software engineering methodologies to formal specification and the exploitation of the relationships between formal specifications and object-oriented or database languages can be cited as encouraging developments. Both of these approaches exploit the formal specification of software which already appears to be appreciated and well established in industry, and both open formalism to a wider audience than might otherwise be the case.

[6]For those who are interested, a useful survey of mechanical support for formal reasoning and theorem proving in software engineering appears in Lindsay (1988).

[7]Private communication with Software Technology Department, British Aerospace, Warton PR4 1AX.

BIBLIOGRAPHY

V.S. Alagar and K. Periyasamy. 'A Methodology for Deriving Object Oriented Design from Functional Specifications'. *Software Engineering Journal*, **7**(1): 247–63, July 1992.

R.M. Alford. 'A Requirements Engineering Methodology for Real Time Processing Requirements'. *IEEE Trans. Software Eng.*, **SE-3**(1): 60–9, 1977.

D. Andrews and D. Ince. *Practical Formal Methods with VDM*. London: McGraw-Hill, 1991.

C. Ashworth and M. Goodland. *SSADM: A Practical Approach*. London: McGraw-Hill, 1990.

S.M. Austin and G.I. Parkin. 'Benefits, Limitations and Barriers to Formal Methods'. SEG E1 N7, DITC, National Physical Laboratory, Teddington, Middlesex, 1992.

C.W. Bachmann. 'Data Structure Diagrams'. *Data Base*, **1**: 4–10, 1969.

R.C. Backhouse. *Program Construction and Verification*. Englewood Cliffs, NJ: Prentice Hall, 1986.

D. Bjørner and C.B. Jones (eds). 'The Vienna Development Method: The Meta Language'. Springer Verlag, *Lecture Notes in Computer Science*, 61, 1978.

D. Bjørner and C.B. Jones. *Formal Specification and Software Development*. Englewood Cliffs, NJ: Prentice Hall, 1982.

B.W. Boehm. 'Software Engineering'. *IEEE Trans. Computers*, **C-25**(12): 1226–41, 1976.

B.W. Boehm. *Software Engineering Economics*. Englewood Cliffs, NJ: Prentice Hall, 1981.

G. Booch. 'Object-oriented Development'. *IEEE Trans. Software Eng.*, **SE-12**(2): 211-21, 1986.

G. Booch. *Object Oriented Design with Applications*. Redwood City, CA: Benjamin Cummings, 1991.

British Computer Society and the Institution of Electrical Engineers. 'A Report on Undergraduate Curricula for Software Engineering'. BCS, 1989.

D. Brownbridge. 'Using Z to Develop a CASE Toolset'. *Z User Workshop*, Oxford, 142–9. Springer Verlag, 1989.

T. Bryant. 'Structured Methodologies and Formal Notations: Developing a Framework for Synthesis and Investigation.' *Z User Workshop*, Oxford, 229–41. Springer Verlag, 1989.

J.R. Cameron. 'An Overview of JSD'. *IEEE Trans. Software Eng.*, **SE-12**(2): 222–40, 1986.

M. Cantu and S. Tendon. *Borland C++ 3.1 Object Oriented Programming*. New York: Bantham Books, 1992.

P.P-S. Chen. 'The Entity–Relationship Model—Toward a Unified View of Data'. *ACM Trans. Database Systems*, **1**: 9–36, 1976.

E.F. Codd. 'A Relational Model of Data for Large Shared Data Banks'. *Comm. ACM*, **13**: 377–87, 1970.

E.F. Codd. 'Extending the Database Relational Model to Capture More Meaning'. *ACM Trans. Database Systems*, **4**: 397–434, 1979.

E.F. Codd. 'Relational Databases: A Practical Foundation for Productivity'. *Comm. ACM*, **25**(2): 109–17, March–Feb 1982.

B.P. Collins, J.E. Nicholls and I.H. Sørensen. 'Introducing Formal Methods: The CICS Experience with Z'. IBM Technical Report, IBM United Kingdom Laboratories Ltd, Winchester, Hampshire, 1987.

O.J. Dahl, E.W. Dijkstra and C.A.R. Hoare. *Structured Programming*. London: Academic Press, 1972.

A. Daniels and D. Yeates. *Basic Systems Analysis*, 3rd edn. London: Pitman, 1988.

C.J. Date. *An Introduction to Database Systems, Vol. 1*, 4th edn. Reading, MA: Addison-Wesley, 1986.

J. Dawes. *The VDM-SL Reference Guide*. London: Pitman, 1991.

T. DeMarco. *Structured Analysis and System Specification*. Englewood Cliffs, NJ: Prentice Hall, 1979.

T. DeMarco. *Controlling Software Projects: Management, Measurement and Estimation*. New York: Yourdon, 1982.

T. Denvir. *Introduction to Discrete Mathematics for Software Engineering*. Basingstoke and London: Macmillan, 1986.

A. Diller. *Z: An Introduction to Formal Methods*. Chichester: John Wiley, 1990.

R. M. Gallimore *et al*. 'UMIST OBJ: A Language for Executable Program Specification'. *The Computer Journal*, **32**(5): 413–21, 1989.

C. Gane and T. Sarson. *Structured Systems Analysis: Tools and Techniques*. Englewood Cliffs, NJ: Prentice Hall, 1977.

A. Goldberg and D. Robson. *Smalltalk-80: The Language and its Implementation*. Reading, MA: Addison-Wesley, 1983.

J.P. Gray and F. Poole. 'An Object Oriented Approach for a Parallel Database System'. In *Proc. Seminar Series in New Directions in Software Development*, Applications of Object Oriented Database Systems, Wolverhampton Polytechnic, England, 1990.

A. Hall, 'Seven Myths of Formal Methods'. *IEEE Software*, **7**(5), September 11–19, 1990.

M.H. Halstead. *Elements of Software Science*. Amsterdam: North-Holland, 1977.

I. Hayes (ed.). *Specification Case Studies*. Hemel Hempstead: Prentice Hall, 1987.

I. Hayes. 'A Generalisation of Bags in Z.' *Z User Workshop*, Oxford, **4**(6): 113–27, Springer Verlag, 1989.

I.J. Hayes and C.B. Jones. 'Specifications Are Not (Necessarily) Executable'. *Software Engineering Journal*, 330–8, November 1989.

C.A.R. Hoare. 'An Axiomatic Basis for Computer Programming'. *Comm. ACM*, **12**(10): 576–80, 583, 1969.

C.A.R. Hoare. 'Keynote Address'. *IEEE Proceedings 3rd International Conference on Software Engineering*, Atlanta, 1978.

C.A.R. Hoare. 'Communicating Sequential Processes'. *Comm. ACM*, **21**(8): 666–77, 1978.

C.A.R. Hoare. *Communicating Sequential Processes*. Englewood Cliffs, NJ: Prentice Hall, 1985.

IEEE Transactions on Software Engineering, **SE-13**(3), 1987.

D.C. Ince. *An Introduction to Discrete Mathematics and Formal System Specification*. Oxford: Clarendon Press, 1988.

International Organization for Standardization. 'Information Processing Systems—Open Systems Interconnection—LOTOS—A Formal Description Technique Based on the Temporal Ordering of Observational Behaviour'. ISO 8807, 1989

IST. *The GENESIS Tool Specification Editor Reference Manual*. Cambridge: IST, 1989.

M.A. Jackson. *Principles of Program Design*. London: Academic Press, 1975.

M.A. Jackson. *System Development*. Englewood Cliffs, NJ: Prentice Hall, 1983.

C.B. Jones. *Software Development: A Rigorous Approach*. Hemel Hempstead: Prentice Hall, 1980.

C.B. Jones. *Systematic Software Development using VDM*. Hemel Hempstead: Prentice Hall, 1986.

C.B. Jones. *Systematic Software Development using VDM*, 2nd edn. Hemel Hempstead: Prentice Hall, 1991.

C.B. Jones and R.C. Shaw. *Case Studies in Systematic Software Development*. Hemel Hempstead: Prentice Hall, 1986.

B.W. Kernighan and P.J. Plauger. *The Elements of Programming Style*. New York: McGraw-Hill, 1974

B.P. Leintz and E.B. Swanson. *Software Maintenance Management*. Reading, MA: Addison Wesley, 1980.

D. Lightfoot. *Formal Specification Using Z*. Basingstoke and London: Macmillan, 1991.

Peter A. Lindsay. 'A Survey of Mechanical Support for Formal Reasoning'. *Software Engineering Journal*, **3**(1): 3–27, January 1988.

B.H. Liskov and V. Berzins. 'An Appraisal of Program Specifications'. In *Software Specification Techniques*, N. Gehani and A.T. McGettrick (eds.). Wokingham: Addison-Wesley, 1986.

B. Liskov and S. Zilles. 'Programming with Abstract Data Types'. *ACM SIGPLAN Notices* (4): 50–9, 1974.

B. Liskov and S. Zilles. 'Specification Techniques for Data Abstractions'. *IEEE Trans. Software Eng.*, **SE-1**, (1): 7–19, March 1975.

M. Looney. *CORE—a debrief report*. Manchester, England: NCC Publications, 1985.

C.F. Martin. 'Second Generation CASE Tools: A Challenge to Vendors. *IEEE Software*, **5**(2): 46–9, 1988.

D. May. 'Use of Formal Methods by a Silicon Manufacturer'. In *Developments in Concurrency and Communication*, C. A. R. Hoare (ed.), 107–29, Reading, MA: Addison Wesley, 1990.

T.J. McCabe. 'A Complexity Measure'. *IEEE Trans. Software Eng.*, **SE-2**(4): 308–20, 1976.

J.A. McDermid and P. Whysall. *Formal Specification and Implementation Using Z*. Hemel Hempstead: Prentice Hall, 1992.

M.A. McMorran and J.E. Nicholls. 'Z User Manual'. IBM Hursley Park Technical Report TR12.274, July 1989.

B. Meyer. 'On Formalism in Specifications'. *IEEE Software*, **2**(1): 6–26, 1985.

R. Milner. *Communication and Concurrency*. Englewood Cliffs, NJ: Prentice Hall, 1989.

'The Procurement of Safety Critical Software in Defence Equipment (Part 1: requirements, Part 2: guidance)'. Interim Defence Standard 00-55, Issue 1. Glasgow: Ministry of Defence, 1991.

R. Monk. *Ludwig Wittgenstein: The Duty of Genius*. London: Jonathan Cape, 1991.

C. Morgan. *Programming from Specifications*. Hemel Hempstead: Prentice Hall, 1990.

G. Mullery. 'CORE—A Method for Controlled Requirements Specification'. In *Proc., 4th Int. Conf. on Software Engineering*, Munich, 1979.

National Physical Laboratory. 'Survey of Formal Methods in Software Engineering', NPL, Teddington, Middlesex, 1992.

P. Nauer, B. Randell, J.N. Buxton (eds.). *Software Engineering Concepts and Techniques*. New York: Petrocelli/ Charter, 1976.

A. Norcliffe and G. Slater. *Mathematics of Software Construction*. Chichester: Ellis Horwood, 1992.

D. L. Parnas. 'On the Criteria to be Used in Decomposing Systems into Modules'. Comm. ACM, **15**(12): 1053–8, 1972.

F. Polack, M. Whiston and P. Hitchcock. 'Structured Analysis—A Draft Method For Writing Z Specifications'.In *Proceedings of the 6th Z User Meeting*. Springer Verlag, 1992.

B. Potter, J. Sinclair and D. Till. *An Introduction to Formal Specification and Z*. Hemel Hempstead: Prentice Hall, 1991.

Roger S. Pressman. *Software Engineering: A Practitioner's Approach*, 2nd edn. New York: McGraw-Hill, 1987.

T. Rentsch. 'Object Oriented Programming'. *ACM SIGPLAN Notices*, **17**(9): 51–7, 1982.

K. Schoman and D.T. Ross. 'Structured Analysis for Requirements Definition'. *IEEE Trans. Software Eng.*, **SE-3**(1): 6–15, 1977.

I. Sommerville. *Software Engineering*, 4th edn. Wokingham: Addison-Wesley, 1992.

J.M. Spivey. *The Z Notation: A Reference Manual*. Hemel Hempstead: Prentice Hall, 1989.

J.M. Spivey. *The Z Notation: A Reference Manual*, 2nd edn. Hemel Hempstead: Prentice Hall, 1992.

P. Thomas, H. Robinson and J. Emms. *Abstract Data Types: Their Specification, Representation and Use*. Oxford: Clarendon Press, 1990.

D.A. Turner. 'An Overview of Miranda'. *ACM SIGPLAN Notices*, **21**(12): 158–66, 1986.

J. Warnier. *Logical Construction of Systems*. Princeton, NJ: Van Nostrand, 1971.

G.M. Weinberg. *The Psychology of Computer Programming*. Princeton, NJ: Van Nostrand, 1971.

J. Woodcock. *Using Standard Z*. Hemel Hempstead: Prentice Hall, 1993.

J. Woodcock and M. Loomes. *Software Engineering Mathematics*. London: Pitman, 1988.

M. Woodman and B. Heal. *Introduction to VDM*. London: McGraw-Hill, 1993.

W. Wordsworth. *A Z Development Method*. Technical Report, IBM UK Laboratories Ltd, Hursley Park, 1987.

D. Yeates. *Systems Project Management*. London: Pitman, 1986.

E. Yourdon and L. Constantine. *Structured Design: Fundamentals of a Discipline of Computer Program and System Design*. Englewood Cliffs, NJ: Prentice Hall, 1979.

INDEX

393